The Re

Frank Lean is the pen name of Frank Leneghan, who was born in 1942 and educated at Thornleigh College, Bolton and Keele University where he read history and politics. He has worked in education in Manchester and now lives in Manchester.

Also by Frank Lean

Red for Rachel
Nine Lives
Kingdom Gone

THE RELUCTANT INVESTIGATOR

Frank Lean

Published in the United Kingdom in 2000 by
Arrow Books

5 7 9 10 8 6 4

First published in the United Kingdom in 1997 by William Heinemann

Arrow Books Limited
The Random House Group Limited
20 Vauxxhall Bridge Road, London, SW1V 2SA

Random House Australia (Pty) Limited
20 Alfred Street, Milsons Point, Sydney, New South Wales 2061, Australia

Random House New Zealand Limited
18 poland Road, Glenfield
Auckland 10, New Zealand

Randon House (Pty) Limited
Endulini, 5a Jubilee Road, parktown, 2193, South Africa

The Random House Group Limited Reg. No. 954009
www.randomhouse.co.uk

A CIP catalogue record for this book is available from the British Library

Papers used by Random House are natural, recyclable products made from wood grown in sustainable forests. The manufacturing processes conform to the environment regulations of the country of origin

Printed and bound by Cox & Wyman Ltd, Reading, Berkshire

ISBN 0 0919 0839 6

For
John, Clare, Angela,
Celia, Lucy and Paul

The author wishes to gratefully acknowledge
the help and encouragement of Brendan Loftus,
John M McLean and Mary McLean

'In her pathetic career as a prostitute Tara Belling had stood on a lot of corners and walked down many streets, but some time shortly before Christmas 1993, she turned the wrong corner. She met the man who killed her. I submit to you, ladies and gentlemen of the jury, that that man is the man you see before you in the dock, the man who has killed at least thirteen others – Billy Fox.'
Charles Aileyn QC. Crown counsel in the case of Regina v. William Fox describing the tenth murder attributed to Fox.

'Your learned counsel has seen fit to state before this court that the evidence against you is circumstantial. Rarely has such an overwhelming mass of evidence been so boldly described. In this case to talk of piling Pelion upon Ossa is an understatement. The jury has rightly disregarded counsel's opinion and found you guilty on all fourteen charges. It is now my duty to see that you are never released to prey upon the public again in your lifetime . . .'
The Lord Chief Justice of England speaking to Billy Fox before sentencing him to fourteen concurrent life sentences with a recommendation that he never be released. It was noted that Fox smiled broadly throughout the sentencing procedure.

1

Wednesday, 12th September

What do you know about serial killers? Probably more than I did when I started my investigation into the background of Billy Fox.

I've been told I'm my own worst enemy so often that I've come to believe it. Even so, I had no idea that accepting the commission from Headstone Books would bring me and mine to the attention of an active practitioner of the craft.

I admit it was ambitious of me to take the job on. The few friends, or perhaps I should say contacts, I have in the police force have always taken great delight in telling me that I'm strictly small-time. My father, Paddy, himself a former Detective Chief Superintendent in the Manchester force, has explained to me my defects as an investigator at such tedious length that I can recite his elegy by heart. The old guy's always been disappointed I didn't maintain family tradition and become a copper myself. I think he fancied steering me into a top job in the force, but I've always been too independent to accept his back-seat driving.

OK. Manchester's a big city, but everywhere I go I meet people I know, people who know the people I know, and people who want to tell me things. But with Billy Fox it was different from the start. Every time I uttered the word 'Billy' faces froze. I should have expected it. After all, Billy had murdered fourteen young women right here in little old Manchester. Chasing up even the most tenuous connections, I collected enough hard words to write my own dictionary of insults, The revelation had created a wave of horror that had left most people numbed. The fact that Billy Fox was a young black man had stirred up a lot of stagnant pools of prejudice.

Some couldn't get over the idea that he'd been a neighbour, an acquaintance, and all the while he'd been quietly butchering those innocent girls. Life in our cosy city hadn't equipped them to understand.

Others reacted angrily right from my first question.

What was my game? Was I trying to make money out of grief?

It's a free country, isn't it? That's what they say. Cedric Liptrot, bestselling true crime author, had every right to 'do' Billy. He'd previously 'done' the Bradford Basher to his own and his publisher's great profit, and Kath and I had every right to help him in his researches. It's a way to earn a living.

The Basher killings had been even more sensational than Billy Fox's. The so-called Basher, Albert Clark, had established a reign of terror over the North of England in the late '70s and early '80s. Known as the Basher because he killed his victims by a single blow to the skull with a heavy hammer, his cries had the full lurid treatment from the media for month after month. Corpses had turned up with mechanical regularity, all bearing the Basher's trademark until he was caught, almost by accident, in 1985.

Cedric Liptrot had made his name as a writer with his biography of Albert Clark. He was like me. He'd become involved in the mass- murder industry through circumstance. Formerly a struggling play- wright living in Bradford, Cedric Liptrot had taken the opportunity provided by the crimes on his doorstep to hoist himself to fame and fortune. We also both had local knowledge of the killing grounds. After all, Billy had lived in Fallowfield, a district where I had spent part of my own adolescence. I had as much right to pry into his noxious past as the crew of journalists who'd arrived from the four corners of the earth when his crimes had been discovered.

I told myself that I was only doing my job.

'Maximise your profits this year,' my accountant had said. Unfortunately the private-investigation industry doesn't work like that. I have to wait for the customers to come to me, and demand for my services had withered over the last few months like the flowers on a week-old grave.

The horror that gripped Manchester while Billy's brief trial unfolded in London had made people unwilling to have their minor problems investigated. Business had sagged all through the summer months as one grim headline followed another.

Who would have guessed that the ineffectual-looking Billy had a hobby that would catapult him into the ranks of infamy?

The discovery had been accidental. A property repairer working on the roof of the Fallowfield house where Billy Fox rented a furnished attic flat had decided to cut a few corners. Billy was out at work, so the repairman let himself in. While looking for a way to get out onto the rafters he found the key to the locked cupboard where Billy kept his collection of severed heads – the gruesome Skull-Rack, as it had since been dubbed.

What a field day the press had. 'Cabinet of Horrors' they called it. The repairman uncovered fourteen large glass jars, each containing the head of a young female, perfectly preserved in formalin. Fourteen of them, peering out of their vessels from behind thickets of floating hair. Billy's landlady said she'd often complained about the smell in his room and Billy had put it down to his job in school biology labs. He'd been such a helpful tenant. 'He always kept his room meticulously tidy, so I didn't press him about the smell.'

Identifying the victims had been easy enough. Each one had a plastic name tag attached by a metal staple through the left earlobe. The little bastard had certainly been painstaking. How had he got away with it? With great ease . . . few of his victims had even been reported as missing persons. They were lonely girls from among the floating population of sixty thousand young people living in flats and bedsits throughout the city. Billy must have carefully selected his targets from among the most isolated.

The media had revelled in guilt. What kind of society was it, they thundered accusingly, where so many young women could go missing without anyone noticing? Ever anxious to deflect blame, the police had been quick with their response. How could they attempt to trace persons whose relatives hadn't even reported them missing? Were they supposed to do a daily roll call of the whole population? In any case tens of thousands of people went astray every year . . . on purpose. They wanted a new life and a freshly minted past.

The press had plenty of cause for grief. Billy's deeds had been done in secret. There had been no long period of 'Terror in the Streets', no lurid headlines as the toll of victims mounted. The revelation had been as sudden and unexpected as a meteorite strike. Arrested in January, tried in April, Billy streaked through the headlines.

His trial was a let down for them too. It raised more questions than it answered. The only thing everyone agreed on, Billy Fox included, was that he was guilty. After his first feeble attempts at denial were brushed aside, Billy had gone along with the big parade – guilty as charged. He was almost cheerful about it. What had he done with the bodies? He'd forgotten. How had he committed the crimes? Again the shake of the head, the grin that convinced so many he was an irredeemable sadist. Experienced journalists said he was revelling in the limelight.

It was the circumstantial evidence that stilled the doubts of the professionally sceptical, that little band of TV pundits and public figures who believe that the police always have the potential to get it wrong. The glass jars and labels were identical to ones Billy used in his work as a lab technician. His fingerprints were actually on some of the labels. Then there were the books about decapitation found in Billy's flat, in particular the gory accounts of how the ancient Aztecs had collected human heads on skull-racks. The jars were part of a consignment of twenty that had gone missing from a stockroom in a school where Billy was working. The remaining six jars were never traced.

Several of the victims had attended schools where he'd worked. Items belonging to them were found in his room. Those curious trinkets and gifts that only girls collected. A mug with the name Sharon on it . . . pottery pigs and plastic trolls each marked with a name . . . fourteen objects in all. A souvenir from each victim, as if the heads weren't enough on their own.

The clincher was a bloodstained newspaper found under the lino in Billy's bathroom, grim evidence as to how he'd disposed of the slain. The police offered the theory that he'd decapitated them in the bath, drained the blood away and then somehow disposed of the torsos.

The brief interval between Billy's arrest and his trial and conviction at the Old Bailey had been something of a record. Some said it was fear of public disorder rather than the open-and-shut nature of the case that had galvanised the authorities into such rapid action. The sooner Billy Fox was incarcerated and away from the public eye, the better. It was as if the case had raised the corner of a carpet under which society had swept some very nasty messes. Billy got life fourteen times over to be served at Greenash Secure Hospital Facility near Wrexham. The Home Secretary was considering requests from families of the victims that he should be brought back to Manchester to help locate the missing torsos. Hypnotists were offering their services to jog his memory.

My part in this story began on a quiet Wednesday afternoon at the beginning of September when my current partner, Kath Headlam, took a call from a friend in London. Kath was bemoaning the unfairness of life. Circumstances had wrecked her career as a TV executive. I was trying to distract her by chasing her round the office with lustful ideas in mind. Well, there wasn't much else to do and I knew that Kath, despite her protests, found a spell of horizontal exercise helped to break the tedium of our clientless afternoons.

Fending me off with one arm, she picked up the phone, 'Dave! Business before pleasure, this is the first call we've had in weeks. Get back!' She threatened to brain me with a heavy glass ashtray and I retreated.

I had to admire the professional way she switched on her telephone manner. Kath had worked as a producer for Alhambra TV before she hit the buffers and landed up here with me at Pimpernel Investigations.

'Felicity! Still at Headstone?' she asked, unnecessarily flashing her prominent teeth at her invisible hearer. The way she always checked that her pals were still gainfully employed intrigued me. Then, as I looked, her expression suddenly became very serious and she gestured urgently for a notebook and pencil. I passed them over. She started scribbling names, dates and figures. I heard her repeating the name Liptrot in reverential tones. It all sounded like a college reunion. I retreated to the inner office. No one can say that Dave Cunane doesn't know his place.

Eventually she appeared in the doorway, doing up the buttons of her blouse.

'That was Felicity Grete down at Headstone. She's got a job for us!'

'Come on Kath, I'm ready for anything but I draw the line at grave digging.' I had no idea what she was talking about, but there's many a true word spoken in jest.

'Headstone Press in London, thicko! They publish all those true crime books. Surely, even you must have come across them at one time or another,' she explained briskly. 'They've got this author, Cedric Liptrot. You know, the one who wrote the bestseller about the Bradford Basher –'

'What?' I interjected. I was startled.

'Headstone have him under contract to do a book about Billy Fox and the Corpseless Head Murders,' Kath continued breathlessly.

'Corpseless Heads? That's a new one, I've never heard them called that before,' I said.

'Don't go off at a tangent, Dave. The title's something their marketing people have come up with,' she explained.

'Since when has it been necessary to market mass murder?'

Kath folded her lips over her obtrusive teeth and stared me in the eye for a moment. 'Don't you dare go all Northern and puritanical on me, Dave Cunane. You peasant! It's only a moment since you were chasing me round the office.'

I knew better than to challenge her expertise. She hadn't spent years in television without learning something about hype.

She looked at me uncertainly, as if assessing my capabilities. No one would say that Kath is a devastating beauty but she has an attractive face that expresses her feelings with precision.

'Dave, this could be the break we've both been waiting for,' she said. 'Felicity's worn out the phone line coaxing Liptrot to leave Bradford and give

Manchester the once over for the book. He came over two weeks ago for a couple of days but then scarpered off back to Bradford before he'd done the business. He says he feels insecure in Manchester. Apparently he's something of a recluse. He rarely leaves his own home. She's had to promise him the services of a bodyguard-cum-investigator and then naturally she thought of me.'

I gave Kath a severe look. It was the word 'naturally' that was a bit hard to swallow.

'All right, Dave. You don't need to give me your best down-trodden-toiler look,' she said, tucking her chin under her face in a way that made her look particularly demure. 'I've been doing a bit of canvassing among my old friends lately. What are friends for if you can't ask them for a job?'

I grinned at her. 'OK, Kath. You said it was a break for both of us. Given that I'm to be this Liptrot's minder, what's Felicity got lined up for you?'

'It's a chance to get back to the kind of work I know best,' she said eagerly. 'She wants me to help Cedric format his work for TV production. Headstone is trying to arrange a tie-in with a multi-national producer so that the book and a TV miniseries will appear simultaneously. It'll save them time and money if I can block out the TV programmes while he's writing the book.'

She spoke so earnestly that I couldn't help getting a bit excited myself. It was a glimpse of glamour, so different from the world of back streets and bent supermarket employees that I usually inhabited. At the same time I realised that if we were successful my chances of maintaining the present relationship with Kath were slim. She wasn't likely to want to hang around with me once the chance to return to her own world was open to her.

'Things have hardly been buzzing round here,' she continued. 'Anyway, we might not get the job, you know. We've got to be approved by Cedric and his mother. Apparently he never makes a move without her say-so. He's got most of the book written. Felicity says they just want scenes and locations and a few interviews with people who knew Billy to give the book some gritty realism. You know . . . the genuine "dirt-between-your-toes" Manchester feel.'

Kath looked at me expectantly. Was I supposed to jump on the desk and shout '*Hallelujah!*'?

'I'll have to give this a bit of thought,' I said cautiously. 'You know I don't work well with somebody looking over my shoulder all the time.'

'I've told you. Liptrot won't be a problem like that,' Kath said heatedly. 'This could be my big chance!'

'But which of us does Felicity Grete want the most?' I asked stubbornly. 'Will she go ahead and get you to help Liptrot with the scripts if I turn the job down?'

'She wants us both . . . Well, at least . . . she sees this as a good chance to get someone working alongside Cedric who knows how to lay out a TV script.'

I didn't speak for a moment. Kath's honesty did her credit. She was hoping to do an acrobatic flip back into television from the broad shoulders of the proprietor of Pipernel Investigations. But where did that leave me if she succeeded?

'I thought we were a team, Dave,' she said, as if reading my thoughts. 'We've been really close these last few months. Don't spoil things.'

'I need to get some fresh air. I'm going out for a walk,' I announced. 'I'll be back soon.'

'Don't take too long, Dave! I might not be here when you get back,' she said pointedly. The trouble was I needed to work out whether I cared if she put her threat into effect or not. Kath and I had reached that point in our relationship where we'd begun to wonder whether it was just a brief fling or if it was going to ripen into something more permanent.

I stumbled out of the office and down the stairs. When I hit the street the weather was playing one of those moody autumnal tricks for which Manchester is renowned. The sky was full of swiftly moving dark clouds threatening rain, but strong beams of light were breaking through the murk like probing rays. Little carousels of litter were gyrating along the pavement. Distant sunlight gleamed and then faded from office windows, highlighting first one building, then another. As I walked along Canal Street I ruminated on how things had slowly changed over the summer.

I suppose having Kath around for the last few months had helped me to straighten out the dent in my ego caused by my former girlfriend's departure.

Yes, I had to face it . . . the fault was mine. Kath had come to me when she was down. Now that she was on her way back to the top again, was I big enough to take it, or would we split up? It was time I sorted myself out. After all, it wasn't as if I was so hungry for material success myself that I had any right to be jealous. I'd been ready enough to patronise Kath. I'd jumped at the opportunity. Now, whatever reservations I had, she deserved my support. I owed her that.

I walked back up to the office. A trot along the canal was no substitute for a long bike ride down the banks of the Mersey as an aid to the thought processes, but at least I was clear in my mind about what the alternatives facing me were.

'Well, macho-man,' Kath greeted me as I entered. 'Is it to be, or not to be?'

'Let's give it our best shot,' I said, with an enthusiasm I didn't feel. 'It's got to be better than debt-collecting or process-serving. I think you should contact your other friends in the media Mafia and ask what they know about Liptrot and his little foibles. I'll see if I can dig up anything about Billy Fox that hasn't already been in the papers.

'What? Start right away?' she asked, as if disbelieving my sudden conversion.

'Unless you've got something else in mind,' I said speculatively, with a glance towards the couch.

'Hang on a minute! I'll just phone Felicity and give her the glad tidings.' She hastily did up the top button of her blouse and returned to the inner office to consult her Filofax.

When I'd said I'd see if there was something I could dig up about Fox that hadn't already been raked over a thousand times before, I'd been whistling in the dark. I knew no more about multiple murderers than anyone else. This is one type of crime that isn't covered in the private detective's handbook. How could anyone develop expertise in investigating serial killing?

In any case, there were few details of the case that hadn't already been exhaustively ventilated in the press: everything was out in the open. What was there for me to do, apart from put together a large handful of press cuttings?

Certainly no one was mounting a 'Free Billy' campaign. There would be no committee preparing handouts showing where the police had gone wrong. There were no aggrieved relatives springing to his defence. He belonged to the local Afro-Caribbean community, but had no friends there. The silence of the usual spokespersons had been deafening.

There was, however, one little feature that had come to my notice throughout Billy's brief trial. His solicitor was the odious Geoff Bartle.

In a previous encounter with him I'd discovered that his seemingly respectable firm wasn't above doing a spot of money laundering for its more bent clients. That was perfectly legal, but using the client account to transfer funds wasn't. I had documents that both the Law Society and the police might be very interested in.

All I had to do now was to find the best method to put the squeeze on Bartle. If he had any information that hadn't already been used to wrap a million bags of chips in, I wanted it. OK, it amounted to blackmail, but having decided to help Kath there was no point in me being squeamish.

The only trouble was I was probably the last person in Manchester that the toffee-nosed git would want to confide in. He knew more ways to wriggle out of an unpleasant encounter than a startled rattlesnake.

Deception was called for . . . I phoned his office.

'Tax District Four, Inland Revenue, here. This is your firm's tax inspector speaking.' This produced a sound of nervous throat clearing, but I continued rapidly before she asked for ID. 'Is Mr Geoffrey Bartle available? . . . He is? Good. Well, don't bother him now, but warn him that we're sending somebody round to verify a declaration he made.'

When I left the office Kath didn't speak. She was busying herself on the phone. As usual, the lift was out of action, so for the second time that afternoon I walked down the six flights of stairs to the dusty street below. The sun had now decided to shine in earnest but it didn't improve the look of the area. It accentuated every sign of dereliction: the never-vanishing litter, the cracked pavements, the crumbling mortar between the dirty bricks of worn-out buildings, the skim of oil over the canal, everything that was best hidden under a protective screen of drizzle. All quite appropriately sleazy for a man on a mission of extortion, I thought.

Back in the flat in Chorlton I found the documents

incriminating Bartle in a suitcase under my bed. I put them in an envelope. I must have had a few qualms about my mission because I decided that I'd fulfil it better if I improved my appearance. I went to the wardrobe and took out a double-breasted navy blue business suit by Hugo Boss. I told myself that it was one of my props. I find it never does any harm to be well dressed when meeting a smoothy like Geoff Bartle.

Having left the car in the G-Mex car park behind the Midland Hotel, I walked along the narrow street between the Town Hall annexe and the Town Hall. The ashlar masonry was sweating dirt as the sun dried the damp walls. There were strapping young men in scuffed leather jackets and beards lying in wait to part me from my change, but for once they'd forgotten about begging. They'd cast their blankets to one side and were quarrelling among themselves about who should sit where. It only needed Charlton Heston in the foreground to turn it into a scene from a biblical epic, I slipped past them into South King Street without being relieved of any cash.

Bartle's office adjoined one of the narrow ginnels. It had a fancy entrance portico lined with pink marble. The name of the firm was emblazoned in gold letters cut into the stonework. I gripped the massive gold-plated handle on the glass door and had to push really hard to swing it open. Thick carpeting spread like a lush green lawn in all directions. A pretty blonde receptionist was buffing her fingernails behind a console that looked like the command module of the Starship Enterprise. She nervously slid the emery board into the desk drawer as I approached with an officious expression on my face. My dark-suited appearance must have fitted her image of an angry bureaucrat on the rampage.

'Tax District Four. Mr Bartle's expecting me,' I announced sternly. 'Shall I go straight in?'

'Oh, you're from the . . . ?' she said, leaving the question in the air, as I briskly walked forward, praying that Bartle still had his office in the same place. She subsided nervously in her seat and started fidgeting with the bank of controls in front of her, presumably to warn Bartle. God! There were so many solid-looking doors with the name Bartle written on them. I had to get the right one first time. There wouldn't be a second chance, Bartle would be heading for cover as fast as his long legs could carry him.

Bingo! When I knocked and opened the door there he was.

Geoff Bartle is typical of those eminent solicitors you see on TV from time to time issuing a statement about some politician's recreational leg-over or footballer's tantrum. A heavy-duty mouthpiece. The type who can frame an impromptu statement, putting the most bizarre behaviour in a good light without batting an eyelid. But now, although immaculately dressed as ever in silk shirt, club tie and pin-striped suit, he was anxiously poring over a pale photocopy of his tax declaration.

He stared up at me in surprise, the light of the green banker's lamp on his desk causing a reflected glow from his brilliantined golden locks to gleam like a halo. He hastily shut the folder in front of him as I advanced into the room.

'Get out, Cunane!' he yelped, before picking up a heavy paperweight which he pitched at me. I fielded it and replaced it on his desk in what must have looked like a menacing gesture. His lower lip quivered slightly.

'Don't be like that, Geoff. I just want to ask you for a favour,' I said pleasantly. 'You owe me more than one and you know it.'

'Get out before I phone the police,' he said, standing

up as if to personally assist my departure. But then he thought better of that idea, sat down and crammed the folder he'd been perusing into a drawer.

'Now Geoff' I said confidingly, 'you do know that any member of the public can make an anonymous declaration about someone's tax return, don't you?'

'You bastard! So that call was from you.' He started up from his seat again, but then slumped back onto it once more, locked the desk drawer and put the key into his pocket.

I took my time in answering. 'It's sometimes hard to get your attention, Geoff. You have a way of being out when I call.' He looked at me nervously and I decided it was time to press home my advantage. 'I didn't come about tax actually, Geoff. The thing is I've been going over my firm's records and I found something that put me in a moral dilemma. You know all about money laundering, I suppose?'

He stared at me blankly.

'I was wondering whether I ought to make a voluntary disclosure to the Law Society about a prominent local solicitor who used his firm's client account to help crooks get millions out of the country. It's all here in black and white,' I said, tapping the envelope I had in my hand.

He made a quick gesture with his hand and I passed him one sheet chosen at random. He scanned it anxiously, sucking his teeth nervously.

'You've got more front than Kendal's, Cunane. This is all perfectly legal,' he whined.

'So you don't mind me sending your legal pals a copy?'

He blanched despite the well-maintained tan and swallowed nervously a couple of times. His brows furrowed as he struggled to come up with a reply. It was good to see him on the hook.

'I knew you were a bastard, Cunane, but I didn't think you were a blackmailer. How much?' he asked. No messing about. Perhaps he hoped to make the payment tax deductible. Still, I was in too much of a hurry to take offence at either his estimate of my parentage or of my character.

'I just want to ask you something about Billy Fox,' I said.

'Billy Fox?' He repeated my words in an incredulous tone. The expression of relief on his face was almost comical, so he probably had been fiddling the tax man as well as washing funny money. Then he began to laugh. 'Cunane, you're incredible! Manchester's last resort of hopeless cases! Please say that you're trying to prove the little swine's innocent!'

I didn't share his jollity. He hadn't got a halitosis problem, but there was something offensively reptilian about the perfection of his teeth.

I shrugged my shoulders. 'No, I'm being employed by a national TV company to dig up more background information about the case,' I said, being only slightly economical with the truth. 'I thought you'd be a useful person to start with . . . there might be some good publicity in it for your firm.'

'And you went through all this palaver for that? I'd have told you all I know for nothing . . . Still, as you have those papers, perhaps I'd better take charge of them.' He gestured towards the envelope I was holding on to.

'Story first, papers later,' I said.

He shook his head doubtfully and his hand started to go for the phone again, but then he shot his cuffs out instead, folded his arms on the desk top and leaned forward.

'Five minutes, Cunane. Five minutes only,' he conceded.

'Just fill me in on the interrogation. I mean were there ever any doubts . . . ?

'Doubts? Doubts, with fourteen severed heads in his bedroom? You must be crazy. The police bent over backwards to be fair to him. As well as his solicitor, me, they had a representative of the local Ethnic Community Forum and a major from the Salvation Army present throughout. It was more like a counselling session than a police investigation. They poured so much tea down the little geek's throat that we had to keep breaking off every few minutes while they took him for a leak.'

'I take it that you didn't approve,' I suggested. 'You'd have liked to see the rubber hoses come out?'

'No, it wasn't that. This soft-soaping of obvious villains is what the police have to do these days to make sure that there's no comeback. I warned the investigating officer, Detective Superintendent Pinnock, that we'd have one of those radical QCs from London up here shouting the odds if they weren't ultra careful.'

'So you were on the side of the police were you?' I said.

'Careful, Cunane,' he warned. 'Stop feeding me lines. If you want to hear what happened just shut up for a minute.'

I waved my hands in a placatory gesture.

'Fox had already made an admission after he was cautioned at his flat. I was brought in to advise him as soon as he arrived at Bootle Street. He was tearful and upset as you might expect anyone to be who's just admitted to fourteen murders. He half wanted to deny everything, but then when he realised that was hopeless he agreed to make a full statement. I've never seen a suspect in such a serious case be so amenable. He was falling over himself to agree with the police. They stopped the questioning and had him examined by the police surgeon at that point to see if he was on something.'

Bartle paused for a moment.

'So, he did deny the charge at first?'

'Only for a few minutes, but it was so blindingly obvious to everyone – he'd been caught red-handed – that even he had the intelligence to own up. So don't you go trying to make bricks without straw, Cunane.'

'I told you, I'm only interested in background. How did he seem?'

'Happy to get everything off his chest. The only problem was that he couldn't remember the exact circumstances of the murders, or at least he wasn't prepared to admit to it. Too gruesome, I expect. The police psychologist thought it was a genuine memory lapse, that he'd blanked out the gory bits.'

'Psychologist,' I interrupted. 'There was no mention –'

'Get real, Cunane,' Bartle sneered. 'Don't you watch TV? Don't you know that the police won't even take their batons out these days without asking a psychologist's advice first? Anyway, this woman, Caulfield, was there to confirm that Fox wasn't just one of these compulsive confessors. Not that anyone thought he was in the first place . . . God Almighty! How could anyone sleep in that bedroom with all those heads in bottles? Do you realise that I had to see all that? All those dead eyes goggling up at me! Caulfield reckons that Fox probably opened the cupboard door so that he could look at them as he went to sleep . . . talk about "Goodnight sweetheart!" According to her, Fox fits the profile of a multiple killer in every particular.'

'When was this profiling established?' I asked.

'Oh, Caulfield's evidence was never needed at the trial. The police had built up a massive train of circumstantial evidence by that time. Anyway, your time's up.'

'Just a minute,' I pleaded. 'How can you profile a suspect when he's already locked up in the cells? What's scientific about that?'

'Cunane, you know I love this kind of inconsequential chat, but thanks to you and your devious tricks I've made an urgent appointment to see my accountant, so farewell!'

'But it must be unethical for you to have had some kind of meeting with the forensic psychologist who was trying to build up a case against your client,' I blustered, clutching at straws.

Bartle showed me to the door. 'I can see that I'll have to set your warped little mind at rest. Although Lauren Caulfield *is* an old friend of mine, we only discussed the case on one occasion when we met by chance in Sam's Chop House. That was well after Fox had decided not to appeal against sentence. So make what you can of that.'

I blocked the doorway. 'Look you haven't even given me five minutes,' I said. 'What about the antecedents? How did Fox meet his victims? How did he kill them? Why?'

Bartle paused, as if humouring the deranged.

'All the system had to do was to establish Fox's guilt and then ensure that society is protected from him. Naturally, the police have tried to establish precisely how each one of his unfortunate victims met her end, but the killings were spaced out over years. Fox has blanked the memory out of his mind and there were no witnesses. The best they've been able to do is to establish that he had the opportunity to meet his victims. But that's necessarily conjectural. What isn't, is the mass of evidence linking him to the murders.'

I wasn't satisfied. 'I'll be in touch,' I said.

'No you won't,' he growled. 'Come near this office again, and I'll slap an injunction on you.

*

I was in a thoughtful mood as I left. Strange how an encounter with the legal profession made me feel that I needed a shower and a change of clothes, There was something rancid about Bartle, but he'd given me more to think about than I'd dared to hope.

There was no doubting that Billy Fox was guilty. If Bartle hoped that I would undertake a 'Mission Impossible' to prove Fox's innocence he was barking up the wrong tree. But it appeared there was lots more interesting material than I'd imagined. If Cedric Liptrot was half the writer he was cracked up to be he'd pounce on the information I'd already discovered. It was unethical to produce a profile after you had a suspect banged up. Anything of that nature was bound to be a self-fulfilling prophecy.

It was too late to think about abandoning the enquiry now. I was hooked.

'The question that is often posed in any discussion about serial killers is *"Are they rational?" I would rather put it the other way round and ask "Is the attempt to find a reason for what they do something we need and they don't?"'*

From *A Son To Us All* by Cedric Liptrot, page 473 – the story of Albert Clark, nicknamed the Bradford Basher, killer of twelve women.

2

Wednesday afternoon.

I shook my head in wonder at my own foolishness. I was now fully committed to a job in an area where I had no expertise whatsoever. A job moreover, on which the most massive resources of tabloid journalism had already been deployed without any success.

I wandered from Bartle's office lost in thought. If Kath and this Liptrot were hoping to make a series about these so-called Corpseless Head Murders they'd have to be geniuses at spinning out a yarn because despite tantalising hints evidence was sparse so far. There was no documentation at all about how each victim had landed up in Billy Fox's clutches. Bartle had admitted that all the police had were conjectures. I walked slowly towards a coffee shop on the corner of the narrow passage between King Street and St Ann's Square, thrusting a coin into yet another impoverished street resident's outstretched hand as I did.

Over a cup of coffee I tried mentally listing my own contacts with the police force. At one end of the scale there was Assistant Chief Constable Sinclair who had barred me from ever again visiting his headquarters. At the other end there was probationary Police Constable Jay Anderson, my former assistant. Between them there was nothing. I'd alienated all other middle-ranking officers nearer my own age in one way or another over the years.

The thought of Sinclair's abrasive sarcasm chilled any desire for an early meet. Sometimes I found it hard to shake the idea that Sinclair was getting at my father through me in some subtle way. He'd been a lowly underling when my father was head of CID in the City of Manchester Police and he derived a certain pleasure from shaking his head at my so-called antics. Despite that, it was advantageous for me to have such a high-ranking officer as an acquaintance. Judicious name-dropping had deflected many a police boot headed in my direction, but it would be better to postpone an encounter with him until it was strictly necessary.

That left Jay Anderson, a former Moss Side resident and son of my old friend Lovena. She'd been in the process of losing a son to the ravages of sickle cell when I first met her. My own spouse Flenki had been dying at that time of the same affliction. It had made a strong bond between us. Lovena had two surviving sons. Jay was the one who gave her the most worry and she'd turned to me for help in keeping him out of prison. Jay was weak, inclined to blame white society for his troubles. It had been a struggle to stop him sliding into the world of petty crime and drug dealing which beckoned to so many in Manchester.

He'd worked for me for two years before joining the police force in the hope of becoming a 'real' detective.

Things are never easy with Jay. There are always some resentments hidden below the surface of our friendship, like submerged logs in a smoothly flowing river just waiting to rip out the bottom of a passing boat. Still, if I was going to make progress in filling in the big blank page that Billy Fox represented, a meeting was in order.

At least, he was bound to have picked up some locker-room gossip about the case. If my memories of the boys in blue were accurate, their tongues would have been wagging about little else for months. After all, the consequences of the case were far from over. They'd still not come up with a single one of the missing torsos.

And then there was the police psychologist, Caulfield. She sounded well worth a visit. How had she managed to come up with a profile? How *do* you profile someone whose memory of crucial incidents is a complete blank? Well, whatever the answer, she'd have to wait until I'd contacted Jay Anderson.

I must have been mulling things over for some time because when I came to drink my coffee it was stone cold. I decided to phone from outside the shop.

Standing behind St Ann's Church I keyed the number of Jay's Moss Side home into my Vodafone. I should have known better than to pause in that locality. The expensive shops were attracting others apart from the well-heeled. I had the feeling of being watched and as I scanned round saw another young male beggar. This one was camped beneath the window of an expensive jewellery shop and his glance locked on me like a missile guidance system acquiring a target. His eyes gleamed like a pair of Rolex watches as he rose and advanced towards me. A whippet guarded his blankets for him.

'Spare me some change, sir?' he asked, courteously enough. I knew better than to refuse, but the constant touting for small change every few yards was getting to me. The beggar's colleagues were stationed on every corner nearby. I rummaged through my pockets and found a fifty-pence coin that he accepted with appropriately meagre gratitude.

'You know, you characters ought to give out stickers like the Flag Day people,' I grumbled just as Lovena Anderson, Jay's mother, answered my call.

'What's that? Who is this?' she boomed down the phone line in her familiar broad Caribbean accent. The recipient of my largesse was hanging around trying to get an earful of my conversation. I scowled at him and he scowled right back. Just my luck to land on a crazy.

'It's me, Lovena. Dave Cunane. Is Jay in?'

'David, we haven't heard from you for months. You must come round for supper. Jay will be pleased to see you. He's sleeping at the moment and then he has a half-day's leave.

'Look, do you mind?' I said to the beggar in an aggrieved tone.

'What's the matter with you, David? Are you in trouble? You sound really peevish, man.' Lovena's voice was anxious.

'There's someone here pestering me. I'm trying to phone from the street,' I struggled to explain.

'I'll wake Jay. I'll send him down to your office if there's someone troubling you. He can sort it,' Lovena said urgently.

'I'm fine,' I said, after a wary glance at the mendicant. 'I'm working on the Billy Fox case and I just wondered if Jay had heard anything interesting.'

I could almost hear the shutters clanging down in Lovena's mind. I was playing the wrong tune. After a lengthy pause she replied.

'Don't know nothing about that David, and I don't think Jay's bosses would be pleased if he talked to you. It was all in the papers, man!'

'Yes, I suppose it was.'

Some of my disappointment must have been discernible because she softened a little. 'Jay was present when they broke the news to one of the victim's mothers. He's been full of stories 'bout her, man.'

'Great!' I said excitedly. 'Maybe you could ask him to call in at the office after all.'

'All part of the service,' Lovena said and hung up.

My satisfaction must have shown because my one-man audience decided to add his twopenny worth. 'They call us scavengers, but you reporters are worse than any vultures. You can't leave it alone can you?'

I took a step towards him. It wasn't that I intended to deck him, although why not? He took a step back in alarm and simultaneously his whippet snapped at my heels. I gently steered it to one side with my foot and scuttled away towards the Square intending to lose myself amongst the throngs on Market Street. Glancing over my shoulder I saw the beggar set off in pursuit.

Once through the Passage and round the corner I found my path blocked. A crowd was pressing forward to observe a piece of street theatre. I pushed myself in among them, taking off my jacket and tie so that I looked like any other casual loiterer.

At first I thought it was a demo against nuclear testing. The base of the statue nearest St Ann's Church was packed with demented-looking people. Trestle tables, draped to the ground with long white sheets, had coffin-like boxes stacked on them. The empty black boxes made a startling spectacle against the white sheets. Between the tables and the statue, people rigged out like gospel singers were waving banners saying VICPAC and chanting a funereal dirge. The whole scene was weird. Keeping a wary eye on the corner of the church in case my pursuer should emerge, I pressed forward to the front. Someone shoved a clipboard with a petition on it under my nose. Normally, signing petitions is against my principles. I'm not in the awkward squad for nothing, but this time I signed up without even reading what I was supporting. Glancing up at the statue I noticed that it was of Richard Cobden, the nineteenth-century Free Trader. He looked down disapprovingly from his plinth.

It was only when I was out of the square and on Cross Street that I realised what they'd been chanting . . . '*Bring Billy Back. Bring Billy Back.*' I shivered . . . fourteen boxes, fourteen victims.

I decided to walk rather than catch the tram. Walking gave me more time to think.

There was another contact who might be able to feed me some police gossip about Billy Fox . . . my father, Paddy Cunane. I didn't like to think what Freud would have made of it but those coffins reminded me of him. The trouble was I hadn't spoken to him for months. My parents were both obsessed with the idea that I should live what they called a regular life – marriage, a steady job, if not with the police force, at least in some reputable firm with a career structure. I failed to measure up to their specifications in so many ways that it made me blush to think about it.

'I suppose I'd better go and see the old fossils,' I thought to myself. Then some instinct warned me to look over my shoulder.

A group of tousled individuals was heading in my direction. It was led by the man with the whippet. I couldn't be sure whether they were after me or heading off somewhere to count the day's takings. Feeling that it was better to be safe than sorry, I dashed through the traffic on Cross Street and ran towards the safety of my own office.

By dodging rapidly through the streets of the commercial heart of Manchester, I shortened my journey somewhat. I stopped outside the Manchester Club, a reminder of the long-gone days when 'Manchester Men' had dominated Liberal governments, and scanned the street to see if I still had company. I couldn't be sure.

I emerged at the top of Market Street and cautiously looked down the sloping street. There was the usual crowd of buskers clustered round the obelisk. This pared-down version of Cleopatra's Needle had been stuck into the top end of the street by the City Council: a monument to the prevailing local industry. No one was taking any notice of me, so I trudged off in the opposite direction.

When I wearily trailed up the six flights of stairs to Pimpernel Investigations I found Kath in a pleasant mood. She had an A4 pad open in front of her and was sketching out ideas for the programmes.

'Do you think "Fox's Lair" or "Fox's Den" sounds better?' she asked.

'How about "Fox in the Hen-house" or "Headless Chickens",' I said.

I'd hardly got the words out of my mouth when there was a heavy thump on the door. I started guiltily. It must be the street people, come to avenge the insult to their whippet. God! I'd only fended it off with the toe of my shoe.

'Aren't you going to see who it is?' Kath asked.

'You'd better go,' I volunteered. 'Say I'm not in if they look menacing.' I retreated to the inner office and closed the door behind me. Almost immediately there was the sound of raised voices from the outer office. There was no way out of it. I flung the door open, ready to face my pursuers.

Jay Anderson, who appeared to have put on at least five inches round the chest since I last saw him, was arguing fiercely with Kath. 'Me Mum said to come because someone was pestering you and you sounded as if you needed help,' he said when he saw me. 'Who is it, Boss? Who's after you? Tell this lady to chill out.'

Jay was at least six foot two and would easily qualify as a basketball player if he kept on growing. Appropriately, he had a Chicago Bulls cap on. He was an intimidating presence. His accent had changed.

'Oh Jay, man! It's all a mistake. Your mother got hold of the wrong idea,' I said lamely. 'I never meant to get you out of bed on your rest day.' The bloodlust, or whatever it was in his expression, took a while to fade.

I laughed. There was something about the way he spoke which puzzled me. This wasn't the music loving, spaced-out young man I was used to. Yet, having already spent two years straightening out Jay Anderson's hang-ups, I wasn't falling over myself to take on any new ones he might have developed in the police force.

Still, laughing at him was the wrong thing to do. This young man took himself very seriously. Evidently he was finding being a young black police officer no easier than he had found being a young black teenager. I should have recognised what the neat dress and clipped accent signalled. Jay was an ambitious, upwardly mobile young man. He must resent the slightest trace of condescension from me, particularly if he remembered that I was credited by his mother with rescuing him from a life of crime.

'Sorry Jay, I didn't mean to dis you. Now you're here perhaps you'd like to tell me what you know about this mother of one of Billy Fox's victims.'

This didn't appease him much.

'Look *Mr Cunane*, I know you're a friend like, and you mean no harm, but I don't know . . . I learned all that officially and Billy Fox hasn't done much for the black community and I think it's best if we don't talk about him.'

'Jay, Lovena said you were always talking about this woman. It can't do any harm to tell me what you told her. Nothing anyone can write can hurt her daughter now,' I said reassuringly.

'I suppose,' he agreed. 'But there wasn't much. Mum exaggerates.'

'Who was the girl then?' Kath pressed.

'Well, she was called Julie Goodchild, a white girl. I found out quite a bit about her from her mother.' Kath was solemnly writing it all down as he spoke. 'They left me with the mother for a while,' he explained. 'The girl had left home to live in a grotty flat. At first the mother seemed more upset remembering that her boyfriend had died than that her own daughter had ended up with her head in a bottle.'

'Did you find out any personal details?' Kath coaxed.

'I don't know . . . This isn't right. The only thing was the mother didn't seem too upset at first.'

'Go on,' Kath cajoled. 'What was the girl like?'

'A quiet little mousy blonde, wouldn't say boo to a goose was how her mother described her.' Kath looked at him in disappointment and he furrowed his brow to come up with further detail. 'She said Julie was a bit what you might call well-endowed for her age . . . you know big –'

'OK. I get the picture,' Kath said, scribbling rapidly. I wondered who she was thinking of casting for the part.

'Anyway, as far as I can tell the mother moved her boyfriend into the house and not long after that Julie moved out.' Kath scribbled away furiously.

'Could we have her address?' I pressed. 'I'll go and see her.'

'I don't know . . . Maybe you should find that out for yourself. Anyway, I thought you were researching Billy Fox, not his victims.'

'Dave feels that we should bring the victims fully into

this story,' Kath improvised, raising her eyebrows at me.

'Yes, we both feel that the victims should get equal coverage with the killer in any story,' I said, picking up her cue. 'After all, speaking as a private detective, the question of how these girls all managed to go missing without anyone starting a major search is what we ought to be looking into. I mean what the hell's going on in this town if young girls can just vanish like this?'

Kath looked at me uncertainly. I had a strong feeling that if Jay hadn't been present the issue wouldn't have occurred to her at all. Perhaps her training in the media made her nervous when anyone achieved a higher state of political correctness than she'd reached herself.

'About that address,' I said to Jay.

'I think it's only fair to let you find it yourself, Dave. After all you are a private detective, and I don't want to upset my mates or my mum, either, for that matter,' he said disarmingly. 'Is there any chance that you've heard any interesting bits of information from the crime scene . . . I mean, you know . . . like a bit of inside information?'

'Thanks Jay, but I'm not looking for a vacancy as a police informer at the moment,' I said rather coldly. I didn't like his cute attempt to swap the address for a tip-off.

'Yeah, well I think it's really interesting. The way he beheaded them and all,' he replied. He wasn't at all ruffled by what I'd said. Whatever his hang-ups were, lack of self-confidence wasn't one of them.

'Dave has your telephone number, hasn't he? Perhaps we can think about your offer. Then we can give you a ring,' Kath suggested in an attempt to tone down my bluntness.

'I know. Don't ring us, we'll ring you . . . that sort of thing.'

'No. Really. Dave often hears this and that. Don't you Dave?' Kath said half-jokingly. I didn't say anything.

Jay looked round the cluttered room where he'd spent so many hours. His expression was guarded. He seemed to be straggling to remember that I'd been his friend as well as his boss . . . He promised to call on us at the flat that evening, then said his goodbyes.

'I hope this doesn't mean you're getting cold feet about this commission,' Kath said when he was out of the room. 'This job could mean a lot to us, Dave.'

I took this as a warning that I was required to show more enthusiasm.

'Look lovey, you know I'm the last one to pour cold water on your ideas but we haven't actually got the job yet,' I said jokingly. 'Don't we have to be interviewed by Cedric and his mummy? I might need to earn a crust in this town for a long time yet and the last thing I want is some sort of reputation as a covert racist. We've got to keep our noses clean on the racial issue. Billy was quite impartial in choosing candidates for his jugs but the fact that he was black means that this whole thing has to be handled very delicately. I hope you and Liptrot understand that.'

By way of reply Kath gave an exasperated sigh.

'You think I'm joking, don't you?' I asked. 'From what Bartle told me, the police were wetting themselves in case the race issue came up during the interrogation and trial. It didn't because Billy was so obliging, but that doesn't mean it's gone away. There are all kinds of racial committees and study groups watching like hawks for anything they can take offence at. If you don't want to wade through pickets with placards saying "Hands off the Community" etc, we both need to be very careful.'

'We're talking about a serial killer here. Who would play the so-called "race card" in a case like that? I don't think many people will be demonstrating in his favour. Felicity rang again while you were out. Cedric's really sold on the idea of working with us, especially me helping with the TV tie-in. She's arranged for us to meet him tomorrow. By the way the fee she's agreed to is a lot more than your usual daily rate. So be nice!'

'Great! Pimpernel Investigations – Detection and Literary Ghosting. Brilliant! I'll have to do some speed reading to get through his other masterpiece, *A Son To Us All,* before we meet them. Touchy about his work is he, this Cedric?'

'As a matter of interest, he's not. I've met him before. He came down to speak to the Drama Society when I was at Oxford. Felicity met him there as well. We put on one of his early plays.'

'Oh, don't say you were all at the same college,' I groaned.

'What if we were? We can't all arrange to go to wildly fashionable places like York University. I made some very good friends at Oxford.'

'Don't get on your high horse, Kath. I love it when you get all indignant about the unfair treatment of the privileged classes in these rough times. What were those latest shocking statistics? The percentage of non-Oxbridge graduates in top media positions has risen as high as five per cent? I don't know what the world's coming to.'

Kath decided to ignore my taunts. 'Let's go home and eat,' she suggested. I loved the cool way she defused me. It was like coming up through a hole in the Arctic icecap into sunshine and warmth.

As we threaded our way through the traffic-besieged streets back to Chorlton, I reflected that one thing we have in common is that neither of us is a food faddist. We can both binge away on the old cholesterols. I have to admire the way she tucks into a fry-up. She claims she learned to cook from her father, a naval officer widowed young and left to bring her up on his own.

It was my turn to cook tonight and I managed to produce fillet steaks with mushrooms and the ever-acceptable chips. The buzzer from the ground-floor entrance sounded just as Kath was washing her dinner down with a pint of Wondermilk.

Jay Anderson announced himself over the intercom.

Apart from the short haircut, life with Manchester's Finest hadn't altered his taste much. He was wearing a skintight, canary-yellow vest and leggings and some very expensive-looking cycling shoes. He was twisting his wrists in that odd gesture of his that I knew signalled embarrassment.

'Hi, Jay, you're looking good,' I said as casually as possible. I knew him well enough to know that I'd get nothing out of him unless I let him set the agenda.

'Hi, Boss, . . . er, Dave. It's been a long time since I was in here.'

'Not my fault, Jay. You can drop in any time, here or at the office. You know that.'

'Yeah, I know. It's just that . . . Well . . . er . . .'

'Mr Sinclair has warned you to keep your distance from me,' I said, completing the sentence for him. His face lit up, complication removed.

'How did you know? Did he tell you as well?'

'I don't have to take orders from Mr Sinclair, Jay. Anyone would know that he wouldn't want one of his best new coppers contaminated.'

'Right, well, here I am. I thought you might like to go for a ride on the Meadows. You used to like it well enough.' He talked incisively, speaking with much greater confidence than he'd ever done when he worked for me. It was interesting to see how after only a few months in the police force he was already taking charge of a situation.

Kath pricked her ears up. She was always interested in gleaning any information about my previous existence. She also had a certain amount of feminine curiosity about my previous partner which Jay could certainly have satisfied for her. I became rather anxious to bustle Jay off the premises.

'Liked to get out a lot did you, Dave?' Kath asked pleasantly. There was a sharp glint in her eye.

I looked at Jay and narrowed my eyes ever so slightly. He took the hint and made no further references to my former existence.

'It's a lovely evening, . . . er, Miss . . . er, Ms . . . er, Mrs Headlam. You could come as well.'

'It's Ms, and I haven't got a bike, and my horse is stabled at Carrington so it would be difficult even to come for a ride on him.'

'Hey, man!' he said, turning to me. 'You got a horse too? Kevin Costner rides the range in Chorlton! Wow! This I've got to see.'

'I haven't, I'm still on two wheels and if you'll wait a minute I'll get changed. You don't mind, do you Kath?'

'Heavens!' she said, flinging up her arms in mock surprise. 'Don't let me interfere with your bonding session, Dave. My years with a TV company have taught me how easily dented male self-esteem is.'

'Well, we could all go for a walk. I don't mind,' Jay offered with a sly smile.

'Yes, you'd look lovely in that suit and those shoes,' Kath said tartly. 'Oh, I'll leave you two old friends together while I go and wash the pots,' she said grumpily, knowing well how to annoy me.

I have this strange fetish that the kitchen is my operating theatre and think-tank. I don't mind her cooking in there but cleaning is my sole prerogative. Scouring the cooker with a Brillo pad is one of the few occasions when I manage to put together a few rational thoughts. I bit my lip and said nothing. If a few months with the fuzz had done wonders for Jay's confidence, the same period of living together had transformed Kath and myself into an old married couple. She knew exactly which buttons to press to wind me up.

Jay was riding a light alloy machine that was about a quarter of the weight of my Raleigh steel mountain bike. When we got out onto the Meadows he kept speeding away from me. I gave up the unequal competition after the second time round Sale Water Park.

'Fancy a pint at Jackson's Boat?' I yelled to his receding yellow backside, 'Or doesn't Mr Sinclair approve of pubs?' He braked sharply and we headed back the way we'd come without another word.

The gardens at the back of the pub were an incongruous spot for a conversation about Billy Fox. There were swings and children's games and young couples holding hands, not to mention the occasional horse rider trotting along the riverside path.

'So,' Jay said. 'Nice to renew your acquaintance.'

I explained the details of the Liptrot commission and Kath's hopes about what might spring from it.

'Hell, that bastard Fox!' he exploded bitterly. 'I've been asked if I'm related to him at least a dozen times. Bloody Billy Fox!'

'Come on, Jay! Stop feeling sorry for yourself. Just tell me what the gossip is. I don't want to start blundering around and then find that I'm treading on some very sensitive toes at Police HQ.'

'I shouldn't think that will happen. They're all very pleased with themselves from what I hear. Detective Superintendent Pinnock got himself a nice promotion out of it. DCS, he is now. The investigation only lasted a few days. All very neat and tidy was Billy. No littering of the scenery with battered corpses like the Yorkshire Ripper or the Bradford Basher.'

'Have you heard anything about the case that isn't in the papers?' I pressed.

'Nothing, except that it was pure chance that he was caught. They say he fits the profile for a multiple killer, and the buzz is that yours truly is shortly going to be involved in digging up half the school playgrounds in Manchester.'

I raised my eyebrows. 'How come?'

'Well, you know we've got the heads. Now the relatives are staging demos. I wouldn't mind but some of them were like this old woman who didn't give a shit for her daughter when she was alive. At any rate, they're demanding that Fox be brought back to Manchester to show us where he disposed of the missing torsos. He worked in at least seven different schools and also in evening centres and everywhere he went he was very handy and obliging with his spade. He'd do a bit of digging anywhere, would our Billy.'

'Sounds like you're in for a fun time,' I commented.

'You don't know the half of it. He can't give specific directions. He's very vague. We're going to have to shift hundreds of tons of soil.'

'What about this radar thing they used in Gloucester? The Geophysical what's-it-called?'

'Yeah, but Fred West gave very precise directions. They knew just where they were looking. We don't.' Jay gloomily downed his pint.

I went inside to replenish our glasses. So far he hadn't told me anything that could be useful to Liptrot.

'What do you know about Fox's background?' I asked, when I returned and carefully put his pint down on the beer mat in front of him.

'Hey, Boss, I don't work for you any more. Am I supposed to be talking like this?'

'Jay, just remember who gave you your early training as a crime fighter,' I joked. It was only half a joke.

'Yeah, I remember all your nasty little tricks and short cuts, but I'm in the navvying division of the police, not the CID.'

I looked him in the eye and for a moment I thought he was going to tell me to get lost, but he gave me that twisted grin of his and supped his ale.

'None of this comes back to me. Right?'

I nodded

'Tracing Billy's background was one hell of a job. Billy knows nothing about who his father is. They only found the father's name because Nancy Fox had applied for maintenance when Billy was a toddler, not that she got any. The dude denied everything, and there's no way we can force him to take a test to prove that he's the father of a mass murderer.'

'Hold on,' I said. 'Who's Nancy Fox and who's the dude?'

'Nancy Fox is the lady who put her name down as mother on Billy's birth certificate. She's dead now. This bloody psychologist, Caulfield, had the town turned upside down to find out more about her. See, she's trying to prove that Billy has reason to hate women. Nancy wasn't married to Billy's father – us black folks don't go in for marriage, you know.'

Jay sounded bitter and he had every right. He was only in the police force himself because his convict father had refused a paternity test.

'Yeah, well purely by chance, they turned up the court record of an application Nancy had made for a maintenance order against this dude. He denied he was the father and cleared off. When we got in touch with him again he threatened to take legal action against the force for defamation.'

'So your psychologist, Caulfield, let the matter drop?' I asked. 'The dude isn't the father?'

'I know different,' he muttered after swilling back

half a glass of ale. 'I know all about him. My mum's followed that creep's career for years. He's an athletics coach. He was working at the YMCA in Manchester when Billy was born. Now he's got a top job with the International Athletics Federation at Geneva. He travels round the world testing athletes for dope. He just turns up with his little bottle and demands that they do a wee-wee right then and there in front of him.'

I laughed at this.

'You might laugh, but the athletes don't. It's perform for him or forget your athletic career. His name's Horatio Bostick, like the glue, but he didn't stick with Billy for long.'

Jay put his head down and stuck his nose into his pint. I thought it was because of his own father who had similarly deserted him, but that was not what was troubling him.

'Can I trust you?' he asked quietly.

'What a question to ask. If you don't know by now you'd better say no more,' I said.

'Yeah, I suppose,' he drawled nasally, stressing the black accent he'd previously suppressed. I don't like it but there is a dramatic side to Jay's character that he needs to vent from time to time.

'You're not too bad for a whitey,' he said mockingly. 'We ain't all drug dealers.'

'OK, Constable Anderson. I've had enough sermons for today.'

'Not a constable yet, still trainin'. The t'ing is, mon, I do know a lot more about Billy and his background than I've let on.' As he spoke, Jay switched from his tedious mock Jamaican accent back to his normal Mancunian. 'It's a relief to tell someone. Not that they couldn't have found out a lot of this if they'd asked the right people, but I'm not going to volunteer anything.

I'm going to become an ordinary police officer like anyone else, not a spy on the black community,' he concluded bitterly. 'Anyway, Billy's father was a right bastard, fits all their stereotypes. My mother knew him when she was young and fancy-free. Billy's got half-brothers and sisters all over the place. Horatio Bostick believed in putting himself around.'

I gave him a questioning look. The way he put it, I didn't know whether to laugh or look serious.

He shook his head, 'You don't know them. Some of them have got his name and some haven't, but you'd better be bloody careful. The police haven't released Billy's so-called father's surname to the press. Among other reasons, they're scared of riots.'

'What about the mother?'

Jay shook his head. 'You don't get it, do you? The father goes round the world collecting samples in little bottles and the son stays here in good old Manchester collecting heads in big bottles. The press would never rest until they'd found Bostick's kids here in Manchester to see what they were all up to, and believe me there's a hell of a lot of them. He was a very athletic guy, was Mr Bostick. There's more. You know my mum's a midwife?'

I nodded.

'Yeah, well while my Mum was training, Billy's real mother was also a nurse, only like, ahead of Mum. She'd finished training. Her name is Lurlene Barnacle. I know . . . don't laugh. Neither of them stuck to each other very well. Anyway, Lurlene was pally with my mum because there weren't all that many other black nurses in those days. You Micks were taking up all the places. This Lurlene says she's having this baby by this wonderful black athlete who's going to win a gold medal at the Olympics and make her all rich and famous.' He paused to quaff his beer. I knew Jay liked the occasional spliff but this was the first time I'd seen him hitting the alcohol so freely. That was police influence for you.

'Anyway, this Bostick keeps stringing her along for months. She buys him this. She buys him that. New shoes one week, a tracksuit the next. Horatio will pay it all back when he becomes a big winner. Then she pops and now she's got the kiddie to look after, as well as him. The dude hits the roof. He blows the coop. She only sees him again when he calls round to "borrow" her wages. Then one time he comes round . . . my mother was right there in the house when he did this . . . lending moral support she was. "Hand over your bloody money, baby-mother," he says to Lurlene. She refuses. So he gets the kid out of the cot and burns it on the arse with a cigarette, thumps my mother in face for interfering and clears off. Only he comes back, time after time, until that baby is covered in burns. Lurlene handed over the money right enough.'

There were tears running down Jay's cheeks now. I moved my chair round to shelter him from the public view.

'Go on,' I encouraged.

'My Mum said she'd go to the police if Lurlene didn't do something. She went in the end, but they said they couldn't intervene as it was a domestic. Weren't so interested in child abuse in those days, not of black kids anyway. So Mum helped Lurlene to leave town. Only without the kid. Billy stays with his grandmother, Nancy Fox. She gives him her name and registers him as her kid so she can collect the family allowance and other benefits, like. Then she abandoned Billy when he was seven. He was too much for her to handle. When my Mum found out it was too late for her to do anything and she couldn't trace Lurlene anyway. The police know nothing about her. Lurlene's in London somewhere and you can bet that she isn't coming forward in a hurry now.'

I was the one who reached for the drink now. It was an ugly little tale right enough. We sat in silence for some time, occasionally fanning a wasp away from our drinks. Jay gradually regained his composure.

'Jay, joining the police was never my idea of a barrel of laughs. You can come back and work with me but then you'll always have the memory of what might have been,' I said seriously.

'Don't get heavy, man,' he said mildly. 'I've got to hack it before I jack it. Hell, I couldn't stand the thought of them buggers laughing up their sleeves if I put my papers in.'

'You're right,' I agreed. 'But don't forget who your friends are.'

'Talking of friends, my career choice hasn't, exactly, made me popular with my neighbours and the old home boys. It's been great going for a drink with someone who isn't a copper.'

'The number thirteen is often regarded as being unlucky. it certainly was for Albert Clark, the Bradford stonemason who had turned his hammer to other uses. He was caught by a trainee special constable on the night he set out to stalk his thirteenth victim.'
From *Madness in the Night – The Story of Twelve Serial Killers* by Muriel Lovejoy

3

Thursday, 13th September

When I woke and sat up bright sunshine was filtering through the venetian blinds making a pattern of light and shade across Kath's bony shoulders. The duvet had slipped off her and she was lying face down in the bed alongside me.

My head throbbed. The names Nancy and Lurlene, Billy and Horatio danced round inside my brain like demented butterflies. I wanted to forget all about them and go back to sleep, but my throat was so dehydrated that it felt incandescent. I clumsily reached over Kath for the large glass of orange juice she kept at her bedside. I drank gratefully and then tried to replace the glass. I didn't quite make it. The glass slipped between my nerveless fingers but then I caught it between finger and thumb.

About a tablespoonful of juice landed between Kath's shoulder blades, ran down her spine and lodged between the cleft of her buttocks. She started to wake. I plonked the glass down and began to mop up with a tissue.

'That's lovely,' she said as she woke, turning over and pulling me on top of her. One thing about Kath, her impulses were too strong to resist.

Afterwards I stayed in the bedroom to dress while Kath prepared breakfast. Although a thoroughly liberated woman, she was willing to accept some division of labour. Or at least she was this particular morning.

'We're meeting Cedric and his mother for lunch at the Swiss Chalet Hotel in Hale Barns at one,' she announced as she dished up my bacon and eggs.

'It so happened that while you were watching TV last night I was hearing things about Wicked Billy that Cedric will give his right arm to know.' I filled her in on Jay's revelations.

'Well, I wasn't exactly idle myself,' she said. 'I found out a lot about Cedric and his mother, and not from *Who's Who* either. I had a word with Cheryl McGrath, who works for the BBC down at Oxford Road. She put two of Cedric's plays on the radio last year. Cedric's written seven plays. One was produced in the West End. The rest have only been performed in provincial theatre or TV. There's one of his on at the Bolton Octagon now. I don't think he's made very much money out of play writing. He still lives with his mother in the same house in Bradford he grew up in.'

This was one of the things I admired about Kath: her ability to concentrate on the essentials in life – such as how much a potential client was worth. I suppose it was only natural, accustomed to an expensive lifestyle as she was. She had to fund the pony stabled at Carrington, holidays in Bali, designer clothes, and, of course, large supplies of bacon and other ingredients for her constant fry-ups. You certainly couldn't fuel Kath for an entire week on a big bowl of muesli.

'You're looking a bit glassy eyed, Dave. Is all this too

complicated for you?' she enquired.

'No, no. Go on. Fill me in on the literary background.'

'Well, some of the plays have been televised but they're a bit too gloomy and introverted to have real mass-market appeal. They've all been well reviewed –'

'– By his old college chums, no doubt.'

'Don't be so cynical, Dave. No, they have what you might call intellectual appeal. Which doesn't get you very far these days. He's only hit the big money with this true crime book about the Bradford Basher. I don't suppose you've managed to read it, have you?'

'Despite being retarded, I'm not completely illiterate! I managed to skim read it last night when I came back from delivering Jay to his lodgings. Who does he think he is? Setting himself up as an expert on crime.'

'Well, he does live in the same part of Bradford that the Basher came from.'

'Get away! His background was completely different. I doubt if he's ever walked through the streets of Bradford. Look what it says on the back of the book.' I picked up the offending tome. 'Son of a farmer who died when Cedric was four, brought up by his mother and an aunt in Bradford. Privately educated, three years at Bradford Grammar, Oxford, and then back to Bradford. The Basher was a monumental mason in Bradford Cemetery, hardly likely to have come across Cedric, mincing his way to his private school with his mother and his auntie holding his hands.'

'If that's meant to imply that Cedric's gay, you're quite wrong. Felicity said she had the greatest trouble in disentangling herself from him when she met him last. Regular human octopus he was.'

'Great, so this is the guy you want to collaborate on TV scripts with!'

'Don't put your underpants on over your trousers

yet. I won't be needing any Superman act from you. I'm a big girl. I know all kinds of ways of discouraging unwanted attention. Anyway, his mother's going to be watching him like a hawk.'

I looked at her and shook my head. 'Are you sure we need this job?' I asked.

She didn't bother with a reply, so I turned the radio on and got on with eating. I sandwiched half an egg and a couple of rashers between two thickly buttered pieces of toast. As I was pausing to wipe the melted butter running down my chin the local news came on the radio.

'The battered body of a young woman has been found beneath a supporting buttress outside the Velodrome near Alan Turing Way, Manchester, in the early hours of this morning. Police are treating the cause of death as murder. A spokesperson for the National Cycling Centre stated that the authorities at the Velodrome have taken every reasonable precaution to prevent the homeless seeking shelter under the buttresses and it is up to the City Fathers to provide accommodation for homeless young people. Police confirmed that the unidentified woman died of severe head injuries. She is the second homeless young person murdered while seeking shelter near a public building. Last month, Yvonne Clutterbuck, 17, was found in a cardboard box. The box was near an air vent at the back of the Churchill Hotel in central Manchester. Her head injuries were similar to those of the latest victim. Police have confirmed that there are similarities but are not yet treating both murders as the work of a single individual. There is an incident room at the Velodrome. The police request anyone with information to phone 0161 872 2378.'

Kath pushed her plate away from her. I poured us a cup of coffee.

'Well, we'll have to get on and find as much information as we can for Cedric, or the public is going to lose interest in his efforts. It looks as if someone is setting off to beat Billy's record,' I said quietly.

'God! It makes you wonder what's out there. You don't think it's some kind of copycat killing do you?' she asked. 'I don't think I could stomach this job if I thought there was someone waiting for us to tell him how to set about it.'

'Forget it,' I said with a shrug. 'Whoever he is, he won't need any help from you, Cedric or me. Isn't that how the Basher did his victims, cracking their skulls with a club hammer?'

Kath nodded, silent.

Neither of us felt like going into the office and we had a few hours to waste until our appointment with the Liptrot family. Kath went back to bed, not to sleep, but to continue with her notes for the TV treatment. I went out to do some shopping.

I walked from the flat in Thornleigh Court to the shops along Willows Road. I could have gone to the crowded little shopping precinct on Wilbraham Road but the role of literary detective drew me to Willows Road with its bookshop. I bought the bacon as required, tucked it under my arm and headed for a long browse around Axon's Second-hand Books.

It took me a moment to force open the rickety door of the shop. Neatly stacked and labelled books filled every available inch of space. Alerted by the doorbell, Gary Axon, the proprietor, emerged from a gloomy recess in the interior.

'Oh, it's you,' he said dismissively when he saw me. Gary looks more like a nightclub proprietor than a book dealer, maybe the owner of a trendy jazz club that's not raking in much money. He always wears loose jackets with the sleeves rolled up. Like many other locals I often go for a mooch round his shelves when on

Willows Road. Unfortunately for Gary, none of us are big spenders. He presides over a very interesting collection of newish books sold to him because no one wants to read them. Either that or other customers remove the good books before I get there.

I told him what I was after and he steered me to the drama section. I soon picked up a cheap edition of Cedric Liptrot's collected plays resting among other discarded masterpieces.

'Not much call for that, had it in for two years,' Axon said, blowing the dust off the spine. 'Tell you what, I'll let you have it for a fiver, as it's you.' I fished a fiver out of my back pocket and he chatted on as he wrapped the book. 'Gloomy stuff! They had one of his plays on at the Royal Exchange but I left at the interval.'

However, I noticed that he had three copies in hardback of *A Son To Us All* on his true crime shelves. I nodded at it. 'That seems to be doing well.'

'It was in the *Sunday Times* bestseller list for nearly a year. Remarkable book, he gets right inside the head of Albert Clark, but I thought he gilded the lily a bit as far as the police were concerned,' Gary commented. 'Shall I wrap one up for you,' he asked hopefully. I shook my head. 'Don't blame you, it's padded out to buggery,' he said. That was the interesting thing about Gary's shop – Gary had read all the books and could give you a quick review of anything you picked up.

On my way back to the flat I reviewed what I knew about Albert Clark, the so-called Basher. He had killed nine prostitutes and three of what the police termed 'innocent' women in the Bradford area before being caught. Altogether the case hadn't marked the Central Yorkshire Constabulary's most shining hour. Apart from constantly making a distinction between prostitutes, presumably regarded as fair game for a killer, and normal women, they'd insistently denied that the first five murders were the work of one man. It had taken them over five years to catch Clark and then it had been by a fluke. A female special constable who had collared him for a parking offence had noticed the club hammer wrapped in a carrier bag on the back seat of his car.

The Central Yorkshire Police had evidently seen Liptrot and his book as a way to redress the well-merited unfavourable publicity. He received full co-operation and in return he'd stressed the relentless nature of the police enquiries; the elimination of thousands of suspects, the blood and DNA testing of a wide population, rather than the chance nature of the arrest. The point Liptrot didn't make was that murder is regarded as an occupational risk of prostitutes and that neither fuzz nor press stirred themselves until Clark started targeting 'innocent' women.

Although it was a warm day, a shiver ran down my spine. Was the most recent Velodrome victim a pro? Was today's killing a sign that some twisted individual was working his way through Liptrot's book about Clark? Would the new book about Billy Fox also breed a host of copycats? I put the idea to the back of my mind. The bookshops were groaning with literature about horrific crime. Dahmer and Nilsen, Sutcliffe and Sams – all competing for space with Catherine Cookson and Barbara Taylor Bradford. Why should we swell their numbers?

Kath was dressed in a green business suit and ready for action when I got back. Her plans for scripts were neatly stored in a folder. I changed into a navy blue 'soft-tailored' jacket and grey gabardine trousers. We looked a promising pair when we set off in Kath's silver Mazda.

Once on the M56 traffic slowed to a crawl. There were massive roadworks under construction, with huge concrete foundations being set in place, big enough to hide a hecatomb of victims of secret crime. I mentioned Jay's gloomy prognostications about having to begin his police career with a spade in his hands but dropped the subject when Kath didn't reply.

The hotel itself was tucked into the remains of a green valley most of which had been inundated under a blanket of concrete to form a runway for Manchester Airport. A similar fate was planned for the remaining pleasant dells and rills of the area. My effort to make light conversation was likewise submerged by Kath's grim silence. I realised that she was psyching herself up for the meeting with the Liptrots, a vital encounter for her and hence for me. Once inside the hotel, all light-oak panelling and discreet Muzak, we were shown quickly up to the suite reserved for the Liptrots by Headstone Press. I was impressed, but then Kath had said that Cedric was getting an advance of half a million. *A Son To Us All* had sold millions in America.

When we entered the sitting room to meet Cedric and his mother I was in good humour but the mood soon leaked away. Our clients sat in comfortable arm-chairs looking out over the remains of the wooded valley. Enough of it survived to give a view of a mixed woodland of sycamore, birch and oaks, just getting ready to shed their leaves. Cedric greeted me warmly enough. He bounded forward and shook my hand with aggressive firmness. Nothing limp-wristed about him. He was wearing a tatty looking navy blazer, black polo neck and grey flannels.

It says something for the power of suggestion that on first glance Liptrot reminded me of Harold Pinter. Apart from Shakespeare, Pinter was probably the only play-wright I could have picked out of a police ID parade. There was just a faint resemblance. Liptrot had wavy black hair worn quite long, and heavy metal-rimmed glasses. With the goatee beard and dark eyebrows it gave his face a gloomy appearance. His face or at least his chin, was long, extended by the neatly trimmed black beard. I studied the hair for some time. It was either a natural 'Melvyn Bragg' or an ill-fitting wig. Either way, I was hardly going to find out.

He looked like an individual to whom doubt was a stranger, a professional dispenser of certainties.

He was older than the forty years advertised on the back of *A Son To Us All*. Nearer fifty, I thought. This wasn't the shy, retiring character I'd been led to expect. I was surprised. He was obviously mad and dangerous.

I sensed immediately that he was more interested in Kath than in me. So did someone else. The son had only the faintest trace of Yorkshire in his speech but the voice that cracked out now was broad Bradford.

'Stop fussing, Cedric. The woman can find her own way to a chair,' his mother rapped out in the unmistakable tone of one who is used to obedience. When she spoke the muscles of her face were fighting her brain to stop the words escaping from her lips. Her mouth was twisted to one side and with each utterance she jerked her head forward as if to assist the words in their passage through her throat.

I studied her carefully to see if she'd had a mild stroke or Bell's palsy, but it seemed to be just a mannerism. Her face was smooth and unlined when she relaxed. Her hair was dyed an unnatural coppery shade of red with white roots showing. The hair clashed with her pink suit and cream blouse.

Cedric gave me a half-apologetic smile, bobbed his head up and down to signify compliance to his mother's orders, then nipped back sharply and perched himself on the arm of his mother's chair. His eyes didn't stray from Kath.

I noticed just the faintest hint of colour spring into Kath's face at being described as 'the woman' but she handled the situation well. She strode towards Liptrot Senior with her hand outstretched like royalty at a command performance.

'I've already rung for tea,' Lena Liptrot said, waving Kath away. 'Well, Mr Cunane, and what makes you think you're qualified to assist my son?' she said, turning to me as if Kath had suddenly swallowed an invisibility pill.

'Mr Cunane's role has all been arranged –' Kath said, interposing herself awkwardly.

'Excuse me, young woman. Let the dog see the rabbit as we say in *Bratfurt.* I want to hear what he's got to say for himself,' Lena said rudely. All this forthrightness was coming out of just one side of the old woman's mouth. It struck me that she might have toothache or a savage abscess, but with just one side of her face she was managing to put the fear of God into me. 'My son managed to write seven plays and one bestselling true crime book without the assistance of a private detective and I want to know if Mr Cunane's capable of –'

'Now, Mother,' the author himself interrupted, orally capitalising the M in mother, 'You know that's all arranged. The publisher –'

'Fiddlesticks! You didn't produce your work for some chit of a girl on the end of a phone in London. It was me that pushed and prodded you and made you write things down on paper.'

No one had a very convincing answer for that, and no one spoke for a moment.

'I know my way round Manchester,' I offered, breaking the awkward silence. 'I know where all the nooks and crannies are. I know how to pry for information, if that's what you mean, Mrs Liptrot.'

'Huh! You know how to blow your own trumpet, at least. I suppose no one else will do it for you. What about your lady friend here? Are you man and wife?' she said, changing tack abruptly.

'We're partners. We live together, if that's any business of yours,' I said with equal bluntness.

She gave her son a sharp look. 'Very modish, I'm sure, though neither of you are exactly spring chickens. Folk that wanted to share a bed got married in my day. But Cedric and I are partners too, in a way,' she said surprisingly, stroking his arm possessively. Cedric looked uncomfortable. 'Yes, when he finished at Oxford it was me who stuck by him and helped him get started as a writer –'

'You mustn't mind Mother,' Cedric interjected. 'She likes to take the credit for whatever success I've enjoyed as a writer.'

'And who's more entitled?' Lena demanded fiercely. At that moment I began to feel better about taking the job. This was a situation I could understand. Looking from mother to son, she adamant and proud, he shiftily examining Kath's cleavage out of the corner of his eye, I found myself sympathising with Mother. If Cedric was a bloody little lap dog, she at least was a thorough-going bitch, as advertised.

'Didn't step foot out of my house for three years until he completed his first play,' she claimed with an air of candour, folding her arms and leaning back to squint at us from behind her massive bosom. 'That's why I need to know all about you two. Frankly, when that Felicity Grete recommended using a private detective from Manchester to help Cedric I wasn't best pleased. I told her –'

'Mother, you mustn't embroider the truth,' Cedric bleated. 'You've never spoken to her.'

His mother wasn't at all put out by this. She smiled at me triumphantly.

'There you are, Mr Cunane, that's my Cedric. You

can tell he's had a fancy education. Bradford Grammar and Balliol College. Do you know what he's talking about? "Embroider", indeed! Without me to cut out all that fancy stuff he'd never have had a word published.'

'Really, Mother!' Cedric pleaded.

Mrs Liptrot ploughed on, regardless. 'Yes, when Felicity said she was going to find us a literary private detective I didn't fancy it at all, but looking at you, Mr Cunane, I must say I'm warming to the idea.' I smiled back at her and then at Kath. It looked as if the old Cunane charm was coming in handy after all. There was no trace of expression whatsoever on Kath's face.

'Just what sort of information interests you?' I asked. 'My partner thought you were looking for fresh material.'

'Oh well, er, obviously we don't expect you to unearth anything too surprising,' said Cedric. He was struggling to make some kind of decision. He stood up and walked towards the window, wringing his hands. 'The thing is' er, actually –'

'What Cedric is trying to tell you is that I did all the local research in Bradford that made *A Son To Us All* such a success,' Lena Liptrot explained. 'It was easy, I've lived there for seventy years after all, but here I'm a fish out of water. That's why we need you.'

'What's stopping Cedric doing his own research?' I asked her, abandoning the pretence that I was having a conversation directly with the author.

'Now, Dave,' Kath intervened cautiously. 'Felicity explained all that.'

'No doubt she said my son was very odd,' Lena said, narrowing her eyes as she looked at Kath.

'Oh, no. Not really,' Kath stammered.

'The truth is, young woman, he can reconstruct a scene better from his imagination than by going out and recording every detail. The way he writes is far more convincing than a purely factual reconstruction. Cedric's work is psychologically true because he can think himself into the mind of the murderer. The Central Yorkshire Police were really interested in what he wrote about Albert Clark. Cedric even suggested details that they'd overlooked –'

Cedric turned angrily from his contemplation of the view from his window, 'Mother, will you let me get a word in?' He looked as if he was getting ready to bash his head against the wall.

'Touchy today, aren't we?' she replied, but she subsided back into her chair and let him have the floor.

'Look, Cunane,' Cedric wasn't looking me in the eye, 'I've got the main details of the Billy murders. Everyone who reads the papers has. According to Felicity, Assistant Chief Constable Sinclair of the police here in Manchester has gone out of his way to offer us his help.'

'Has he? That doesn't sound much like the Sinclair I know. He's a friend of my father's,' I interrupted. It was the wrong thing to say. Cedric paused a moment, glared at me, and then pressed on.

'The thing is, despite the gruesome details, . . . twelve decapitated heads found in the brute's bedroom . . . there isn't really enough nitty-gritty to make much of a book. At least the sort of book I can write.'

'Actually, it was fourteen heads,' I butted in.

'Whatever, but the trial was over in two days, and Headstone Books expect me to produce another best-seller and a TV script.'

'Yes,' burst in his mother, unable to contain herself any longer. 'There's not enough to knit a paragraph out of, still less a five-hundred-page blockbuster.' There was tremendous emotion and animation in her face. She looked as if she were auditioning for all the parts in a Greek tragedy at once. I felt intimidated again. 'The public is dying to know what that little shite-hawk got up to while he was killing all those poor wenches, but the police admit that they're stumped. Find that out and we'll have a world-wide bestseller.'

Lena folded her arms across her formidable bosom once more and relaxed into her seat. With her stout arms and full thighs pointing in my direction she looked like a great battleship swinging at anchor; immense power and force lying in repose.

'Do you get our drift, Mr Cunane?' she demanded. 'There isn't ever going to be much you can dig up. We'll have the police records and photographs. There might even be a chance for us to visit Fox at Greenash. We think you should take a reduced fee, and as for Ms Headlam . . . we don't need her at all. I've heard one or two things about her and I don't think it'll do Cedric's image any good to be associating with the likes of her.'

I heard a sharp intake of breath from my partner.

'Get the police to bung a load of PR stuff at you, and then let your son's imagination have free rein. Is that your idea of investigative writing, Mrs Liptrot?' I said scornfully.

Cedric studied my face intently. His eyes were a very washed-out shade of blue behind the metal-rimmed specs. I could almost read his mind. 'Thick yob', that's what he was thinking.

'I'm not in the business of true-life crime stories, Mr Cunane. Imaginative reconstruction, getting inside the mind of a killer, that's what my public want. I am a dramatist after all.'

'Well, bully for you! Kath and I'll wait until you've finished your book before we release our own information about Wicked Billy, then.' I was dying to throw a spanner into his works, actually rather than metaphorically.

'Eee, what are you on about, lad?' chipped in the

human battleship from the depths of her chair. 'What information? There is none, Cedric. Take no notice!'

Kath joined in. 'I don't think any TV company will be interested in your book if there is piles more factual information coming out that you've discounted,' she said. 'Felicity says the TV deal isn't actually finalised yet,' she added cattily. 'I've seen lots of promising projects come to grief at the final stages.'

Cedric turned a pale shade of puce. 'What is this, Cunane?' he screeched.

'I've discovered some very interesting background material about Billy Boy, that's all. Now that you've decided to give Kath the elbow and offer me less, I've got to consider what it's worth to someone else,' I rapped back.

'That's right,' Kath chimed in. 'I'm sure the *Sun* would pay plenty to learn that –'

'No. Don't say a word,' I ordered. 'Let's get out of here.' I stood up to leave and Kath rose to follow.

The old dame in the armchair realised that she'd overplayed her hand. I think she'd wanted us both on our knees begging for our jobs and tugging our forelocks like the servant class did in her youth. Perhaps she now realised that it wasn't very bright to muck up the publisher's arrangements.

She pulled Cedric down towards her while she whispered something urgently in his ear. Whatever it was, it gave him a jolt.

'We ought to reconsider,' he mumbled, avoiding my gaze. When he looked at Kath there was a peculiar expression on his pale face, he was almost licking his lips. 'Look Cunane,' he whined. 'We'll keep you on at the agreed rate, plus a bonus for any new information. It comes out of my royalties. You can't expect us not to drive a hard bargain.'

'And Kath? What about her?'

'I'll look at this,' he said, snatching the folder of notes out of her hand. 'But, I can't promise anything.'

'We both work as previously agreed or neither of us does. Phone me when she makes your mind up for you,' I said, nodding in the direction of Mrs Liptrot.

So they thought they needed me but not Kath. 'Why?' I asked myself.

Lindow Man: On Friday, 1st August 1984, a naked body severed at the waist was discovered in a peat bog at Lidow Moss near Wilmslow. Police were called. it was only after prolonged forensic investigation that it was decided that the body was the surviving evidence of the druid practice of human sacrifice two thousand years ago and not a recent cadaver. The body was carefully preserved and is now kept in the British Museum.

4

Thursday afternoon

On the way out of the hotel Kath fumbled some change into a cigarette machine and retrieved a packet of Benson and Hedges from the tray. She hadn't smoked for months. It went against the grain for Kath to show her disappointment by cursing and swearing. Instead she preferred to turn the air blue with tobacco smoke. The quality of her silence indicated her anger. I wasn't sure whether she was just angry with Old Mother Liptrot or with me as well.

I must have been nervous because coming out of the hotel car park I took the wrong turn and headed off towards Wilmslow, rather than Manchester. I had an impression that someone had followed us out, just a glimpse of a grey van in the mirror. We drove along the road for some way without speaking and as the silence lengthened it became impossible to admit my mistake. Then I saw a sign on the right that gave me the excuse to pull over. It was a site of special scientific interest – Lindow Moss – a local nature reserve open to the public. I drove confidently into the car park. The grey van went on by. I got an impression that the driver was a middle-aged man. We sat in silence for a moment, contemplating the dense screen of bushes and woods in front of us. I was determined not to be the first to speak.

'What's this then?' Kath said at last, in a low dispirited voice.

'I thought we might go for a walk for a few minutes and talk things over –'

'What is there to talk over?' she said angrily. 'That bloody woman! Who does she think she is?'

I got out of the car and Kath followed, still seething.

'This is where they dug up the remains of Lindow Man,' I confided knowledgeably, indicating the moss-land in the distance. 'The police treated that as a murder case until they found that the remains were over two thousand years old.'

'Shut up!' Kath replied. 'Stop wittering. I can't bear it! Felicity said he was eccentric but I didn't expect that kind of treatment.'

'Actually, I think you made rather a hit with him. His eyes were out on stalks. I think it's Mother who's the real obstacle, not him.'

'The man needs analysis! Imagining himself into the mind of a murderer while his precious mother gives him directions. Talk about an Oedipus complex! Did you see the way he sat on the arm of her chair? A grown man fawning over that horrible old creature! It's depraved.'

'Spare me the amateur psychology, Kath. This knockback might be a good thing if it makes us both face up to reality.'

'Reality! – A broken down office at the top of six flights of stairs!'

Now it was my turn to feel angry. You can't win. I'd done everything she wanted. Now she was throwing my efforts back in my face. We walked along in silence. I made a point of studying the scenery and Kath lit another cigarette. The path wound its way through a dense growth of dwarf birch and oak. There was still plenty of greenery in this sheltered spot.

Eventually we reached the Black Lake at the centre of the site. Apart from a couple of OAPs with their grandchildren at the other side of the lake, we were on our own. My partner was still fuming. 'What have you brought me here for?' she asked. 'I've got things to do.'

'Why don't we sit down for a while? You might feel better.'

She looked as if she was on the point of striding back to the car park but then she thought better of it. We sat at opposite ends of a bench. Some time passed. I was idly observing the insect life when some faint movement caught the corner of my eye. I looked round quickly. There was nothing, but I had a strong sensation that we were being observed. It was that sort of place. The dense undergrowth could hide a regiment of Peeping Toms.

I looked round again. The bushes stirred faintly. It could have been the breeze or my imagination. Kath must have caught my mood. 'Let's go. I don't like this place. There's a creepy, shut-in feeling to it.' We stood for a moment looking out over the waters where druids had once performed their ugly rituals. There were dragon-flies flitting about but no sign of a hidden observer.

Before we plunged into the bushes I threw a stone into the lake, watching the ripples spread out. It didn't dispel the atmosphere. Kath strode ahead briskly. I set off after her. The path back took us past little ponds with neat observation decks and explanatory pictures of newts and water-boatmen. Eager children were bending perilously close to the edges to peer into the hidden depths while anxious parents hung onto them by their clothing.

I kept turning round and taking a glance over my shoulder. There was nothing; nothing but that uneasy sensation. 'What's the matter?' Kath asked.

'Nothing, I just thought I spotted someone in the bushes back there.'

'Probably kids,' she said. I could see that her temper had improved. She scanned the area. 'This place is likely to be crawling with perverts and sex maniacs. That's the trouble with these carefully fenced-off bits of nature. They attract the deranged.'

A grey van, similar to the one that had followed us from the hotel, was parked across the exit from the nature trail. I walked past it. There was no one in it. We drove away and took the M56 back to Manchester. I drove in the slow lane and kept one eye on the rear-view mirror. There was no one following us.

Kath seemed more like herself so my little diversion at least had one good result.

'I thought I might go up to Hawkshead and spend a long weekend with Daddy,' she said. 'It's been ages since I saw him last, and he's not getting any younger.'

I raised my eyebrows and looked at her questioningly. Daddy was her port in a storm, not me. Her father, a retired naval commander whose entire service career had been spent in submarines, had elected to spend his retirement in the Lake District. I thought it was because the constant drenching offered by the local climate reminded him of his former life beneath the waves.

'You can come too,' she offered. 'Daddy would be delighted to see you.'

The lie was so blatant that I laughed loudly. Daddy thought I was a lower-class lout who shouldn't be banging his daughter, even if it was done with her enthusiastic agreement. That wasn't just my alleged lower-class chip-on-the-shoulder talking. He'd told me so in as many words. The Headlam family were certainly direct. Daddy was a traditional naval officer, with a broken nose from his rugby playing days, a deadpan expression that gave away nothing, and no nonsense about endearing himself to the other ranks. My sort was there to work the ship and man the guns as directed by the officer class. He would have been totally at home on the quarter-deck of one of Nelson's first-rates or the bridge of a heavy cruiser at Jutland.

'I've one or two loose ends to tie up here,' I said. 'I'm worried about Jay Anderson. I think he's being given hell by some of our lovely little red-neck coppers. I'd like to take him up to see my old man. I haven't seen my parents for a while.' It didn't do any harm to remind Kath that I also had roots and came from a background that could be just as disapproving as her own.

'We're an odd couple, aren't we?' she said.

'If you don't like the arrangements we can always change them.'

'Touchy, aren't you?'

'Me! Touchy?' I exploded. 'It was you –'

'Oh, come on Dave! You wanted us to face reality.'

'That old besom back at the hotel did make one or two cuts that were close to the bone. All that stuff about whether we're married.'

'She was only saying that for her precious Cedric's benefit. The old harridan's still living in the Victorian era.'

'I have been married, you know,' I said belligerently. 'I'm not incapable of forming a permanent relationship.'

'I never said you were.'

We drove in silence for some time as I negotiated the

complicated interchanges leading off the motorway towards Chorlton.

'Dave – is this your round-about way of proposing? she asked eventually.

I shrugged my shoulders. She'd have to take it in whatever way she preferred. It was true that neither of us was getting any younger.

'I've no objection to a spot of mating. You know that, Dave. It's the rest I object to. Can you see me toiling at a sink, up to my armpits in dirty nappies,' she said earnestly.

I looked at her closely. She wasn't joking.

'They don't use them these days,' I chided.

'Well, as long as it's only a spot of . . . fresh air and healthy exercise you're interested in why don't you come up on the Saturday or Sunday? You can bring me the tidings from the Liptrots. You know Daddy will be out roaming the Fells.'

That was it. I could tell from the firm set of her lips that the topic was closed.

We parted when we reached Chorlton. I drove on into town in my car, a battered old second-hand, red Nissan Bluebird. Sometimes, I wished I had something a bit more adventurous to drive. It was as ponderous and stolid in cornering as a truck, but it did have the advantage of being virtually invisible wherever I went in Manchester. I managed to find a space in the car park at the back of the courthouse in Minshull Street. I wasn't feeling too pleased with myself as I walked to my office in the Atwood Building. The roof of the old listed warehouse was sagging even more noticeably than usual in the bright sunlight of the afternoon. It gave a new meaning to the word 'listed'.

I hadn't been in the office long before I heard the fluting tones of the fax machine on Kath's desk. Four sheets of paper scrolled out. It was a contract from

Headstone Press with a covering note addressed to Kath from Felicity Grete.

Dear K.

There seems to have been a mix up between you and Cedric. He's just called to ask me to correct any wrong impressions you may have. He's delighted with your work on the TV script and instructs me to tell you that he will insist on you receiving full credit (name below his)! There's a contract of employment here for your partner, guaranteeing one calendar month's work at 10% above the previously agreed rate. Get him to sign it and post by return. Also very good news on the police front. One of your local bigwigs in Manchester called Sinclair has suggested bringing Cedric in as a kind of consultant about some recent murders you've had up there. So I think we can take it that the police will be very co-operative with info for the Billy book.

Yours ever

Felicty.

PS. I don't know what you've done to Lena and Cedric but I've never known them to be so co-operative. Nil desperandum, things are looking up for you on the job front.

I read my contract carefully. I was to be paid for the full month regardless of how long Liptrot required my services, which was nice. What wasn't so nice was that I was required to divulge any information I discovered in the course of enquiries exclusively (in so far as the law allowed) to Liptrot alone. I was required to accompany Liptrot in any capacity he required in his travels round Manchester.

After today's performance any information he got from me was going to be' carefully edited before he saw it, but, for the rest, shepherding him round Manchester was no hardship. Assistant Chief Constable Sinclair was in for a surprise when I showed up at Liptrot's elbow.

Thinking of Sinclair made me wonder just what kind of public relations exercise was going on here. Sinclair was a sly old bugger. Yet, he was normally so secretive that people in his own office had little idea what he was up to. Now here he was offering a publishing firm invaluable publicity.

What could be the reason? Was the GMP under pressure from on high to play this case with a bit more imagination than the Central Yorkshire Police had managed to do in the original Basher killings? Could there be a more sinister motive? Had Sinclair already decided that his force wasn't going to catch this new killer of two women in a hurry? Random killings of loners on remote sites are notoriously difficult to solve. Did he want to involve Cedric Liptrot, the so-called expert in serial killings, at an early stage? Then if things went wrong, he could always say they'd been following the best advice, furnished by the country's leading authority.

If he was setting Liptrot up as a fall guy he would have my full support. It couldn't happen to a nicer fellow. That might not be the reason though. With Sinclair it was often months later that you realised just why he'd taken a certain course of action. He thought well ahead.

Just to be on the safe side, I spent part of the afternoon typing up my notes about what I'd learned from Geoff Bartle and from Jay. I looked through the phone book for any mention of Bosticks. If Horatio had spread himself around as thoroughly as Jay claimed there should be plenty of entries There were twenty-odd Bostocks one Bostic without a 'k' and five Bosticks. Three of the Bosticks were in Moss Side and two in Old Trafford Quite a number of the Bostocks clustered round the inner city as well, I sat and pondered for a while The information was certainly relevant to any story about the genesis and development of Billy Fox but it had come from a confidential source. I decided to sit on it for the time being. I locked my notes in the safe.

Headstone hadn't been paying me at the time I discovered it. Anyway, there should be many other ghoulish details to glean if half of what was said about Billy's upbringing after Nancy Fox abandoned him was correct.

Shortly after four the phone rang. It was Liptrot.

'Mr Cunane, has the Headstone Press been in contact with you?' he asked diffidently. I gave an affirmative grunt. 'Is everything all right then?' I responded with another grunt. 'I wonder if you could come out to the hotel right away? Assistant Chief Constable Sinclair has been in touch. He wants me to offer him any insights I can into the murder of this girl at the Velodrome last night. The way he put it, it was an offer I can't refuse. It'll be a kind of quid pro quo for whatever he lets me have about Billy.'

'That's great Mr Liptrot. What's the problem? You and your mother are bubbling over with insights, aren't you?' I asked breezily. If he wanted my help in anything that wasn't in that contract – and accompanying him to meetings with Sinclair about murders not involving Billy certainly wasn't – he was going to have to humble himself. He and his blessed mother had really rubbed my nose in it this morning. I could sense his hesitation.

'It's like this, I need . . . oh hell. Look, I can't tell you over the phone. Can't you come round? Please put what happened earlier behind you. It was all a mistake. I can only tell you face to face.'

What he meant was that he needed Mother there to

give out the instructions. I listened to him clearing his throat nervously before I replied.

'OK, I'll be with you when I can make it through the traffic. Expect me when you see me. It'll probably take me an hour at this time of night.'

I had no intention of scurrying off to do his bidding at the drop of a hat. I had business of my own.

I gave Kath a call but neither she nor her father was in and she didn't carry a mobile these days. I left the good news from Grete on her answer phone.

Before I left the office I phoned my father at his moorland cottage to tell him about Jay and his troubles.

'It's never easy,' Paddy said. 'They put me through hell because my father was on the force and because . . . well, never mind. They knew I was never going to prance around with my trouser leg rolled up. There was one particular bastard, Jack . . . anyway, he died of prostate cancer the other week, so I'll say nothing ill of the dead . . . but you know what the bastard did? He used to spit on my food. Wanted me to thump him, then he could get me sacked. My sergeant and inspector were in the same lodge as him. They'd have backed him all the way. I knew if I as much as breathed on him they'd have me out on my ear. They got tired of it after a while when they saw I wasn't going to rise to their bait.'

'Yeah, that's all right, Paddy. That was you and this is him,' I explained. 'Don't forget that you had Grandad to advise you and there were lots of others in your situation. Black coppers from Moss Side are a much rarer breed . . .'

'Correct,' he said in his flat official sort of way. 'Give me his number and I'll ask him up here for the week-end or whenever he's free. A bit of fresh air and solid food will work wonders for him. Can't have the lad feeling sorry for himself, can we?'

I gave him Jay's number and muttered my thanks, but he wasn't done with me.

'Is this one of your annual phone calls then, David? You know your mother worries about you. Why don't you keep in touch? Are you still with that high-flown madam from the TV studios?'

'Hold on. There are about six questions there. You know I don't phone because you give me a load of earache every time I do. I'm still with Kath, just about. She's cleared off to the Lake District for a long weekend with her father.'

'If she can visit her family, why not you?'

'I've got a lot on. I'm helping this author write a book about the Billy murders.'

There was a long silence after that.

'Just what help are you giving him?' he asked in a low tone.

'I'm helping him with the Manchester background and a bit of investigating into a few loose ends.'

There was no warning rumble before he spoke next but I knew he was going to blast me.

'Why the hell you didn't get yourself an honest job, I'll never know. It's not for want of effort on my part, or your mother's. I must tell you that writing these stories about dirty little freaks like Fox is on a par with grave robbing in my book. They just glorify the scum and make others want to copy them. What somebody should be doing is building a very large memorial to the victims of his crimes. It's bloody immoral the way this country's run these days.'

With that he slammed the phone down.

He was probably right but I'd bet he'd be watching the TV dramatisation of *Fox's Den* or whatever title they settled on along with about twenty million other upright citizens. I think the old curmudgeon relished nothing better than the chance to give me a flea in the ear. He was like Dial-a-Conscience, the voice of the moral majority speaking from his lofty pinnacle in the hills. At least he'd do something for Jay. The Chief Constable would be on the receiving end of an awkward phone call if Paddy found that Jay was being victimised. Relentlessness, whatever that was, was one thing I'd inherited from him.

Once out in the hydrocarbon-rich Manchester air I walked angrily towards the car, trampling along the cracked pavement. A Chinese family coming towards me hopped smartly out of my way.

As I had predicted, the traffic was dense. It took me half an hour to get to the end of the Parkway and onto the M56. I drove wildly, crossing lanes and ignoring the fifty-mile-per-hour limit whenever I got the chance. I wasn't the only one. The traffic was fierce. If I got done, I could send the fine to Headstone Press.

Cedric Liptrot must have been on the look out for me because he came running out before I'd even locked the car.

'Thank God you've come,' he gasped. 'Come on up, Mother's waiting.' He practically dragged me into the hotel. I took the stairs two at a time. I couldn't help noticing that Cedric was puffing and panting alongside me like a steam-engine gone wrong. Evidently the sedentary writer's life left him short of energy.

When I got into their suite Lena was lying on the sofa fanning herself with a copy of one of Cedric's plays.

Cedric had set out a table in the sitting room as a work desk. There was a printer with a stack of paper sitting alongside his compact computer. 'Wonderful box of tricks, 540 megs and a fax-modem attached. I'll give you my e-mail address,' he offered with the special pride of those who feel that they are on the crest of the technological wave. Not to be out done, I took out my pager and gave him the number I could be reached on.

He appeared suitably impressed.

'Will you boys stop bragging about your toys and come over here?' an imperious voice rapped out from the sofa.

Cedric and I seated ourselves facing her.

'What are we going to do? That fool of a police officer Sinclair thinks that Cedric is some sort of expert criminologist! And it suits us for him to go on thinking that. He's invited Cedric to look at where this young lass was murdered at the Velodrome and to attend the autopsy with his officers. Then tomorrow, he's calling round in person to take Cedric to the flat where Billy Fox lived.'

I didn't see what the problem was. Then I looked across at Cedric. His momentary affability had evaporated. He was wringing his hands. His helmet of dark locks was plastered onto his scalp by sweat, beads of which were trickling down onto his glasses, effectively blinding him. He looked like a lost, day-old kitten. I turned back to Lena.

'You see what the problem is,' she said out of the side of her mouth. 'He's so squeamish he used to run a mile if he saw me cutting up a fish, let alone seeing some young wench's liver and lights being pulled out under his nose. So I told the police officer that he'd be bringing an assistant with him and he didn't mind. You'll have to go and prop him up.'

Lena's unsubtle comments had done nothing to soothe her son. He'd turned green.

'There's nothing in my contract about this,' I said coldly. 'I'm being employed for the Billy Fox enquiry.'

'Ten-per-cent bonus on top of your total gross earnings if you do it. I want you to see him through these meetings without any fuss, and I mean complete discretion. He's got his public to think about.' As she made the offer her facial muscles were doing aerobics to a Stockhausen concerto.

'Twenty per cent,' I said coolly. After the way she'd treated Kath I was in no mood to be generous.

We settled on twelve and a half per cent of total net earnings. I insisted that she type out the addendum to my contract on Cedric's fancy machine and fax it off to Headstone.

'You can start earning this right away. They're coming for him in an unmarked car in twenty minutes,' she informed me when she finished. She was very proficient with everything for a person in her seventies. I began to wonder again just how far her collaboration with Cedric went.

'Is he always like this?' I asked her, looking at Cedric. He was completely paralysed. There was no way he was going to inspire the GMP in this state. She nodded.

'Bloody hell,' I muttered to myself. I stripped my jacket off and advanced on him. 'Shower for you,' I said, taking him by the arm.

When he was in the bathroom Lena came in and laid a new shirt and dark suit out on the bed. I selected a stripy tie for him. 'That's his Balliol College tie,' she said proudly.

'Let's hope the GMP are suitably impressed,' I muttered.

When he came out of the shower I stayed with him while he dressed. I noted with a twinge of disappointment that the hair was his own. For some reason I'd have preferred it to be a wig. His face had lost its puffiness and bad colour and he wasn't trying to drwnon himself in his own sweat anymore, but he was still shaking and trembling.

'God Almighty! What have I let myself in for?' I wondered. He looked like someone coming down from a bad trip.

I gave his case and drawers a quick scan. I didn't find any pills, potions or powders. If he'd been using whiz there was none about now. Meanwhile he was just sitting on the edge of the bed like a slowly deflating balloon.

'Get a grip on yourself!' I shouted at him, but a cod on a fishmonger's slab would have shown more life than Cedric. He just didn't respond. There was no time to rush out and get him a prescription for Prozac. I pulled him through into the living room towards the hospitality trolley. I took out a half-pint tumbler and filled it with vodka and tomato juice in about equal quantities and made him drink it down in one. Signs of life began to dawn.

'More, he'll have to have more,' I insisted.

'He can hardly go visiting the police with a vodka bottle under his coat,' Lena said venomously.

'Oh, God. They'll be here in three minutes.' I fixed him another large drink and poured it down his neck. 'Look, phone reception and ask them to send up their two largest hip flasks. There's a display in the lobby.'

Scowling fiercely, she complied.

I found a jar of silverskin onions on the trolley and forced Cedric to chew a few. He protested weakly, the first sign of normality I'd seen from him. The flasks arrived and I managed to fill the last one with vodka just seconds before there was a rap on the door. Cedric now had a portable supply and I had a backup for when he got through the first.

Our escorts were an ill-assorted pair. A tall detective constable wearing a neat blue suit, five-o'clock shadow and a scowl, was accompanied by a cheerful, roly-poly detective sergeant in a shell suit. Sartorial elegance isn't a big thing in the GMP, or perhaps he'd been working undercover in Liverpool. The constable was very uneasy, the Swiss Chalet was the last place he wanted to be, but the sergeant was very pleased with himself.

'Not every day I get to meet a famous author,' he burbled as he led us out to his blue Sierra.

Cedric wasn't saying much, but he managed to nod and smile as well as anyone could with the best part of a pint of vodka inside them. When we got in the car the first thing the sergeant did was to open the glove compartment and pull out a copy of Cedric's masterpiece. He'd no sooner got it in his hand than Cedric reached over, took it off him, whipped out a pen and signed it on the title page.

The sergeant, whose name was Cullen, received it back gratefully and then proceeded to talk nonstop about the Albert Clark case all the way to North Manchester. Cedric was required to do no more than agree and nod his head at intervals. I began to relax a little. Thinking of the grey van, I remembered to ask Cullen if the police had been doing any surveillance at the hotel. He was mystified by the suggestion. By the time we reached the Velodrome I guessed Cedric was back to about fifty per cent of what passed for normality with him.

Points of similarity between the murders of Yvonne Clutterbuck and Stacey Shawcross: 1) Both victims were 17 and of similar physical type. 2) Both were homeless. 3) Both were drug abusers. 4) Both had chosen an isolated spot to sleep in. 5) It was likely that both were followed to the locus by the killer. 6) Both were killed by a single hammer blow to the base of the skull. 7) There was no sexual assault or robbery in either case. 8) The bodies were not staged after death. 9) The clothing was not cut or disarranged in any way. 10) Both murders took place on a Wednesday night.

GMP Internal Memo.

5

Thursday evening

When we arrived dusk had already begun to fall. Seven o'clock in mid-September and it was already growing dark. After alternating between cloud and sunshine all day, the weather now seemed to be set for rain. There was a moderate easterly breeze gusting in from the Pennines. It carried a hint of the chill of winter.

A stout chain-link fence surrounded the Velodrome site so the police had installed two cars as a roadblock by the gate. Negotiating this took us some moments. A crowd of sightseers, children and youths on mountain bikes milled about aimlessly. They pressed forward and pushed their faces up against the car windows. Cedric Liptrot winced under their moronic stares.

The murder scene itself was highlighted by glaring lamps that created a harsh contrast with the dull autumnal backdrop. Long shadows radiated in all directions. Uniformed police and groups of men and women in plain clothes were standing around earnestly discussing the situation. Their radios were crackling away as they talked. It was as if a vital industry employing hundreds had sprung up. There was a generator thudding away somewhere nearby.

The long white GMP serious-incident trailer was parked in front of the building. A temporary awning had been hoisted over the locus. It was flapping in the wind and straining against its guy ropes. A line of technicians clad in white overalls and hoods were on their hands and knees, scanning the ground with lenses. They looked like an oriental cult at prayer. When we arrived there was a momentary hush. A path opened before us. We were admitted to the inner area around the angle made between the massive concrete buttress and the brick wall where the victim was found. An officer ticked our names off on his clipboard.

'We have to preserve continuity of evidence,' Cullen whispered to us. 'The pathologist has already been.'

We walked along a temporary wooden duckboard. A large cardboard box, labelled Creda Cookers, lay on its side next to a duffel bag made of cheap hessian material. A sleeping mat lay crumpled up in the corner. A tatty magazine, *Just Seventeen,* lay beside the mat. Paraphernalia consisting of a piece of scorched and crumpled metal foil and half a dozen used matchsticks showed that the victim had been consoling herself with crack.

Uniformed officers, CID, forensic technicians and scientists all gazed at Cedric with a curious beady-eyed solemnity as if expecting an immediate pronouncement from the oracle. He shuffled nervously from foot to foot like a guard trying to keep his circulation going. Looking from face to face, I sensed barely suppressed anger, but not directed at us.

The time and expense going into this investigation were massive. The victim was probably receiving more attention now than she ever had in her brief life. A fraction of the money spent on her welfare would have ensured that she need never have ended up sleeping rough in this lonely spot. There were no houses for hundreds of yards in any direction except for a few terraced streets cramped up by the car park. How her killer must have relished finding her here.

This whole area, once a cosy huddle of terraced streets and factories, had been swept clean. In the middle distance, only the gasometers were left as forlorn reminders of the immense jumble of industry that had once cluttered the area. Further away, the stubby upthrust shapes of blocks of flats completed a bleak skyline. The stately dome of the National Cycling Centre had been decreed as' a kind of consolation prize for the complete disappearance of productive industry in North Manchester.

I guessed that the victim must have chosen this lonely site as a place of safety. Perhaps she'd come up from the canal bank not far away. 'Sport for All' hadn't done her much good.

A scene-of-crime officer, clad in white overalls, demonstrated the exact position of the corpse for our benefit. His effort was superfluous; we could see from the splatter of bloodstains where her battered head had lain. Still, it showed how seriously the police were taking Cedric. Despite all their science and their technical aids, the police were looking to him to supply them with an intuition about what had happened. He studied the locus as if transfixed. He certainly looked impressive enough.

'Identity,' I muttered to him. He gave me a corpse-like stare.

After what was a very long moment for me, he

turned to Cullen and said, 'Have you established who she was yet?' To my relief, he spoke incisively enough, no slurring.

'Yes, sir. A social worker identified the body about half an hour ago. No parents. Stacey Shawcross, her name was. Homeless,' he said bitterly, emphasising the last word.

'How did she get up here, with the fence round the perimeter and the access road all closed off?' I asked. 'Could she have come up along the canal bank?'

'We've not established that yet. There was a cycling competition here last night that finished after ten. Someone may have given her a lift to that and left her here. She certainly didn't bring the cardboard box with her. She salvaged it from one of the rubbish skips at the back.'

'So the killer might have been stalking her all day and followed her up here, or he could even have been the one who gave her the lift,' Cedric suggested. A trace of colour had returned to his cheeks.

Cullen nodded at this display of sagacity. 'Yes, we thought something like that. There were only a few thousand people at the competition . . .'

We stood in meditation for a while longer, then Cullen moved us on. 'Next stop, mortuary. The Boss wanted you to get an idea of where it happened, like. We have a Home Office pathologist here in Manchester and the forensic scientists have gone over the scene. They taped the clothing and skin before removing the body and that took a while. It's only just been removed.'

Cedric turned to me for a whispered explanation. 'Contact traces, they try to pick up any fibres or dust that might have fallen off the killer,' I said.

He wobbled and I thought he was going to tumble off the duckboard and damage the evidence. I gripped him firmly by the arm and steadied him as we walked back to the car. I looked around as we tottered back. The silvery roof of the Velodrome was gleaming from the reflected glow of the police arc lights. Poor Stacey had certainly picked her spot. Maybe she had only wanted to show her friends that she was 'well hard'.

I briefly mentioned some of this to Liptrot as we got back into the rear seats of the Sierra. Cullen was using the radio and the blue-jowled younger detective was studiously avoiding speaking to or looking at us. Shepherding a pair of civilians around a crime scene was obviously beneath him. Cullen referred to him as Gobbo which was appropriate in the way that fat men are sometimes nicknamed Slim. We swept out of the Velodrome and slowed to pass the police cordon at the main road. The crowd of idle spectators had been dispersed. However, the press remained on station. A cluster of journalists and photographers scanned the interior of the car for want of anything else to occupy them. Out of the corner of my eye I saw one of them turn excitedly to his colleagues and make some comment about Cedric.

The author was starting to look hot and bothered again. Having got my man so far, I didn't want him to fall at the last fence. I tapped the hip flask in his back pocket. 'For God's sake, take a mouthful,' I suggested urgently. He fumbled for it and took a swallow. The flask was still in his nerveless fingers when Cullen turned round, nonchalantly took it and had a pull himself.

'That hits the spot,' he said, before offering the flask to the driver who angrily brushed it aside. 'OK, be like that,' Cullen murmured. 'Mr Liptrot's only trying to be friendly. Aren't you, sir?' He took another healthy swig before handing the flask back to Cedric.

The public mortuary is in a narrow street behind

Piccadilly Station, near the River Medlock. When we reached the tiled room used for hacking up corpses, formalities were at a minimum. A tall, angry-looking individual with untidy bushy red hair shouldered her way through the group surrounding the green-shrouded cadaver and pressed right up at Cedric with aggression written all over her face. As I reached forward to restrain her, I felt her arm. She was a strong person. There was a lot of wiry muscle there concealed in her loose-fitting cream linen trouser suit. She shrugged me off like a prop forward going through a tackle.

Interposing myself between her and Cedric, I turned to Cullen. 'What's going on? Who is this character?' I asked urgently.

'Take no notice. This is Dr Caulfield, our official forensic psychologis. Gets a bit overwrought on these gory occasions,' he said. His tone was very contemptuous, that of a pro describing an amateur.

'Shut up, slime-ball,' Caulfield responded. 'At least I haven't had a formal reprimand for drinking on duty.'

'Not yet! But you're working at it, from what I hear,' Cullen sneered. He turned to me, shook his head and then tapped his forehead with two fingers. 'Nutty as a fruitcake!' he said.

'You're impertinent!' she snapped.

'Yeah, and I wish you'd remember that you're only a civilian employee of the GMP, not the Queen of the May,' Cullen returned.

This was by no means the hushed reverential display I'd been expecting. I was so startled by the display of discord in the police ranks that I failed to prevent her from pushing past me and confronting Cedric Liptrot.

'I see. Got your minder have you? Think you're some kind of rock star, I suppose,' she rasped at Cedric, ignoring me. 'Caulfield's the name, forensic psychologist, and if you think you're going to shove me off this investigation you can think again.'

Cedric shied away from her. 'No, oh no. No, that's not my idea at all,' he said. He looked ready to wet himself. 'No, no,' he repeated.

I got a dose of Caulfield's breath. It wasn't hard to guess the source of her forensic intuitions. She'd been on the juice just like Cedric. Irish whiskey by the smell of it.

'I've a fair idea of who sent you here. Just let me warn you I've got friends in high places too.' She was in a furious temper. 'This is my job! You've no right to be here at all. I've been ordered to co-operate with you, but I'll smack your silly head if you get under my feet,' she said menacingly.

Cedric cringed. I inserted myself in front of her again, ready to defend my client. Caulfield shoved her face right up at me. 'You're the so-called researcher, are you?' she snapped. 'Geoff Bartle told me all about your game. Don't think you're going to drag my reputation through the mud. You've even less right to be here than Liptrot.'

Cullen intervened again, speaking more judiciously than before. 'Hold on a minute, Dr Caulfield. Technically speaking, Mr Liptrot has as much right to be here as you,' he said in a very reasonable tone. 'This gentleman is his assistant and they're both here at the invitation of the Chief Constable to see if they can shed a little light. You'll get your chance to do a profile later.'

Caulfield subsided, and when she'd returned to her place at the mortuary slab, Cullen whispered to me. 'Not a woman to tangle with. Quite unreasonable when she's been on the happy. She's the reason that the Chief and Sinclair invited your man. They're far from pleased with the Doc. She's too erratic. If she attacks Mr Liptrot again, deal with her. No one will mind – apart from herselL that is.'

'Oh, yes,' I thought. 'Thanks a bunch! Just what Bartle and his friends would like to see. Me wrestling all over the floor at the scene of an autopsy.'

'Right people, if we're all ready we can begin,' the pathologist announced, interrupting further bitter ruminations. An attendant whisked the green cloth away from the body bag containing the puny cadaver of Stacey Shawcross and pulled down the zipper. However hardened you may think you are, nothing quite prepares you for the sight of an innocent victim of violent crime lying on a slab. I felt a rush of hot, sour anger against the man responsible. What had Stacey ever done to ask for this?

My own eyes ached. The attentiveness of the onlookers was tangible. I glanced round the group. Caulfield seemed to have subsided, though her shoulders were still heaving slightly. Then Gobbo, the bristly detective who'd driven our car, suddenly turned on his heel and left the room.

'I've got a kid of my own that age,' he said over his shoulder, his voice shatteringly loud.

Cullen turned to Liptrot. 'Can't take it, some of these lads. Though I can't say I go for this fashion of crowding round corpses like a bunch of medical students much myself.' He looked distinctly queasy. 'Got another nip of that vodka, Mr Liptrot?'

Cedric was frozen to the spot so I offered Cullen the full flask that I was keeping as backup. He drank deeply.

'Christ, you two came out prepared. Been to many of these?' he asked matily. I shook my head, 'I've been to more than I care to remember,' he said.

The drink partly sustained me through the slow process that followed, that and the fascination of watching the meticulous work. Each item of clothing was removed and photographed separately by one technician, while another made a video recording of the arrangement of the clothes on the body. The pathologist took his time removing the jewellery; earrings, nose studs, seven cheap-looking rings. Then there was more taping of the skin for traces and scraping of the fingernails. It all took the best part of an hour.

By now the corpse was stripped and there was a feeling of pity mingled with anger in the group of onlookers as we took in the emaciated frame. She looked like a concentration camp victim. Her ribs stood out like a row of coat hangers, her breasts hardly more developed than those of a ten-year-old. There was very little flesh on the thighs, arms or legs either. The faded blonde hair at the back of the head was spotted with blood. Her features were sharp, the thin little nose and drawn skin giving her a beaky look. The skin looked like opaque and shrivelled clingfilm wrapped round a bag of bones, all angles and corners. Her eyes were open.

Over the next hour every inch of skin was examined under a strong light. The external wound to the head was probed and measured from every angle. Powerful UV lights were used to reveal any external traces of semen. By this time I'd seen enough. I told myself that I wasn't squeamish, just that the pathologist had already passed on most of the relevant information that he was going to find.

Throughout the examination Dr Caulfield was making notes. She was not an unattractive woman physically if you go for these hefty types. I've nothing against people working out and pumping iron, it's just that in her case the assertiveness training seemed to have gone right over the top. The red leonine mane blended with her manner well enough – startling appearance, startling conduct. This was not a person to be trifled with.

It was her behaviour rather than her muscular appearance that made an odd impression. While the pathologist laboured, she kept up a busy conversation with herself, humming, occasionally talking. The woman was completely oblivious to her surroundings. She might have been an eccentric but bright student in a college science lab watching a demonstration. She asked the pathologist questions and seemed particularly interested in the arrangement of the victim's clothing. Surprisingly to me, he seemed to accept her presence as routine. With the help of a technician he demonstrated to her that the girl's clothes hadn't been interfered with. He showed her how the traces of lividity present, blood gathered just under the skin, proved that the victim had been in a sleeping posture when killed and not subsequently disturbed. There had been no staging of the body after death. Caulfield seemed to make a great play of this, scribbling copious notes and even a little sketch.

The only sign of unease I detected in Caulfield was that every so often she hauled a large handkerchief out of her shoulder bag and pressed it to her lips. It was only when I heard the chink of glass as she put the handkerchief back that I realised that she was topping herself up with whiskey.

I was unable to maintain Caulfield's alcohol-assisted pose of scientific detachment. I began feeling sick when the pathologist began swabbing out the genitals and rectum. I knew what was coming next. They'd already wheeled out the trolley bearing the buckets to receive the internal organs.

'Do we need to stay?' I asked Cullen as he passed the flask back for about the fifth time. I felt a need to get hold of the politician who'd approved the spending of millions on a new cycling track and force him to watch all this in my place. A few thousand quid spent on a homeless hostel and Stacey and Yvonne might still be alive.

'You can hear everything you need outside, the pathologist's commentary is relayed to the waiting room,' he said eagerly.

'Right, come on then, I've seen enough,' I said, tugging at my client's arm. Once again, though, he'd lost all mobility. Nevertheless, I'd have got him and myself out of that room, if Caulfield hadn't chosen that moment to put her oar in.

'Lost your bottle, Mr Writer? Not like books is it?' she sneered at Cedric.

Liptrot ignored her but gave me a very discouraging look. 'Take your hand off me, Cunane, I'm stopping. I want to see this.' He pulled out his hip flask without any prompting.

I should have expected that. A complete about-face was the predictable response from him. I'd had to pump him full of vodka to get him as far as the murder scene. Now, he wanted to witness the goriest part of the autopsy.

I shrugged my shoulders and was about to turn away when I was on the receiving end of more interference from his rival.

'Yeah, leave him alone, hard man,' Caulfield said. She then put a restraining arm round my client. I wasn't having that. When I tried to prise him away from behind she took a step back and rammed me in the face with the point of her elbow. The blow was totally unexpected. I could feel my knees giving way and I sagged towards the floor. Cullen grabbed me by the arm and hauled me up before I landed flat on my back on the tiled floor.

'Not in here!' he hissed urgently, assuming, wrongly

as it happened, that I was about to go for Caulfield. He dragged me out of the room. Our little contretemps had passed unnoticed. Everyone's attention was riveted on the pathologist, now beginning the incision from neck to pubis.

Cullen wiped the blood off my face with his own handkerchief. 'You can do that bitch for assault. What she did was completely unprovoked.'

'It's all right. She's only given me a bloody nose,' I mumbled. Cullen was more indignant on my behalf than I felt myself. In so far as I felt anything at all, apart from stunned, I blamed myself for letting her thump me. Some minder I was.

Cullen went to the toilet for water and when he returned, continued mopping my face, then he gave me a cold compress. I felt odd and embarrassed. I wasn't used to being cared for by the police. There'd been times in the recent past when they would have formed a queue to punch me in the face. Caulfield's elbow had caught me on the left cheekbone and side of the nose. I looked at the detective suspiciously. In my experience solicitude from official quarters is usually the preamble to being asked to shove your head into a bag full of poisonous snakes.

'Hadn't you better get back?' I asked. I gave him a searching look. In his loose-fitting purple shell suit, T-shirt and old trainers he seemed as incongruous a figure as Dr Caulfield. I was beginning to feel trapped between the pair of them.

'No, I'm only here as escort for you and Liptrot. Taxi driver, that's all I am. I'm not involved in the investigation. Anyway, it's all a load of balls, this routine of standing round while the victim is dissected. The pathologist has already told them most of what they need to know. He'll give a summary at the end, as well.'

'Oh,' I said. I was pleased to have missed the dissection myself. 'What about your partner?'

'He'll be in the car. Proper sorehead he is. Doesn't approve of drink.'

Taking the hint, I offered him my flask again. After he'd swallowed a slug, I did the same.

'Better than anaesthetic, eh?' he said with a smile. 'Doesn't take much to upset Dr Caulfield,' he said, priming me for a discussion of the incident. I shrugged my shoulders. Least said, soonest mended.

'Yes, she has a habit of taking things very personally has our Lauren,' he expanded. 'Mind you, you wouldn't think a convent schoolgirl would be so rough, would you? Went to the same school as my wife. Youngest of a family of six, has five brothers.' He chuckled to himself at the thought. 'Lauren's not her real name you know, she changed it from Carmel.'

'Just let it drop. It was probably an accident,' I said. 'You and I were the only people who saw it happen.' I wasn't anxious to have the fact that I'd been put down by a drunken female broadcast round town.

'Look, if you don't want to report Caulfield do me a favour. Keep quiet while I talk to her about it. I'd like to put the frighteners on that arrogant tart. Acts as if she's the Duchess of Manchester.' He was speaking quite venomously now, joviality forgotten.

I looked at him more closely. If Cullen wanted to pursue a private vendetta against the good doctor, the last thing I wanted was to get involved. 'Just what's up?' I asked. 'Manchester's Finest don't usually get their knickers in a twist when a private detective gets a bloody nose.'

'It was assault,' he said. His face assumed a genial and completely innocent smile. He looked totally sincere, like Pat O'Brien playing a priest in one of those '40s films.

'Come on, give or I'll go back in there and ask her what's going on,' I warned.

'OK. No more bullshit,' he said with a sly grin. 'Well, a little bird tells me that she gets to behave in such a high-and-mighty way because she's the very special friend of a certain very senior policeman,' he admitted.

'Hell, are you trying to commit professional suicide?' I asked.

'It makes no difference to me. Her boyfriend has already put the blockers on my career,' Cullen said. 'All they can do is to force me into premature retirement and I'd quite like that. Your father was in the job, wasn't he? I remember some of the old timers talking about him. Well, you must know what can happen if you have a disagreement with the wrong knob-head.'

'Well, who is he?' I'd had a sudden wild stab of fear that Cullen's enemy might be my father's old pal, Assistant Chief Constable Sinclair.

'Might be better if you didn't know,' Cullen said cautiously.

'It's not Sinclair is it?' I demanded. I was getting tired of his sly equivocation.

He burst out laughing. 'I'd heard you were a bit of a wag, Cunane, but that takes some beating. I don't think Sinclair's looked at a woman since his old Scottish mammy kissed him goodbye when he set off to join the police force.'

I had to smile myself. The thought of the ascetic Sinclair, the proverbial confirmed bachelor, compromising himself with Caulfield was funny. The old relic was married only to the job.

'Look, assuming you hang around near Caulfield long enough, and that you survive the experience, you'll find out who the boyfriend is soon enough.'

I couldn't let it rest. 'You want me to help you hassle

Caulfield so you can get back at her boyfriend then?' I asked.

'Get off! Soft lad!' he said in mock indignation. 'I'm sworn to uphold the law. That woman's violent and she needs to be curbed.'

I couldn't tell whether he was serious or not. Possibly he thought that the threat of prosecuting Caulfield would give him the edge in his tussle with the senior officer. Anyway it was something I didn't want to get involved in.

'Is she into violence in a big way?' I asked. I was expecting him to reel off a series of similar assaults by Caulfield. When he didn't I knew that it was all internal police politics.

'Her nose is out of joint,' Cullen commented, then looked at the blood on the handkerchief he'd used to swab my face. 'Sorry, mate,' he continued. 'I'm probably saying too much to a civilian but you are involved in a way . . . You know Sinclair don't you? He's trying to ease Caulfield and her profiling out of the GMP. Can't stick it you see. That's why he's gone out of his way to invite your boozy boss, Liptrot, to give us all the benefits of his wisdom. One in the eye for her! Ooh! Sorry!' he said, swabbing my face with the bloody handkerchief again. 'In a way you can blame Sinclalr for this. It was really him she was lashing out at.'

'Yeah,' I mumbled doubtfully as I put a hand to my damaged face. It ached like hell.

I settled down to wait for Liptrot, and Cullen sat down beside me. He must have felt he was off duty because his way of relaxing was to come out with a well-rehearsed stream of dirty jokes that would have made Bernard Manning blush. My face, already bruised, began to feel tired from the effort of maintaining a fixed grin.

We stayed in the waiting room listening to the

commentary. It was a genuinely surrealistic hour, Cullen's well-honed patter mixed with that grim soundtrack. The bit where the pathologist's assistant sawed the top of Stacey's skull off with the electric trephining saw was the worst.

Then the pathologist droned away through his summary in a matter of fact voice . . . There was a distinct rectangular wound expressed through the crushed dura mater, skull and on into the cerebellum. The base of her skull had been crushed by a single blow, expertly delivered. There was no sign of frenzy, repeat blows or defence injuries. Death would have been instantaneous. There was evidence of substance abuse, she'd been injecting behind the right knee and into the groin. The drug was yet to be identified from a blood sample, possibly a cocktail of amphetamines or temazepan. There was no sign of sexual assault. No secretions or fluids of any kind on the body or on the victim's clothing.

It was an age before it was over. The sky had cleared and the moon was shining when we emerged. Watching the others come out, it occurred to me that Lena Liptrot wasn't as well informed about her son as she thought. He'd displayed no sign of squeamishness at the autopsy. The viewers formed one party with Cedric and Caulfield in their midst. They were reluctant to separate, like a bunch of nervous Christian survivors coming out of a Roman circus. They milled around, peering at each other in the light of the sodium lamps.

Cullen, his surly driver and myself – the non-viewers – formed a detached group.

Cullen drew me over to his car. He ostentatiously took his notebook out and appeared to consult it carefully. 'Right, thank you very much, Mr Cunane,' he said loudly. 'All you need to do now is to come into the station and sign the statement and we'll take it from there.'

We looked at each other and then at Caulfield. She pretended that she hadn't heard anything, turned her back on us and walked to her car, a red BMW. I went over and retrieved Cedric who came with me meekly enough this time. Despite the fact that Cedric was my employer and that he was paying me over the odds, I'd rather have been getting in the BMW with Caulfield than nannying him. There's nothing like a good smack in the gob to make you sit up and notice someone. I had a sneaking admiration for Caulfield. At least she had the courage of her convictions and was consistent. If Liptrot had a touch of one or the other he'd have told Sinclair to go to hell when he got the invitation to attend the autopsy. As it was the pantomime was continuing.

'We're to attend the conference back at the Velodrome. I'm to report and Mr Liptrot to observe, that is, if you don't mind,' Cullen informed us. Liptrot didn't mind. At least he made no objections, or response of any kind.

When we got back to the National Cycling Centre the conference was already assembling inside the building. Clusters of coppers stood round coffee urns. Despite the late hour, after eleven, there was a lively feeling in the place. It was like a meeting in some big consumer products company. The police had installed a portable framework in the centre of the cycle track. It was the sort of thing a touring sales team might cart around with them and supported lighting and all kinds of visual aids, projectors and screens. There were eight rows of seats occupied by uniformed and plain-clothes police. The atmosphere was disorderly, almost rowdy.

There were dozens of photos on a pin-board. Folding screens contained reports on different aspects of the investigation. Officers sat around fondling their laptop computers. With the high bank of the cycle track all round us and the tiered seating beyond, the setting felt claustrophobic, like sitting in a swimming pool with the water drained out. The only access to the area in the middle of the cycle track was via an underground passage.

Sinclair was presiding, seated at the table up front behind a battery of microphones and recording equipment. Assistant Chief Constable Sinclair had been a detective sergeant when my father was the Chief Superintendent in charge of the Manchester CID. They'd heen quite close and still were. Sinclair was unusual for a high-ranking officer in that he'd only ever served in Manchester and had never sought promotion elsewhere. The reason for his success was that his deep knowledge of the local criminal scene allied to his supple mind had made him invaluable. He'd been unable to stem the rising tide of crime in the city once drug dealing and nightclubs became major growth industries. Despite that, it was generally agreed that without him things would have been worse. Much worse.

Sinclair is unusual for a modern copper in that he inspires a degree of fear among the criminal classes. This is because behind the carefully maintained front of old world courtesy, there's an absolutely ruthless determination to bang up wrongdoers. Once he gets his claws into someone he rarely relents. I imagined that at his rank he could pick and choose his cases, which must help. His presence here, at this late hour, showed the commitment that the GMP were putting into solving this crime.

In the curious manner of the police, the three officers at the trestle table were entitled only by large plastic signs bearing ranks not names – ACC (Crime), DCS (Force HQ), and DS (Divisional Officer) in descending order of rank. I supposed that the ready-made all-purpose signs came with the portable incident room fixtures. It was odd, almost designed to promote insecurity in the higher ranks. I felt as if I were involved in one of those plays they stage at country hotels where the guests all have to choose roles. The trouble was, I wasn't entirely clear what my role was.

Although Sinclair was the senior officer present the meeting was chaired by a keen-looking detective chief superintendent from Force HQ of about my own age. He looked young to be in charge, especially flanked as he was by two silver-tops, Sinclair and the Divisional Detective Superintendent. He was casually dressed in a black sweatshirt over a white T-shirt, creating the odd impression that he was wearing a clerical collar. His sleeves were rolled up, revealing long hairy arms with well developed forearms. A squash player, I wondered. There were liver spots on the arms so he wasn't quite as juvenile as he preferred to appear.

His slightly pendulous lower lip didn't detract from his star-like appearance, or was it that thing they called charisma these days? His hair was shaped, it must have been styled. He had a moustache and his dark hair was beginning to be peppered with grey, but it was the image of alertness and intelligence that he conveyed which impressed me strongly. The mobile phone he urgently clutched in his right hand completed the picture of a man going places.

After seating us at the back, Cullen hurried forward and conferred with him at length.

'Right, come to order,' the Detective Chief Superintendent commanded through his microphone. 'We're treating this as a major crime. That is why Assistant Chief Constable (Crime) Sinclair and myself are here.' He didn't bother to introduce himself or the Divisional Superintendent next to him.

'Philip Pinnock's his name,' Cullen whispered into my ear as he sat down beside me. 'Ambitious bugger, off to the Senior Command Course at Bramshill when he's finished here,' he muttered more to himself than me.

Ambitious or not, Pinnock briskly whisked us through the reports of the various specialists and operational squads doing house-to-house checks. Then he had Liptrot up on his feet, introducing him to the brainstorming free-for-all session.

'What do you think?' Liptrot asked me urgently as he sat down while Pinnock continued his masterly *tour d'horizon*.

'What?' I grunted, startled at his lucidity.

'Give me your impressions on the case so far,' he demanded urgently.

I did, and a few minutes later had the pleasure of hearing him relay them to the meeting almost word for word. He even added some of what his mother described as his embroidery for good measure.

Stacey Shawcross was stalked. It was probably by someone who wasn't a stranger to the homeless scene, quite possibly someone known to the girl. She was killed with an implement, not necessarily a club hammer like the Bradford Basher had used. They mustn't delude themselves into thinking that the killer would appear to be an obvious nutter or sexual deviant. He might betray no external signs of his violent sideline. This could be a copycat killing. The perpetrator was a man, definitely a man, who was repaying society for some incident buried in his own childhood. He would feel that something had given him the moral right to kill. The neat way he'd killed with a single blow suggested a degree of professionalism and self-restraint. They could be looking for a skilled manual worker, builder or carpenter. It must be someone who was used to gauging the force of a blow. Then again, the control shown in inflicting death with a single blow suggested that it could be any professional who was used to accepting restraints in his work, a lawyer, a teacher, a doctor, even a policeman –

'That's bloody rubbish and you know it, Liptrot.' Caulfield was on her feet at the front of the meeting, shouting the odds before Cedric had finished speaking. This was handy because I don't think Cedric could have supplied the rationale behind his interesting hypothesis.

'Narrowed it down a bit, haven't you?' the red-haired forensic psychologist continued jarringly. 'Well controlled, a professional, no record of sexual deviancy. Huh! That applies to more than half of the male population. Anyone can see that this crime was committed by an angry man whose anger will present itself in many other ways. The single blow was to register his contempt, not his self-control. It is stereotypical of male violence. We're looking for your run-of-the-mill male nutter. There are probably men in this room quite capable of it.' A stir passed through the gathering as she said this. She was looking directly at me. 'But the method of attack suggests a particular type of perverted male to me.'

Caulfield confidently strode out into the aisle between the two serried rows of officers. I saw Sinclair raise his eyebrows at Philip Pinnock, but neither of them objected to Caulfield's grandstanding.

'Let's look at the facts. The culprit's targeted a young girl, not some weary old tramp, so the sexual motivation is obvious. He almost certainly will have had other sexual adventures in the past characteristic of lonely frustrated men. Check out men who've exposed themselves to school children, loners who've assaulted prostitutes. The failure to rape Stacey indicates that the guy is sterile or impotent. Maybe that's what's enraging him. It would fit the typical pattern of blocked sexuality. He might be living with an elderly parent, still a virgin at thirty. Check the hospitals, this could also be someone who's lost his goolies in an accident. He'll be having hormone treatment now. Look for men with heavy tattooing or facial deformities and difficulty in forming relationships with women. Probably he attended the cycling competition, so look for sports fans, in particular cyclists who've had an accident with their crossbars.'

There was a ripple of laughter at this witticism.

'Above all, this was a crime of opportunity. The killer won't have stalked Stacey. He found her here by chance.'

Then as swiftly as she'd risen and held forth, Caulfield left centre stage. She strode towards me. As she passed me, she puckered up her face into a scowl. Her eyes were too closely set together, I thought, but she wasn't a bad looker, I put her just on the cusp of thirty. She didn't look like an habitual lush. Maybe she only drank so she could get through autopsies. There was something about the confident walk and to-hell-with-you shrug of the shoulders she gave as she left that inspired guarded admiration. When she exited down the steps that led from the central area I couldn't help noticing that she had a very neat rear end.

'Well, I'm sure both of the last speakers have given us something to think about,' Pinnock concluded soothingly. 'We may be dealing with a serial killer limbering up to beat Billy Fox's record. I'd have invited Mystic Meg along if she had an idea of how to stop this bastard before he kills again. Right, pack up now, and before you go, remember, it's important to keep your minds open. Briefing's at nine thirty, Bootle Street.'

Whether it was the drink, delayed shock or my natural cussedness, I'll never know. Perhaps it was because I knew that I'd never get another chance to address such a dense scrum of police persons unless they brought back capital punishment and had me on trial for my life. I tugged Liptrot's sleeve urgently. 'You're not going to let that domineering madam get away with rubbishing you, are you?' I demanded angrily. 'Get on your feet.'

Such was his suggestible state that he obeyed.

Pinnock caught his eye immediately and gestured to the gathering to sit down again.

Cedric looked at him for a long while. The silence in the hall deepened. Finally, Pinnock lost patience. 'You have something you wish to add, Mr Liptrot.'

'Er, yes. That is my assistant . . .' He pulled me to my feet alongside him, and then sat down abruptly. All eyes swivelled to focus on me. Sinclair rose to his feet with an expression of horror on his face when he recognised me. He looked at the gathering anxiously, as if fearful that I might corrupt them in some way. Then he sat down again. There was nothing else he could do. If he denounced me, he'd have to explain just who had invited Cedric Liptrot along in the first place and why. He pulled out a handkerchief out of his pocket and mopped his brow. He must have been wondering what he'd let himself in for.

'Dr Caulfield tried to rebut Mr Liptrot's ideas but all she did was totally confuse the issue,' I said. My voice sounded unnecessarily loud. Beside me Sergeant Cullen began clearing his throat, but I didn't care if he was warning me to get back into my seat. I was angry.

'Get your forensic medical textbooks out and look up the effects of castration on sexually violent men. I'll give a grand to the first one of you who finds a single recorded case of a castrato going round knocking off the opposite sex.'

'Right mate! Good one,' Cullen shouted and began to clap. A buzz of noise passed round the enclosed area, bouncing off the wooden racing track.

'Mr Liptrot explained all this to me – He didn't say

that the man who did this might not have a previous record – obviously you've got to start there. But this man is fastidious, he has a revulsion, maybe he hates the homeless or drug addicts.'

There was another burst of clapping from Cullen and further general discussion. I felt that the place was turning into one of those revivalist meetings that Lovena Anderson had occasionally taken me to.

'That's why there were no bite marks,' I said, warming to my theme. 'There was no spittle, no semen, no rape. This scumbag thinks he's doing society a favour, clearing up the social problems of Manchester. He's targeting the weakest in society.'

I sat down. There was a buzz of comment and then a scattering of applause. We were in a sports arena after all.

Pinnock leaned towards Sinclair and I could read Sinclair's lips: 'A private detective . . . Cunane.'

'Let no one say that the GMP discourages vigorous debate,' Pinnock said. 'Mr Liptrot's views have certainly been forcefully expressed to us, but I'd caution against completely abandoning what Dr Caulfield said. One of our consultants suggests a sports fan with no balls. The other – a man with his equipment intact, but shy about lowering his undercarriage. May I just add that we're going to look at all possibilities!'

There was a roar of unforced laughter at this and the meeting broke up. Looking at Sinclair and Pinnock sitting together, apparently so genially, I wondered what the agenda was. Everything seemed to be sweetness and light between the two. Which one of them was using the profiling issue to gently slip a sharpened dagger into the other's back? Despite my customary distrust of the boys in blue, I was impressed by Pinnock's style and by Sinclair for backing him in his open-minded approach. Maybe they'd catch this new killer before the number of his victims reached double figures

As I was shepherding Cedric towards the steps, Cullen grabbed my sleeve. 'Eh, cocker,' he said, 'that was one hell of a performance you put on there. I was going to pull you back into your seat but it seemed a shame to spoil it. Guess who La Caulfield's boyfriend is.' He gave a mischievous laugh when he saw the expression of dismay on my face. 'Yes, you're right. It's Philip Pinnock.'

It was midnight before I got Cedric back to Mother. She stood up to greet us, thrusting her bosom out like a swimmer testing water wings. She was an imposing character, taller than I'd thought, swathed in a heavy green dressing gown.

'How did he get on?' she asked me anxiously.

I chose my words with care, 'He did great, the star attraction at the Police Officer's Ball.' Cedric had thrown his jacket onto a chair and gone into the bedroom. I heard the shower running. 'You'd better level with me Mrs Liptrot,' I said 'What's his problem?'

'Lena, you must call me Lena,' she insisted. 'Come and sit on this sofa next to me.'

I obeyed, finding it interesting how nearly everything the woman said was a command.

'You think we're very odd, don't you?'

I shrugged my shoulders.

'A pair of oddities.'

I said nothing.

'Cedric's father was quite a bit older than me. A prosperous farmer in the Vale of York. His first wife had died and he had teenage children. I was supposed to be the housekeeper. The first time he came into my bedroom I told him, "Either you make this official, or I pack my bags in the morning." He must have decided that a wife would come cheaper than a mistress, because we got married at the Registry Office in Beverley.'

I could imagine the scene. He must have been desperate.

'The children hated me, but I thought "I'll see you lot right . . . I'll have a family of my own, that'll really get up your stuck-up little noses." 'Course, Liptrot didn't want me having kids, but that was something he couldn't completely control. So, when Cedric finally arrived there wasn't a great deal of rejoicing round the family hearth. Cedric's own father was far from delighted to see him, I can tell you. But these things have a way of evening themselves out . . . Really took to the baby he did, the senile old fool, but the others hated him like poison. They encouraged Cedric to play near the combine harvester or the hay baler. I had to keep my eye on him, I can tell you.'

She paused and looked at me speculatively before going on. Once again, I wondered which of the Liptrots was the dramatist.

'Yes, things balance out. The old skinflint moved into a separate bedroom, said he didn't want me taking advantage of him again, if you please! Have you ever heard the like?'

I shook my head encouragingly.

'Took to the bottle for comfort, he did. Then one night he tried to drive his tractor up a sixty-degree slope. It tumbled over and broke the old fool's neck. Served him right. He was that pig-headed. Anyway, they took a door off its hinges and laid him out in the kitchen. While he was still lying there, not yet stiff, his two bitches of daughters went upstairs and started packing my bags. "We want you off our property," they said, bold as brass. The older son sat there with his shotgun across his knees, trying to see how quickly he could empty a bottle of gin, just like his fool of a father.'

She studied my face again to see what effect this everyday story of country folk was having on me. I tried to keep my face blank.

'Cedric and I left without a word. Didn't even go to the funeral. But did they get a surprise when the will was read out!' At the thought of this she gave a cruel little laugh. I gently slid a little bit further away from her and she took her hand off my knee.

'Cedric got the lot. "I'll be putting a manager in at the end of the month, so if you can be gone by then that'll be convenient," I told them, cool as you please. Oh, you should have seen their faces,' she said with another cackle. 'Then I told them the farm was up for sale. It had been in the family for four generations. The Mormons have it now.'

'This is all very interesting . . .' I cut in, before she got to her feet to give me a visual demonstration of the eviction of her stepchildren.

'Yes, well, when we moved to Bradford to live with my sister in a nice tidy house in Manningham, Cedric started having panic attacks whenever he had to go out. He's had them ever since. That's why he needs me. That's why I've told you all this.'

Her story explained a lot.

'Tell me, Lena, have you ever thought of writing stories yourself?' I asked. 'You'd give Catherine Cookson stiff competition.'

She glowed with pleasure. 'I have thought about it more than once, but Cedric needs me.'

'Right, well it sounds as if he's getting ready for bed now,' I said as pleasantly as I could. 'You've got my number and you can reach me on the pager if you need me, so I'll get off to bed. Busy day tomorrow.'

'I suppose Kath Headlam's waiting for you,' she said.

'As it happens, she's gone to stay with her father. The way she was treated today upset her.'

'There's harder knocks than that in this life,' the old woman said bitterly. 'She's got her way now though, hasn't she? TV treatment! As if I couldn't have helped him.'

Back at the flat I made myself some cheese on toast before going to my lonely bed. I was in a deep sleep when the insistent ringing of the phone woke me.

Cedric Liptrot's voice echoed down the line.

'What's she been saying? What version was it this time?' he demanded without any preliminaries. 'Don't tell me – "the ill treated farmer's wife".'

I struggled to grasp what he was raving on about. He sounded as if he'd really fallen out of his pram.

'You do realise that she's quite mad, I hope?'

'Listen, Mr Liptrot, I do hope you realise that the last thing I need at 3 a.m. is a discussion on your family history.'

He gave a snort of contempt but didn't say anything else so I put the phone down. I couldn't get back to sleep then. I kept hearing the whine of the saw as they tookoff the top of that girl's skull. After about an hour I slipped into a light doze.

At six the phone rang again. It was Lena this time.

'Mr Cunane,' she said, shouting down the line, 'would you get round here right away. I want you to take me for a ride round Moss Side, Fallowfield and Hulme and all those places where Billy Fox lived or worked. And get a move on! I want to go before there's too much traffic.'

'What about Cedric?' was the only half-rational comment I could bring myself to make.

'He'll be coming too,' she snapped.

I groaned. A look out of the window confirmed that

it was another day like yesterday – scudding clouds, threatening rain, brief gleams of sunshine.

Our arrival outside the big three-storey house in Fallowfield where Billy had rented attic rooms did not go unnoticed, even at six forty-five in the morning. Spotting the zoom lens of Cedric's camera poking out of the back of the Nissan a milkman came over and leant against the car.

'I knew him, you know. Tourists are you?' he asked knowingly. 'There's people here at all hours. They reckon they're going to pull the house down and build an old folk's home, but I think they should preserve it as a tourist attraction. You know, like the Ripper Trail in London.'

Mindful of my role as investigator I asked him how well he knew Billy.

'I delivered his milk. Saw him lots of times. Liked to go out for a jog in the morning. Always pleasant, said "Good morning" like. Not like some of his lot, certainly had a civil tongue in his head. Helped me to push the cart one morning when I got stuck with a low battery. Very obliging, you'd never have thought he was collecting human heads up there. It just goes to show.'

'Show what?' I asked, anxious to test the water now that I had a live member of the public willing to talk about Billy.

The milkman narrowed his eyes, and pushed his cap to the back of his head. 'Not press, are you?' he asked suspiciously. 'They've been roaming round here like a pack of hungry wolves.'

'No, we're just interested,' Lena volunteered.

Looking at her settled the issue for him. The Sun was hardly likely to put an overweight seventy-year-old woman out on the news trail.

'These blacks, you can't trust them,' he said confidentially. 'It was all white girls he killed, wasn't it? Just goes to show.'

'I thought at least four of them were black or mixed race,' I said hesitantly.

'No, they just put that out to stop a race riot. There's plenty of people round here were ready for one, I can tell you. Anyway, must get on.'

My next call was at the school in Whalley Range where Fox had been working at the time he was arrested. At least one of his victims had attended. We drove down the street past the rusted chain-link fence without stopping because a police van was parked outside. A gap had been cut in the fence and contractors were manoeuvring an earth mover off a low-loader. Further along hessian screens were being erected round the rose beds by the main entrance to the school.

'Looks like flowers weren't the only things Billy planted in there,' Lena said with a chuckle.

'Yes, Mother, I think Cunane and I had managed to work that out,' said Cedric fretfully.

'Grumpy this morning, are you son? They do say blood and bone meal's good for a garden.'

We turned right then and I took them on the tour of Moss Side, round Yarburgh Street and Claremont Road, then down Lloyd Street and Moss Lane East. There was nothing startling to see really. Some of the older Edwardian terraced streets were showing signs of dereliction but mostly the housing was as good as you'd find in any inner-city in Europe. Better than most. A clue to some of the area's problems was given at one intersection – there was a brand new Jobs Centre, complete with steel shutters on all windows. Standing opposite, across the road was a Probation Centre, equally new and fortified. A little bit further on there was a big Welfare Rights Office.

I drove as slowly as I could but even at that early

hour there was plenty of traffic. We had a look at the Champs Gym and the Afrikan Klub and as we finally pulled up at the lights to cross the Parkway into Moss Lane West, a car drew up alongside. It was driven by a wild-eyed white person, sporting a dog collar and a mass of prematurely grey hair. There were three sullen-looking black youths with her.

'Do you think she's taking them to church with her?' Lena asked eagerly as they eyeballed her in her red tracksuit.

'Is she a priest? She doesn't look like one,' muttered Cedric. 'New fangled ideas.'

'I think she's some sort of amateur social worker taking them to see their probation officer,' I surmised.

He started to open the window to take a photo.

'I shouldn't do that,' I said, clicking all the doors shut with the central locking switch.

We carried on with our journey. I showed them the surviving traces of the deck-access flats in Hulme – the dismal attempt by the city council to realise Le Corbusier's dream of a city in the sky in the rain-drenched streets of Manchester. The remnant, preserved as accommodation for New Age travellers, was similar to the much larger demolished building where Billy had spent part of his meagre childhood with Nancy Fox. I didn't tell them that she hadn't really been his mother. That was a revelation I'd save for another occasion.

When we finally turned back towards the Swiss Chalet Hotel there was dense traffic heading into town on the Parkway.

'Well, that didn't look like the heart of darkness,' Lena said as we reached the M56. 'I don't think it's all it's cracked up to be. I wouldn't mind living in one of those nice new houses in Hulme myself.'

I made no comment.

'All trace of this abode of evil should be wiped from our city. It has been suggested that the land should be used for an old folk's home. I think this is an obscene idea. No, the site, in fact the whole street, should be cleared and turned into a garden where children may play in the hope that one day what happened there may be forgotten.'
Extract from a Manchester city council debate about the future of the Billy Fox residence.

6

Friday, 14th September

It was half eight before we got back to the hotel. ACC Sinclair, acting as a public reiations officer rather than as Manchester's senior detective, was due to take the Liptrots on the official tour of Billy Fox's chamber of horrors at nine. Shortly before then, a message informed us that the great man was running late, so I had a couple of hours to myself. Lena had retreated to her bedroom. Cedric was tapping out his impressions of inner-city Manchester on the portable, sharpening up a few phrases in which he could capture the essential squalor, as he put it. Seeing that it was only yesterday that we'd attended the autopsy of one murdered citizen, I didn't feel in any position to lecture him about the joys of life in Manchester. Still, the city was no worse than many others and a hell of a lot better than some. I made up my mind to put the best possible spin on anything I reported back on that might put the old place in a bad light.

I racked my brain thinking of contacts who could

supply authentic information about Billy. The trouble was the Billy murders had really brought the whackos out of the woodwork. Cedric's book needed facts, not another rendition of the collective scream of rage. The tabloid trawlers had already thoroughly sieved the town for news, cheque books at the ready. However, they might have let a minnow or two slip through their nets . . .

At the time of the trial I'd read about a social worker, Angie Mallory, who'd looked after Billy for a while when he was a kid. She was the only person who'd had a good word to say for him, and much good it had done her. Poor woman, she'd had her work cut out, a character witness at the trial of a mass murderer. They'd pelted her in the streets when she emerged from the Old Bailey, although some said the indignation had been staged to give the press something to shout about. Mallory might welcome the chance to explain her point of view.

Then I thought of the female priest I'd seen earlier. She shouldn't be too hard to find. The churches certainly had a closer involvement in the area where Billy grew up than the police did. But perhaps not. I'd heard that relations between the civil power and the ecclesiastical branch in Hulme and Moss Side weren't exactly rosy. She might be inclined to lump an intrusive private detective amongst the irredeemable, along with the fuzz. My own memories of dealings with the clergy belonged to a dimly remembered past. I hadn't been in a church since I was sixteen, except for the odd wedding or funeral.

I was being paid to come up with something new, not with a load of excuses. There must be people out there who'd known Billy well, but most of them were keeping their heads down. I'd do better to use my own skills and delve into the world of lonely young people stranded in bedsits, or even the homeless. They were the ones who might know something but hadn't had the chance to communicate it. Yes, that was it. I'd spend a few nights on the streets and see what I could come up with there. Happy to have decided on a plan of action, I fell asleep in the chair.

It was Sinclair himself who woke me.

'Well, Davie boy! This is a surprise. Mr Liptrot tells me that he's employing you as a guide to those disadvantaged parts of our fair city that you know so well,' he fluted in that posh Scottish accent of his. I goggled up at him in dismay. He still had the purple crosshatching at the top of his hollow cheeks.

'I was with him yesterday as well, didn't you see me at the Velodrome?' I blurted out, feeling the familiar spurt of annoyance that Sinclair's face always provoked in me.

'Aye, I could hardly miss you. That was quite a performance you put on. I was a wee bit confused as to which of you was supposed to be the famous author when you sat down. I found it hard to believe that it was the son of my old mentor up there spouting off.' This was all said in a gentle, faintly querulous tone.

I had to grin. His trick nowadays was to pretend that he was a dreamy old-age pensioner a bit confused about what was going on. His deceitful ways had lulled many an unwary suspect into thinking he could confide in the nice Scottish gentleman. The eyes gave him away. They were still as sharp as any vulture's.

'Yes, I was saying to Mr Liptrot, you're the man to get to the bottom of things. You might have to upset the apple cart in the process but you'll get down to the essentials, eh Davie?'

Old Mother Liptrot emerged from her bedroom at this point and Sinclair turned his attention to her. She was still clad in the red tracksuit she'd worn earlier. By miraculously subtracting fifty years from her present age and transplanting her to a Californian beach, you might have thought she was attractive in an overblown *Baywatch* sort of way. Nevertheless, Sinclair positively swooped towards her and seized her by the hand.

'Dear lady, I've heard so much about you. I'm delighted to meet you at last. I believe you're the inspiration for your son's remarkable book about Albert Clark. Believe me, we're all looking to him for inspiration about this latest horror to descend on our city.' He spoke so earnestly that his sentiments could almost be genuine, but knowing Sinclair as well as I did I was certain that it was all a subtle send-up.

Lena blushed to the roots of her oddly coloured hair. 'Charmed,' she murmured truthfully.

'I'm sure you're aware that the autopsy findings on Yvonne Clutterbuck and Stacey Shawcross show that they both died from a single blow of a hammer.' Sinclair spoke with the solemnity of the head undertaker at a state funeral. Cedric and Lena exchanged nervous glances. 'The similarities to the Bradford Basher murders are remarkable,' he continued.

Lena's face lost its rosy hue.

The visit to the house of horrors in Fallowfield was a total anticlimax, at least as far as I was concerned. There was nobody living in the building. All the windows were boarded up but the police had preserved Billy's room exactly as it was, pending a decision to demolish. It was like any one of tens of thousands of other little boxes set aside for a solitary life. Thousands of hidden existences are passed in such spaces but there was nothing to tell us why the occupant of this particular one had embarked on his career as a homicidal maniac. It was distinguished only by its neatness. An exception was the chest of drawers stuffed with an amazing jumble of bric-a-brac. It looked like the lost property box from some enormous orphanage.

'He didn't like throwing things away then,' I said.

'No, fortunately for us, he was something of a squirrel,' Sinclair replied gravely.

The fatal and famous cupboard was bare. We examined it carefully. The cupboard door fitted flush with the wall and was very neatly carpentered. There were traces of wallpaper round the frame.

'The heads have still not been released for burial,' Sinclair announced grimly. 'We're under tremendous pressure to find the missing torsos.'

'Do you think Billy actually killed his victims here?' I asked, as we crowded into the tiny bathroom.

'The bloodstained newspaper found under the lino indicates that he did, but as with so many details of this case, we just don't definitely know. It's possible that he lured those poor girls up here, rendered them helpless and decapitated them in the bath. His landlady took little notice of his comings and goings.'

'Yeah, but surely lugging fourteen headless corpses down all those stairs, she must have thought he was in the wholesale meat trade.'

'Davie, I hope you're not going to give us the benefit of that corrosive scepticism of yours,' Sinclair commented.

'No, no. I'm sure he's as guilty as hell,' I said quickly.

'There may have been another location, but that's just one more of the things Fox has "forgotten".' Sinclair hunched his bony shoulders and peered at me down the length of his beaky nose, defying me to challenge him.

Sinclair, with his certainties and his sly ways, always brings out the teenage rebel in me. 'Whatever Fox may or may not have forgotten, he's in the pokey and they're still going missing, aren't they?' I said slowly.

'You're incorrigible. You're not suggesting we've got the wrong man are you?' he asked crisply.

I shook my head.

'Or that there's any connection between what went on in this room and the recent killing of Yvonne and Stacey?'

I shook my head again.

He turned to Cedric, still with a mean glint in his eye. 'There were one or two puzzling aspects, as you know. Some features of Fox's confession suggested that he'd carefully studied your book about Albert Clark.'

Cedric and Lena began speaking at once in their eagerness to refute Sinclair's inference. The hint of copycatting really needled them. For purposes of literary profit killers have to be singular in personality, plural in deeds, and without a crowd of imitators to render their feats commonplace.

'Any resemblance between Fox's confession and what I wrote about the Albert Clark case is purely coincidental,' Cedric said stiffly when he'd succeeded in shutting Lena up.

'So you wouldn't say he'd studied that?' Sinclair said, reaching over and pulling out a well-thumbed copy of *A Son To Us All* from Fox's narrow little bookshelf. Next to it sat *Herbaceous Borders*. Then *The Aztecs* and *The Mayas* by Michael Coe and *Embalming for Beginners*.

'Look, Mr Sinclair,' Cedric said huffily, 'a mind as limited in its capacity for expression as that of Billy Fox may well have drawn certain phrases from my work. In speaking to the police he may have sought to excuse his deeds in some of the ways I surmised that Albert Clark did. Remember, though, what I wrote were my guesses about what was going on in Clark's head. Anyway, if Fox did use words he'd read, I don't see how that affects his confession.'

'I'm certain you're right,' Sinclair said reassuringly.

'How many times have I seen criminals try to justify their actions by quoting something they've read? Usually something about the unfairness of life. It used to be the Bible, but now you'd think some of them sat down and studied *Guardian* editorials before setting out on their careers of economic redistribution.' He chuckled at his own joke but Cedric didn't miss the barbed hint in his words.

Lena licked her lips nervously and looked at her son. The room suddenly became very cold and she looked old and tired. We were certainly in the Fox's den but looking at Sinclair I wondered who was the real fox?

'You're understandably distressed, Mrs Liptrot,' he said, suddenly changing tack in that unpredictable way he had. 'We've stayed too long. This room of horrors has that effect on the more sensitive. Let me take your hand.'

Once outside in the sunlight, Sinclair conducted us round to the back garden. They'd excavated to a depth of nine feet, right down to the clay layer, without finding a trace of human remains.

'We're starting to dig elsewhere today,' he said. 'You must tell me anything that strikes you, Mr Liptrot. Share with us any clue you have to unlocking the secrets in Billy Fox's mind. I'm quite sure you have insights into the criminal mind that the rest of us don't.'

Cedric looked less worried.

'Ask him about the profile,' I whispered as Sinclair preceded us back down the garden path.

I'd forgotten how sharp-eared Sinclair was because he immediately stopped in his tracks. 'The profile was useful confirmation. Dr Caulfield has had tremendous experience all over the country. She suggested several lines of enquiry, the sexual offences for one. Did you know that Fox got the sack at Hoggett's Wood High School when a girl complained that he'd made improper advances to her during a biology practical?'

'That hasn't been mentioned anywhere,' Cedric said eagerly.

'We don't want the girl, Cynthia Royton, to suffer from unnecessary publicity. However, the incident fits the pattern of repressed sexuality turning to brutal violence which Caulfield said we'd find. Others said that Fox exuded a sexual atmosphere when he was working near them. That's been widely reported now. Then there were the tattoos and the body piercing. Caulfield said that was typical of the self-hatred found in many serial killers. Billy had rings through his nose, eyebrows, lips and both nipples, not to mention his penis.'

Lena Liptrot gave a little snort at this. It certainly was news to her. I had a chilly feeling in my bones as I walked up the narrow passage leading from the back garden. I supposed it was due to the damp rising from all that rearranged soil. A man at the corner of the street looked as if he was watching us with interest.

Sinclair turned to go. He had an engagement at a Rotary Club and we'd previously agreed to return under our own steam, but before he went I tried another question.

'How certain are you that Billy only had fourteen victims? I mean he was so handy at disposing of the bods and all.'

This didn't please Sinclair much. 'Speculation, eh?' he muttered. 'There are many, many unresolved cases of missing persons in this city. You know that, Davie.'

'Yes, but how many of them were young and lonely single women who lived in this area?' I persisted.

'More than fourteen,' he admitted reluctantly as he reached his car. I looked down the street as he drove away.

'Well, I don't know whether he was trying to help us

or accuse us,' Lena said angrily. We watched Sinclair's car disappear round the corner at the end of the short tree-lined avenue, heading off towards Ladybarn Road.

'He suspects everyone. It's only his precious police officers who are allowed to have spotless reputations,' I said bitterly.

She turned to me. 'Right, well use your thingummy to get us a taxi,' she snapped, pointing to the pocket where I had my mobile phone. 'You needn't think you're coming back with us to snooze on a sofa. Get busy. I want recordings of anyone who knew Billy – relatives, friends, schoolmates, anyone.' She fished a small cassette recorder and a handful of cassettes out of her shoulder bag. 'Get out and earn your fee. Cedric needs material. He'll be writing all weekend, won't you, son?'

Cedric nodded his agreement. His face wore the long-suffering expression of a sick supernumerary agreeing to leave the tent on a doomed Antarctic expedition . . .

Fox's landlady, Mrs Colquhuon, was unavailable for our questions. She was in a nursing home at Kent's Bank near Grange-over-Sands in Cumbria. So, my first stop was the newsagent's shop on the corner of the road. The Asian proprietor gave an exaggerated sigh of disgust when I explained my mission.

'We're tired of this. When is it going to stop? Fox came in here once a week to pay his paper bill, always very pleasant, very agreeable. He made no complaints; never argued about his bill.'

'Anything at all unusual?' I pressed.

'He used to buy some of those and take them home in a brown paper bag, if you call that unusual.' He pointed to the porn mags up on the top shelf.

'What about other things? The police said he had an extensive collection of sadomasochistic books.'

'*Big and Bouncy*, that was all I supplied him,' he said between clenched teeth, leaning forward so that I could see the baseball bat standing against the counter beside him. 'I used to save him a copy.' He began fingering the bat and I decided it was time to conclude the interview. None of the pictures I'd seen of Billy's victims fitted the category of 'Big and Bouncy' – more like 'Skinny and Scrawny'.

By the time I'd finished my twelfth such interview of the day, I was feeling hot and bothered and in need of a cold shower. The pattern was always the same – I was met with contempt, followed by either a demand for money or a door slammed in my face. I knew canvassing the neighbourhood was the wrong approach but I was following Lena's orders. I was filling up the tapes and some sort of a picture was beginning to emerge. Unfortunately most of the people I'd interviewed had only learned Fox's identity after his crime was revealed. The little pervert had kept himself to himself. No night owl, Billy left his flat after six in the evening only on rare occasions. He must have recruited his victims from contacts he made at work and then visited them by stealth. Maybe he chatted them up on the phone.

I plodded on, trying to reconstruct the sort of movements Fox must have made – to the shops, to the off-licence and the chippy; anywhere he might have gone. My mission was in vain. No one had anything interesting to say about Fox that they hadn't read in the papers. Just as Billy had recycled psychological information from *A Son To Us All* when being questioned, so in turn the public retailed lurid details about him. I needed an uncorrupted source.

Two o'clock on a Friday afternoon is not a good time to go visiting a secondary school. Fox had attended comprehensive school in Didsbury from 1977 to June

1982. Hoggett's Wood High School occupies a large campus that it shares with the Rural Studies Centre which had employed Fox from '93 to '94, so if anywhere had a link with him this was it. I was in luck. The school prided itself on its 'open door' policy and the mention of Cedric Liptrot's name, coupled with the sight of Liptrot's letter of authority, opened the door to the Head's study.

'He never made any mark on this school when he was here,' Peter Turner said sorrowfully. As if to check, he looked out from his widow over the neat lawns and flowerbeds laid out in a courtyard below his office. 'But he's going to! The police have notified us that they're going to dig up the whole shooting match. God knows when we'll ever get it straight again. You can't get any funding for gardens now.'

Turner was the model of a modern headmaster. A light-blue suit fitted his slim frame to perfection. His black leather shoes were highly polished, and his dark hair neatly combed. A red paisley-patterned silk tie supplied a splash of colour. There was a fax machine on his desk, as well as a telephone console with more buttons than I could count. On a table behind him, a computer with an outsized display unit and a basket full of print-outs hummed away quietly. Everything that could shout 'Wired up!' was present. As a concession to old-fashioned academia there were even a few printed books on a low shelf by his desk.

'You're in luck. I was Fox's head of year for the first two years he was here. I remember him particularly well because he was one of the last pupils I dealt with before I left classroom teaching and moved into administration in '79. I worked in another school before coming back here as Head.'

I put the tape recorder on his desk and switched it on.

'I'm surprised that the police haven't asked me about this but I suppose they know their business.'

'Well, we're trying to write a book about his whole life. Whereas they're just interested in the murders and of course they had all the evidence they needed about that.'

'I did have the forensic psychologist, Dr Caulfield, round. What I told her made her angry. She said she wished teachers would stop trying to be "Damned amateur mind-readers". Quite aggressive she was. Yes, she slammed that door when she went out, but you get used to that in this job,' he said.

'If you tell me what you told her, perhaps I can tell you what it was that annoyed her.'

Turner swivelled his chair round to the computer, tapped a few keys and seconds later paper was emerging from the laser printer. I was impressed.

'Here's a copy of Fox's complete school record including reports. The first thing I did when I became Head was to have all records computerised. To retrieve, all I need are the name or date of birth,' he said proudly. 'Billy was what teachers call "easily led" when they're trying to soften the blow for parents, although, of course in his case there were no parents, just Ms Mallory, his social worker. He lived in a home here in Didsbury, close to the school.

'Billy was always in trouble, mainly vandalism to school property, but occasional wild things like firing a catapult at a teacher, until I worked out what the problem was. Some other kid would say "Why don't you pull that door off?" Then he'd do it straight away. He was just very, very suggestible. So I gave him tasks to occupy him every moment he was here. He spent hours weeding the paths.'

'Did you notice any signs of violence,' I prompted.

'Not particularly. That's what got your friend Caulfield

annoyed. She didn't like me saying that. If I had a school full of Billy Fox types now, life would be quite peaceful once I'd got them all programmed correctly.'

'I expect the teacher he fired the catapult at wouldn't agree with you.'

'That teacher was me, and it was typical of Billy. Totally suggestible. Another boy had brought the catapult in, supplied him with the pellet and told him who to aim at. It was during wet break in the hall.'

'I bet it hurt you.'

'Not much, it was a piece of plastic. Hit me on the head. He owned up right away. I had him out trimming the lawn edges every day for the rest of that term. Of course, we couldn't do that now. He'd have to be up before a sub-committee of Governors. He'd have his own solicitor present and everything,' he said with a sigh.

'I suppose he was pretty retarded,' I said.

'We don't use that word,' Turner said severely. 'We use the terms "learning difficulties" or "educationally disadvantaged" and Billy was neither of those. I told you he was suggestible. Put him in a classroom with a teacher who had good control and he'd get on with it. Put him with a weak teacher and he'd start doing what some of the other kids wanted instead. No, he was a good reader. In National Curriculum terms –'

'But he ended up as a glorified gardener in a school biology lab,' I interrupted.

'Are you suggesting that you have to be a moron to like gardening?'

I hastily apologised and asked him about Fox's sex life. 'Apparently Fox created an unpleasant atmosphere of sexual innuendo around him? There must have been complaints from some of the girls.'

'Not when he was under my control,' Turner said. He looked as if he knew something he wasn't telling me.

'But he was only thirteen when you left the school.'

'That's usually young enough to spot these things, and there was no suggestion of abnormal sexuality. I'm telling you I knew that boy well. I think I was closer to him than anyone at that stage in his life. It was when I said that, that Dr Caulfield stormed out. She didn't believe a word I was telling her.'

'Perhaps teachers weren't as quick to report sexual harassment in those days.

'Yes, they were. I was his pastoral head. I'd have known if Fox was going round slagging girls off. He wasn't. He spent his time committing vandalism on request for other pupils, and playing football, both normal occupations for boys of that age. I don't know why people think teachers are blind. We can spot boys who have an abnormal, or at least a premature, interest in the opposite sex a mile off. Fox didn't.'

'He must have had *something* wrong with him,' I said. 'I've just seen the cupboard where he kept fourteen severed heads. That's hardly normal.' I could see why Caulfield had got annoyed. Turner was just a little too complacent and confident of his own expertise.

'I'll grant you, that is worrying,' he said with a rueful smile. 'But that side of him must have come out later. He had a bloody awful childhood you know, being passed from one home to the next. The one here in Didsbury closed down while he was at the school. There were no relatives for him to go to. At the risk of sounding like an amateur psychologist, it must all have had its effect. While he was with me I tried to give him a normal childhood. I encouraged him to take up gardening and put him in charge of the Pets' Corner. I don't believe in being too severe with kids like him. Although he's done terrible things I still feel a bit sorry for him at times.'

For a moment I thought Turner was going to wring

his bleeding heart out all over the desk. 'Come on, Mr Turner, no one's blaming you,' I said.

'Aren't they? You should have been at the last Governors Meeting. Fair isn't in it. I'm supposed to have been able to spot his tendencies when he was eleven years old.'

'Go on, even Adolf Hitler was a choirboy at that age.'

There was a silence while Turner surveyed his doomed flowerbeds. 'What about Cynthia Royton, the girl he propositioned during a biology lesson?' I asked.

'Someone's given you inaccurate information about that. It was a rural studies class conducted in co-operation with the Rural Studies Centre with which we share this campus. Although all the papers said Billy was a lab assistant here, he worked for them not for us.'

'Have you got her details?'

'Sorry, Data Protection Act. I'm not allowed to let anything out about her without her written consent.'

I looked at him sternly. He'd handed over Billy's details quickly enough. He turned to the computer and did something to it.

'Look Mr Cunane, I'm just going to get myself a cup of coffee. I'll leave you on your own for a moment, if you don't mind.' Turner gave a nod towards the computer, and I realised that he was ready to go to great lengths to clear the name of his school and of himself.

When he obligingly closed the door behind him I went to the computer. He'd left it set at 'Pupil Files'. I typed the name Royton in and was rewarded with her address in seconds. She lived in Fog Lane, Didsbury. At least, she had lived there when attending the school.

I waved to Turner on the way out. He was standing by the coffee dispenser in the registrar's office. He winked. I wondered if any of what he'd said would appear in Cedric's book. Turner was obviously hoping to put himself in a good light. After all there was no way he could deny that Billy was now the most famous old boy of the school. I suppose he could claim that everything that should have been done for Billy by Hoggett's Wood High School had been done.

When I got outside the school I stood on the pavement to phone a taxi. As I waited, school let out. I scanned the eager young faces of the kids dashing towards the bus stops or idling about to exchange insults and taunts. Was one of them destined to become a serial killer? Was it that mild-looking boy over there, weighed down by his sports rucksack? Was the population infested with killers, multiplying like maggots on a piece of rotting meat?

As I slumped in the back of the taxi I felt weary. My interview with Turner had left me with that drained, inadequate feeling I'd so often felt in the presence of my own headmaster as a boy.

When I got to Cynthia Royton's home in Fog Lane it was deserted. I decided against waiting. I was in the wrong part of Manchester to find anything out about Billy's early childhood. His earliest days had been spent in Hulme and Moss Side. But even in his short lifetime the whole place had changed.

Pub crawling round inner-city Manchester on the off-chance of meeting someone who'd known him as a kid wasn't likely to be a very healthy occupation. So I told the taxi driver to take me on to the Central Reference Library. Billy's old neighbours back from when he lived in the deck-access flats in Hulme must have some remembrance of him that wasn't coloured by the ravings of the tabloids. For most of the first decade of his life Billy had lived in Rolls Crescent with his gran. His former neighbours would have been dispersed following the demolition of a large part of

Hulme. I hoped to compile a list of who they were, and where they might be, from the voter registration lists kept in the library.

'Forensic psychology and the profiling of potential serial killers are the greatest advances in criminology since the advent of fingerprints. Used scientifically, they give us the chance to stop would-be mass murderers before they reach their victims. I would like to see predictive profiles done of all violent sex offenders as a matter of routine.'

Director of the FBI on inaugurating the VICAP database of victims of violent crime.

7

Friday evening

I was cross-referencing the names I'd gleaned from the voter lists against the current telephone directory when my pager bleeped, causing hostile glances in my direction from the students working all around me. At least, some of them were working; others were more interested in chatting up the opposite sex. I'd been working for over an hour. It was just after six.

Removing myself from public gaze behind one of the stacks, I phoned. It was Dr Caulfield, the fighting forensic profiler.

She wanted a meet. She was in her favourite haunt – Sam's Chop House, just a couple of streets from the library. I warily considered my options before replying. The person who'd orally and physically attacked me at a postmortem with fuzz standing shoulder-to-shoulder might think nothing of a repeat performance in a restaurant.

'I'm sorry Dr Caulfield, but I'm in the library doing

research at the moment. What do you want to see me about?'

'I'd rather not say over the phone but if you come round you might learn something to your advantage,' she said cryptically.

'Sorry. I can't make it,' I said flatly.

'It's about that complaint,' she continued.

'Can't it wait until next week?' I said. When she said the word 'complaint' I began to regret going along with Detective Sergeant Cullen's little trick about the alleged assault. The more I thought about it, the more her blow seemed like an accident.

'Well, there was something else. Cunane, I'm the official forensic profiler for the GMP, right? I ought to know if you find anything about Billy Fox that hasn't come out yet. I'd make it very much worth your while.'

'Brilliant!' I thought. She bawls me out and bruises my ugly mug one day, then she's trying to shove a bung into my hand the next. Life was complicated enough without this.

'Sorry, Dr Caulfield, I only work for one client at a time.'

'Don't hang up,' she wheedled, but I did.

I returned to my task in a glow of virtue. It was one of those boring jobs that take forever because you have to keep going back and forth between various sources. Half the microfiche machines didn't work properly which was no help. Eventually I looked at the short list of names I'd compiled on the back of a Council Tax demand. There was one that I'd only managed to trace because it was such a rare name – Mrs Z.Y. Pilatski. Mr and Mrs Pilatski were listed as Billy's next-door neighbours in Rolls Crescent for seven of the nine years he'd spent there. I found another Pilatski in the phone book. Mrs Z.Y. Pilatski was the only person of the same name that I could find living in a twenty-mile radius of

Manchester. She was out at Macclesfield. Just to test the water I phoned her.

'About Billy Fox? You know, I've been expecting to hear from someone for ages. I practically brought him up as a child,' she said. Her voice was firm and self-confident. The accent was local and she sounded well educated. 'Yes, I could tell you a lot about him.' Delighted though I was by her response, I remained cautious. The woman's eagerness was definitely suspicious.

'Would you be willing to give me an interview?' I asked.

She said she would be perfectly happy to see me but it would have to be tonight because she was off on her holiday tomorrow. I was exhausted after trudging the streets of Fallowlield all day without even a lunch break, but I was anxious to add to the meagre store of background information I was building up. The more I could learn that hadn't appeared in print somewhere, the happier I would feel when the imperious Lena Liptrot demanded that I come up with the goodies.

The shiny brownstone façade of the Midland Hotel opposite was gleaming in the evening sunlight as I stepped out into the portico of the library.

'Cunane!' There was a 120-decibel screech in my ear and as I swung round a heavy hand landed on my shoulder. I tried to shy away but the grip was firm. It was Lauren Caulfield. Her face was flushed and beaded with sweat. 'Hell!' I thought, realising that by disclosing my location I had broken the most important rule in the undercover agent's handbook. She was in the same crumpled linen suit she'd been wearing yesterday and was carrying a large leather satchel slung over her shoulder.

'I'm so glad I caught you. I just want a word with you. Come back in the library, or we can go to a pub.

The Square Albert's just round the corner,' she spoke politely enough, but I could sense her underlying desperation. My instinct was not to get involved.

'Look Doc, I'm busy,' I said curtly, before turning on my heel and walking towards the taxi rank in front of the Midland. I intended to get a taxi out to the Liptrot's hotel in Hale Barns and pick up my car from there.

She caught up with me and took hold of my arm again. 'Please, I must speak to you. I'm sorry about yesterday.'

'Forget about it,' I said, trying to give her the brush off. 'I'm sure that was an accident. I can't stop now. I'm in a hurry. Perhaps we could arrange a meet sometime next week.'

'Damn, damn, damn,' she said bitterly. 'I knew you'd be difficult. It's my own fault.' She sounded so forlorn that I experienced a minute's twinge of sympathy.

'Aren't you interested in following up what you said at the Stacey Shawcross meeting? You know, about your highly restrained and uptight killer?' I turned to look at her. 'Where are you going? Maybe I could give you a lift. Look my car's just there,' she said beguilingly. The red BMW was parked diagonally across two spaces in the disabled parking area in front of the library.

Like a fool I told her that I was on my way out to the Swiss Chalet Hotel at Hale Barns. I was expecting that the prospect of a half-hour crawl through the rush-hour traffic would make the idea less appealing.

It didn't, and I found myself seated beside her as she drove over the pavement, then across Peter Street against two lanes of traffic. I was curious by now. What did she want with me? It certainly couldn't be a romantic interest. Anyway, a lift would save me the taxi fare and the profiler had originally been on my list for an interview.

As we careered round the back of the Midland onto Lower Mosley Street she almost ran straight into a tram. I grabbed the wheel and jerked us to a halt against the kerb just in front of the grandiose new Concert Hall.

'What the hell's the matter with you, woman?' I stormed. 'You're kettled, aren't you?'

By way of confirmation, she touched the window button, wound it down and vomited elegantly over the side of the car. Having completed this she started struggling with her massive satchel.

'Tissues,' she muttered weakly before dumping the bag on my lap. I discovered that it contained a comprehensive selection of whisky miniatures – all empty, an IBM laptop computer, bills and receipts going back to the year dot, but no tissues.

'Keeping these for recycling?' I asked, holding a handful of the miniatures under her nose. It was the wrong thing to do. She shoved her head out of the window and began retching again. In desperation I opened the glove compartment. There were tissues, baby wipes and another pile of miniatures. Full ones. I got out onto the pavement. There were no police cars in sight but they'd be along at any minute. The BMW was parked on double yellows obstructing the tramlines. All I needed to do was to walk away and Sergeant Cullen's dream of petty revenge on his boss would be reality.

It didn't take much conscious thought to decide. I sprinted round to her side, yanked her out with difficulty and pushed and pulled her limp and unresisting body onto the back passenger seat. It was a very ample body, I noted. Then I got back in and drove off. Fortunately, the traffic lights were in my favour both at Bridgewater Street and Whitworth Street and I got away and out of the immediate vicinity. I wasn't a moment too soon. A police car flashed by me with siren wailing. The tram that Caulfield had missed by the thickness of a coat of paint must have telephoned for help.

I sped past the former British Council Building to the interchange under the Mancunian Way. I was shifting a bit when I hit the start of Princess Road. Driving a red BMW with vomit stains down the side has that effect on me. As I came up to the huge brewery at the start of Moss Side my passenger began groaning again. I bobbed into a garage and with almost comical timing Caulfield threw up again, out of the back window this time.

I got in the back seat with her and tried to clean her up a bit. She'd lost the greenish colour she'd retained after her first session and now looked almost normal.

'Never, never call me "woman" like that again, you sexist pig!' she muttered between clenched teeth.

'Fine! That's easily arranged,' I said, stepping out of the car.

'Don't go! Please!' she implored.

'Look! What the hell is going on?' I growled. By this time the staff inside the armoured petrol sales point were peering out at us anxiously. It wouldn't be long before they put the fuzz onto us again.

'Please, I wanted to speak to you about something personal,' she said. A faint greenish tinge was returning to her features.

'Where do you live?' I asked. 'I'll drop you at home and you can sleep this off.'

Curiosity kills the cat, but I was itching to know what was going on. As well as the stale smell of vomit, my nose detected a hint of scandal in the air.

She told me she lived in Brooklands. Apart from giving occasional directions she didn't speak until we arrived at her home. It was a small detached house at the end of a cul-de-sac, a black and white timbered mock-Tudor affair.

'Are you going to come in?' she asked.

'Who's waiting for me?' I responded cautiously. 'Husband, boyfriend, a heavy mob from the police force?'

'No, nothing like that,' she said seriously as if the possibility had been considered. 'I live on my own.'

I followed her in, professional eagerness overcoming prudence. Caulfield obviously had a lot she could tell me about Billy Fox and the killing of Stacey Shawcross at the Velodrome. Not that the latter was any of my business. Her place was full of comfortable old furniture draped with rugs and frayed cushions. There were family pictures and ornaments everywhere. It wasn't what I'd expected at all. Enough cricket bats and discarded golf clubs were lying around to equip a sports club.

'They belonged to my brothers. They don't live here now. This was my parents' home,' she explained. 'I bought it off them when they retired to a cottage in Wales. I haven't had time or inclination to do anything to it yet. Make yourself at home.'

She went upstairs to change and I went into the kitchen to make some coffee. I examined the kitchen leerily. It was like the rest of the place – antiquated, full of more cast-off equipment, and not particularly clean. There were no Brillo pads. I busied myself by washing several days worth of pots. Whatever she had to tell me had better be good, I mused. I heard the toilet flushing and later a bath emptying. My stomach gave a loud involuntary rumble in sympathy with the out-of-date plumbing. In desperation I had a look inside her fridge. There were a few blackened slices of corned beef and an old carton of Greek bio-yoghurt. Most of the space was taken up with ice cubes and bottles of Canada Dry

Ginger. Obviously she preferred to take her calories in liquid form.

When Caulfield returned she'd managed to put herself back together again. In glamorous 'Lauren' rather than homely 'Carmel' mode, she was wearing a heavy navy blue silk shirtwaister designer dress that must have cost a packet. Her untidy red hair was brushed smooth and she looked very striking, if pale. She favoured me with a warm smile.

'What's the big deal, then?' I asked.

She hesitated dramatically before replying, 'I've found out some new things about Billy.'

'Like what he did with the bodies?'

She gave me a very odd look. I was infuriated by her coy hesitation. I had no time for guessing games.

'I'll have to go in a minute,' I told her. 'I've got to see a woman in Macclesfield who claims she practically brought Billy Fox up.'

The effect my words had on Caulfield was far stronger than I'd expected. She began breathing heavily and looked as if she was going to have a panic attack.

'What is it?' I demanded, getting hold of her by the arms to steady her. She calmed down and caught her breath. 'You know something strange about Fox and you're frightened that I'll find it out as well, aren't you?'

'Not at all. Everything the police know about Billy has been made public. I've nothing to hide.' Her voice shook.

'Tell me,' I said, standing practically toe to toe with her. I caught a strong whiff of an expensive perfume. Her close-set eyes were an attractive shade of green. She stuck her chin out defiantly.

'Show me what you've got or I'm going.' If I didn't get food soon whatever she had to say would be of abstract interest only. I'd be flat out on the floor.

She had a lot. The IBM laptop held a complete account of each murdered girl's brief life. The annotated database she'd prepared could be of interest but it was too soon to let her know that. Sinclair had already promised to send over copies of his files on the victims so her stuff wasn't vital. I'd no intention of passing on what Jay Anderson had told me about Horatio Bostick and Lurlene Barnacle. Whatever it was she was hiding, or was frightened I might find, would come out eventually. I was being paid to dig up background material about Billy not to put the world to rights.

'Dr Caulfield, there's nothing here I can't find out elsewhere. I'm faint with hunger. I want to get my car and I want to get off to Macclesfield.' With that I got up to go. I didn't reach the front door. She got me by the arm and tried to pull me back. God, she was strong!

'Let me come with you,' she shouted as if her life depended on it. There was no way I wa going to shake her off without getting really rough. I didn't think it would look too good if I laid her out, and anyway what if her significant other, DCS Pinnock, should turn up? I pulled free and put my hands up in surrender. The woman was deranged. Short of the handy arrival of a couple of men in white coats bearing a straitjacket it seemed I had no choice.

'Why don't you phone someone?' I suggested, not wishing to reveal that I knew about her relationship with Philip Pinnock.

'I want to see the woman,' she insisted stubbornly.

'Right, you can come, but we're doing this my way,' I said. I made her promise to keep her mouth shut while I interviewed Mrs Pilatski. She grabbed a black leather jacket eagerly and opened the hall door, passing me her car keys as she did so.

Hunger and desperation having overcome fear of indigestion, I drove into the McDonald's in Chorlton. The chip shops were all shut, so it was either that or go back to the flat and put something together there. I didn't feel like traipsing Caulfield round my flat. The 'woman', as I defiantly thought of her, was far too intrusive already. I'd only known her for a day and she was already muscling in on my investigation. I had a faint hope that a quick visit to the drive-in eatery might sicken her again, giving me the opportunity to dump her.

No such luck! The sight of kiddies running about wildly and grown men and women eating with their fingers had the opposite effect. She quaffed coffee while I struggled to wrap myself round the outside of a quarter-pounder with cheese. Her colour came back and she began to look almost normal, if a little out of place.

Watching her, I wondered what Pinnock would make of my presence here. There was also Sinclair. He wouldn't be too pleased either. According to Detective Sergeant Cullen he was trying to ease Caulfield out of the GMP. I was annoyed with myself for becoming involved in the never-ending intrigues of the GMP. The only consolation was that through Caulfield I might get an interview with Pinnock. Sinclair had handled the PR with the Liptrots so far, but as the actual arresting officer, Pinnock's account might put some real zest into Cedric's masterpiece. Even so, anger at being used got the better of me when she seemed to be taking too long over her coffee.

'Will you get a move on?' I asked impatiently. I walked out without waiting for her and unlocked the car.

She leapt into the passenger seat like a startled hare and we shot out of the car park like the space shuttle leaving Cape Kennedy. I drove straight out onto the road in front of an articulated lorry, which gave us a blast of its horn.

'Calm down now,' Caulfield said, bracing herself in her seat as I sped towards the traffic lights. The sight of her – nervous, despite her own exploits behind the wheel earlier – amused me. I calmed down.

'Got any friends you'd like me to pick up, Dr Caulfield?' I asked jauntily. 'We might as well make this investigation into a real picnic.' She didn't answer and we drove on in silence for a good part of the journey.

I was almost certain that the Pilatski female would also have nothing to say. It's almost a rule in investigation that people who cheerily volunteer their services have damn-all worth telling you. Anyway, if Pilatski turned out to be a total waste of time, my unwanted passenger would only have herself to blame.

I reached Macclesfield, which I had always thought of as a pleasant rustic haven of tranquillity, without any more trouble. It was just before eight and I found my way to Zara Pilatski's address easily enough. Her home turned out to be a semi, one of many well-maintained houses on an 'overspill' estate. At the end of the street a broken down barbed-wire fence gave way to green fields with copses and farm buildings in the middle distance. The late-evening sun was casting long shadows across the fields. Youthful figures could be seen prancing about beneath distant trees. We got out of the car. The air smelled good. It hadn't got the dry-roasted flavour I was used to in Manchester. In the distance an ice-cream van was playing the repetitive chimes of 'Teddy Bear's Picnic' over and over again. There were dogs yapping, children yelling hoarsely and motorbikes revving: all the normal indications of life on a sedate English council estate. Very faint sounds of destruction wafted to us on the breeze. I assumed that there was building work going on in the vicinity.

I made my dispositions. Despite my suggestion that it would be nice to have hubcaps and wheels when we came out, Caulfield refused to stay and guard her car. She looked at her face in the car mirror and applied a dab here and a dab there with a wet wipe. She looked a hell of a lot fresher than I felt.

Ruefully, I repeated my earlier instructions. She was to be the silent partner. Caulfield gave me a mocking grin, as if the suggestion that I could exercise any control over her was ludicrous, but she agreed to keep quiet. Despite her bravado, I don't think she knew me quite well enough to test me out.

I rang Pilatski's doorbell.

I could see that the woman was unhinged as soon as she opened the door. A white woman in her mid-forties, she had an intimidating fixed stare. She was wearing a grey cardigan over a faded blouse and a long dull Indian-cotton skirt down to her ankles. I sensed that there would be no Mr Pilatski on the scene. She continued to glare at me and I tried to smile back. She grabbed my arm.

'Oh you've come! You'll bring him back won't you? He won't listen to me,' she said urgently, her short mousy hair shaking as she spoke.

'Bring who back? What are you talking about?' I asked, trying to discreetly check that I'd come to the right door. The woman's fierceness was directed at me. Although her clothes were old and faded, her blue eyes were startlingly bright.

'My Lennie. I have a teenage son. Well, he's out there, and he's going to do something awful. He's with the others.' She waved her hand vaguely towards the peaceful rural scene that provided the setting for the estate. Her eyes were rather prominent. Iodine deficiency or something, I decided. The woman was so anxious that I turned and scanned the horizon for some minutes. Lauren Caulfield did the same. I couldn't see anything, only hear the faint highpitched cries from children playing beyond the line of trees.

'Who are they?' I asked.

'They're animal rights activists. They hate this nearby farm. They think old Mr Malpas is holding the animals prisoner.'

'Have you called the police?'

'Hours ago,' she said. 'They never come.'

I realised that Caulfield was waiting for me to resolve this problem. She was looking at me with a faintly amused smile on her lips. Obviously she felt that Mrs Pilatski would have benefited more from her professional expertise than mine. However, she remained tightlipped, which suited me.

'They're only kids really. Playing at being important,' offered Mrs Pilatski. 'If you were to go over there –'

'What?' I asked.

'I expect they'd run off.'

The complexity of this case was increasing by the second. I turned to Caulfield, 'OK, let's get out of here. Get back in the car.' The psychologist gave a superior smile and moved as if to comply. This trip was turning into a fiasco.

'You're not going?' my potential interviewee asked.

'I didn't come out here to sort out the rural crime scene. Get in touch with Social Services if the police won't help,' I said.

'I just thought, a man's touch . . .'

'Has he done this before? What happened last time?'

'Lennie will survive,' she said. 'It's just that we're going away.'

'Look, give me the interview and if he's not back when we've finished I'll go with you to look for him.'

This offer satisfied her. Having achieved her desire for male assistance my prospective interviewee now looked relaxed and pleased with herself. I felt nervous and apprehensive.

'You are the person I spoke to?' I said, as it suddenly struck me that I didn't even know who she was. 'Mrs Pilatski? The one who was a neighbour to Billy Fox at Rolls Crescent in Hulme?'

'Course I was. Practically brought him up. If I'd had a pound for every hour I looked after him, Lennie and me wouldn't be in the mess we're in now, stuck here on income support, I can tell you. I looked after him week in and week out while Nancy went to the Out Patients at MRI. Real good neighbour I was.' All this was gabbled out at top speed. It took me a second to take in what she was saying. I wondered if I could trust anything she said.

'Now, when *I* need a neighbour, where are they?' she said resentfully, gesturing theatrically towards the silent houses all around her. It was a good question. We looked at the houses. Here and there curtains were twitching, but there was no sign of anyone rushing to assist a lady in distress.

'What about your husband?' I asked tentatively.

'Slung his hook years ago! Couldn't stick it. Too quiet for him in Macclesfield. Went back to Hulme. No, it's the teenagers who rule the roost round here. Everyone in the neighbourhood is scared of them. But my Lennie's a decent lad and they're not going to make him like themselves.' A real Mancunian, she pronounced Hulme as 'Oom'.

'Nice car you've got,' la Pilatski said brightly, indicating the vomit-stained BMW. Cauffield managed to refrain from speech as our hostess ushered us into the narrow little hallway of her home. There was a stack of cases at the foot of the stairs.

'All ready for the off first thing tomorrow,' she said happily. 'That's why I don't want Lennie getting in any trouble.' She then began locking the door behind her. I noticed that she had several locks and bars fitted. The door was a modern Georgian-type with separate window panes. The one directly above the main lock had been replaced by a plywood cutout. Obviously the Pilatskis had had a break in. A common sight. What wasn't common was the damage done to the plaster at the side of the door. A circular patch had been blasted away at the intruder's head level. I must have goggled at the sight.

'It is what you think it is,' Mrs Pilatski confirmed. 'Lennie heard someone trying to get in. I came down with my shotgun. It was just bad luck that I missed. We haven't been troubled since.'

I looked her over again. I obviously needed to assess just how crazy she was. She smiled back, pleased with herself. She was attractive in a hard sort of way. Her features were ordinary, even plain, but the intense blue eyes made her face interesting. Her mousy hair had originally been dyed blonde but I could see she'd skipped the last rinse. I tried to work out her age. If Lennie was sixteen she could perhaps be a worn-looking thirty-six or youthful forty-one or so. Sensing my interest, and mistaking my intentions, she favoured me with a very cosy grin. I think she imagined it was seductive.

'You haven't told the police?' I asked.

'What use are they? They'll only turn out round here when they're sure they'll get the right type of headlines in the local papers,' she said bitterly. 'My sister lives in Florida. We went to stay with her last year and I brought this back as a souvenir.' Leading us into the kitchen, she opened a cupboard at shoulder-height and took a lethal-looking Remington pump-action shotgun out of an old sports bag. 'Here, have a look,' she said, casually passing it over.

It was loaded and the safety catch was off. I carefully put the catch back on and replaced it in the bag.

'You're lucky that your burglar didn't report you,' I commented. 'I'm surprised that he hasn't demanded compensation.'

'Oh, but he did! Armed police came and turned over a house three doors down belonging to a soldier who'd been in the Gulf War. They had the whole street cordoned off. I think my burglar was so stoned when he tried to break in that he sent them to the wrong house. Anyway, they got lucky with Fred Jarvis. He brought all kinds of weapons home in his kit bag. Still has some. I don't think that it was just fireworks that he was letting off last November fifth.'

I gave up the unequal struggle.

'Well, what am I supposed to do? Lie awake at night waiting to be raped and murdered in my bed. No, I sleep with this beside me.' Then she suddenly looked at me seriously, 'You won't turn me in, will you?'

I reached over and put my hand on the bag. 'Yes, I'm afraid I will. I'll keep this and hand it in to the police tomorrow. I should tell you that Dr Caulfield here is with the police herself.' I was remembering my resolution to be ruthless. The crazy woman was lucky she hadn't blown her own head off before now.

Her mouth formed a perfect round O of surprise. I watched her run through things in her head and come to a rapid decision. I felt that my character was deteriorating. This was the second time in this case that I'd tried using a little blackmail. Oh well! Fame and fortune beckoned . . . for Kath Headlam if not for me!

'Look, how about us all simmering down and having a little discussion?' she volunteered. 'I did live next door to Billy and I practically brought him up during some stages of his childhood.'

If she was ready to talk, I was ready to back down.

She led us into the lounge and opened a well-stocked drinks cabinet. I sat down but kept a firm grip on the sports bag. While she dished out drinks I took in my surroundings. Pilatski was certainly into wildlife. Almost every surface was adorned with statuettes of animals. There were even ducks dangling from the low stone pediment surrounding the gas fire.

Pilatski put a glass of whisky in my hand. She looked warily at Lauren Caulfield before handing her a glass.

I put the tape recorder on the low coffee table in front of us and switched it on. 'Tell me about Billy,' I said

She lit a cigarette and blew the smoke towards me. 'The reason that you haven't seen my name in the papers is that I can't believe any of this stuff about Billy. It's as if he's become another person.'

Caulfield began coughing loudly at this. She subsided when I scowled at her.

'He's confessed to it all,' I pointed out. 'The heads . . .'

'Yeah, when I heard Billy had confessed I wasn't surprised, he always owned up when he'd done anything wrong as a child. Proper little George Washington he was.'

'So, what's your problem then?' I asked.

She shook her head. 'Billy sometimes confessed to things he hadn't done. You know, to stop Nancy or me fussing. He was soft-hearted like that.'

'Soft-hearted enough to have killed at least fourteen girls that we know about,' I said with a glance over at Cauffield. She glared back at me with an expression of disbelief on her face and then drained her tumbler of whisky.

'One day he came back from the shop with the

wrong change. There was a fiver short. Nancy was just getting her coat on to go and sort out the Paki shopkeeper, when Billy owned up. He said he'd given the fiver to some friends. Nancy tanned his backside for him. She did that a lot. An hour later the Paki called to apologise and hand over the change. He'd mistaken Billy's ten for a five.'

'Billy's a killer,' I insisted.

'All right,' Pilatski whined, 'but when I knew him he was always giving his toys away to other kids. You had to watch him though. He'd do anything they said. He once saw a programme of this Roald Dahl story about this marvellous medicine that turned grown-ups into giants or something. He tried pouring it down Nancy's throat when she was asleep. Bleach and all sorts there were in it.'

'There you are! He was dangerous, even as a child!' I said. Dr Caulfield nodded eagerly. The psychologist was having trouble keeping to her vow of silence.

'It wasn't like that. It was just one of those tricks that all kids get up to,' Zara Pilatski said firmly. 'The others put him up to it. He cried for hours when he saw that he'd hurt her. Inconsolable, he was.'

'Still . . .' I said, reluctant to discard the idea of an early start to Billy's murderous career.

'See? You're just like the papers. Out for sensation. He was lovely really. He'd look up at you with those big eyes of his and do what you told him to. It was a shame. Nancy was too old and ill to look after him properly. She always said she was his mother, but I wondered. She had a daughter, much older than Billy, who was a nurse at Paddington Hospital in London.'

'Nancy abused him, did she?' I asked. 'You said she tanned his backside.' This conversation wasn't following the pattern I'd expected at all.

'Well, if you call letting him have more or less

whatever he wanted abuse, she did. When she smacked him it was only to teach him right from wrong, like I've done with my Lennie. She did show me burn marks on his little bottom once. She said his father had put them there, and if he ever came round asking for her I was to say I didn't know her.'

'Did she say who he was?'

'Only that he was a big, athletic dude and he'd be wearing a tracksuit and trainers.'

I paused to think for a moment. This was the second recorded conversation of the day that was unlikely to bring much joy to my employers. If Billy had been abused again it must have been later, when he was in local authority care.

I was jogged from my thoughts by Zara. She laid a hand on the lapel of my jacket.

'Look at your beautiful suit. It's all flecked with something. Why don't you take it off and I'll sponge it down for you?' She was beaming at me tenderly. Caulfield was choking with embarrassment. The suit must have picked up traces of vomit from the car seat.

'Don't bother. I'll take it to the dry cleaners.'

'It's no bother. You're not shy, are you? It'll only take a minute.' She leaned forward to let some of her Chanel No. 5 waft over me. 'You can wear a dressing gown if you like. There's one upstairs in my bedroom. Your friend won't mind if you go upstairs for a few minutes. Will you, dear? Come on. I'll show you.'

Her forwardness led me to speculate how she was able to afford holidays in Florida while living on income support. Was she on the game, I wondered? It might explain her handiness with the shotgun if she had no pimp to protect her.

'I don't think so,' I said, standing up. I realised that she was craftily trying to separate me from the bag containing the shotgun. I was spared the necessity of making an immediate decision because at that precise moment a long, emaciated-looking youth, aged about fifteen, came in. I took him to be the famous Lennie.

His eyes were blazing with excitement; he had the same prominent eyes as his mother. He ignored us and spoke to his mother.

'It was terrific,' he enthused. 'There was this gang of us trying to storm the old man's milking parlour to let the cows out. He tried to chase us off with a high-pressure hose. Talk about Port Apache, but this was better.'

While Lennie was explaining how the savage hordes of animal lovers had been beaten back, I pondered what to do about the shotgun. The pump-action was illegal and, in Pilatski's hands, likely to be lethal. I decided it would be better if I disposed of it. Before we left I explained that I was going to dump it in the Mersey. Lennie looked relieved but his mother was clearly livid.

As we left the house I happened to look at the airline labels on her bags. The destination was Orlando. God knows what souvenir Zara would bring back with her this time – an Armalite or a rocket launcher or some such.

'Well, what do you make of all that?' Caulfield asked impatiently when I got back behind the wheel of the BMW.

'None of your business,' I said laconically.

I drove the BMW towards her home in Brooklands, intending to take a taxi back. She shut up for a while but it seemed as if our departure had unleashed a torrent of comments. She was bubbling with indignation. She kept asking, 'Just what are you trying to prove?' My weary denials that I was trying to prove anything only provoked more questions.

'You do understand that that woman is a compulsive liar, don't you?' she demanded.

'I don't know,' I said guardedly. 'Some of what she said sounded pretty authentic.' Mad though she was, Pilatski had partly verified Jay Anderson's story about Billy's mother. I had no intention of revealing that to Caulfield.

'Rubbish! The story about the father burning Billy was a lie – obvious guilt transference on Nancy Fox's part – athletic dude indeed! Social Services credited Nancy Fox with those burns. The woman was a prostitute and she probably had no idea who Billy's father was.

I made no comment, which infuriated the profiler. Apparently it was permissible for her to refer to Nancy Fox as the 'woman' and suggest that she was a prostitute although no one else had.

You'd prefer it if Liptrot retailed a load of sentimental twaddle, wouldn't you?' she said aggressively.

'And you'd prefer to twist the story to make Billy a deviant, malignant from birth, wouldn't you?' I countered. I felt really angry. What is it with you?' I asked. 'You want to categorise everyone into neat little compartments but life doesn't work like that.'

'Brilliant!' she said, dripping sarcasm. 'The man wants the killer of poor Stacey and Yvonne to be seen as icy calm and controlled. Yet he objects to me saying that the accounts of Billy's childhood from that wet headmaster Turner and crazy Zara don't hold up.'

'They've got the evidence and you haven't!' I snapped back.

'All right, Mr Investigator! I'm telling you Billy was a sadist. An abused kid who decided to repay with interest everything he'd received from Nancy Fox and other people!' she shouted.

The quarrel was so furious that I drove across the

Mersey Bridge without stopping to dump Zara Pilatski's illegal firearm. Lauren Caulfield went on and on trying to convince me that I was wrong. I kept telling her that I hadn't formed any conclusions. The truth was she was trying to convince herself. When we arrived in front of her house I was out of the car like a shot. I had the mobile in my hand to phone for a taxi when I spotted the gun.

'You'll have to get rid of it,' she said. 'It was your idea to take it. I expect you intended to keep it all along.'

'Don't be stupid!' I snapped. 'You can get serious time for having a gun like that. I was doing her a favour.'

This sparked off another argument. She refused to take the gun or come with me when I dumped it. I now decided that dropping it over the bridge into the Mersey was too public anyway. There were too many prying eyes and hidden cameras these days. The result was that we drove to Chorlton. I proposed to dismantle the gun and lose it bit by bit.

'Why don't you give it to Detective Chief Superintendent Pinnock? I'm sure he'd dispose of it for you,' I said nastily when we arrived in front of the garages at the rear of Thornleigh Court where my flat was. I'd decided to stash the thing in my own lock-up rather than indoors.

'What do you know about him?' she flared angrily.

'Nothing much,' I said truthfully.

I'd opened the floodgates. If she'd been noisy and demonstrative before, she was a hundred times worse now.

'I expect someone told you that I was his mistress,' she said, more in a bellow than a whisper. 'There's more gossip round the police stations in this town than in any old women's sewing circle.' She was seething with indignation. There was a chance she might tell me just what was burning her up so much about the Billy Fox case. Burning so much that she thought it was worth her while to waylay me at the library and then trail around with me all night.

Even so, I had no desire to take her up to my flat. I didn't want her there and the gesture was far too open to misinterpretation. We conducted our sparring match in the car. I was expecting lights to come on at windows and noisy complaints from the other tenants but nothing stirred.

'I'm not a lush, you know,' she continued quite gratuitously. 'I've had post traumatic stress disorder after attending postmortems. I feel that drink helps me to counter the stress.'

I smiled unpleasantly.

'Philip's a pig, too. He led me to believe that he was going to leave his wife and that we'd be getting married. Then three days ago I got an e-mail message from him on my laptop putting it all off. He feels a divorce wouldn't be good for his career at this stage. I've given him five years of my life and he sends me e-mail!' Having unburdened herself thus far she looked at me for some contribution. Somehow, I just did not feel like offering comfort to the lovelorn.

'I'm being paid to research Billy Fox and you're threatened by that,' I spoke harshly.

'You fool! You and your pathetic employer, Liptrot, are being manipulated to discredit me and ruin my career. That profile on Fox that I did –'

'Yes, what about the profile?' I asked, getting involved in spite of myself. 'Even your friend, Geoff Bartle, had to agree there was something highly unusual about it.'

'Bartle's Philip's friend, not mine. I expect he told you that hoping you'd make trouble.'

'Don't be paranoid. Bartle wouldn't give me the time of day unless I had his arm twisted up his back.'

'I wish I'd never done it. It seemed like an innocent request at the time. Philip's based his career on the offender profiles I provided him with. He shot up the senior ranks thanks to me.'

'Oh, come on. Other coppers must have seen them,' I said.

'They did, but they're all old-fashioned types like Sinclair or your friend, Cullen. Philip really believes in profiling. We did the profile on Billy Fox as an exercise to show ourselves how he fitted the parameters and, of course, he does. Now if the case went to appeal his lawyer would claim we'd fitted him up. Philip's terrified. They'll shoot him down in flames if there's any slip up.'

'There's something you're not telling me, isn't there?'

'This case is so unusual. Even for "Stranger Killing" it's weird,' she explained. 'There was no crime signature linking one man with a series of separate killings. All the victims were found at once. The lack of bodies meant that all the usual indicators used to build up a picture of the killer's needs were absent. We don't even know how he killed them.'

'Decapitated them didn't he?' I interrupted.

'That could have been postmortem. He could have shot them or stabbed them first.'

'So what did your profile say about the killer?' I asked.

'Mainly that the urge to collect heads as trophies pointed to a man like Billy. That he exhibited a pattern of abnormal relationships with the opposite sex throughout life consistent with obsessional killing.'

'OK. That was your profile, but right or wrong it was never needed. It was irrelevant. Billy was convicted by material evidence and his own confession. There's got to be something else that's needling you . . .'

I looked at her for a long time. She was almost on the point of telling me but then she shook her head.

'Billy committed those murders, as for the rest . . . You know so much, why don't you find out?'

'. . . trailing clouds of glory do we come
From God, who is our home:
Heaven lies about us In our infancy!
Shades of the prison-house begin to close
Upon the growing boy.
But he beholds the light, and whence it flows . . .'
Intimations of Immortality, William Wordsworth

8

Saturday, 15th September, morning

I'd been in bed just long enough to fall into a deep sleep when the phone rang.

'Cunane! Where've you been? I've been trying to reach you all evening,' Lena Liptrot's voice squawked when I picked up the receiver.

'Lena, if you have trouble sleeping, I don't,' I said mildly. 'It's after two a.m.'

'I was worried. Your car's still in the car park. Cedric thought something might have happened to you.'

I was wide awake now and I knew that I'd have trouble getting back to sleep. I filled Lena in on the interviews with Turner and Pilatski and made only a token objection when she demanded that I deliver the tapes straight away. I didn't mention Caulfield. Still, the suggestion that I was being manipulated played on my mind. I decided that I was going to find out exactly how mother and son intended to use the material I was supplying.

I showered and dressed in black jeans and two layers of polo shirts. There was plenty of traffic heading from the outskirts to the city centre when my taxi reached the motorway, so much in fact that it set me thinking. Even at this late hour there were plenty of people whose evening was just beginning. They were heading downtown for fun and frolics. That was where the money was these days: supplying booze, music, sex, drugs, etc, etc. I remembered an old school friend, Dennis Quince. He'd not been overly endowed with brains or knowledge but he did know one thing – how to make money. After a few ventures that failed, he'd hit on the idea of theme pubs and got into the market early. Now he owned five and was on the way to his second million. He was also onto his second wife, I recalled. A pretty blonde just turned twenty.

Here I was, cruising down the motorway to an appointment with my third crazy woman of the evening. I hadn't even a pension plan to my name. I almost decided to tell the taxi not to turn off at the interchange for the Swiss Chalet Hotel but to go on as far as the M6 and head up north to Kath. Then I wondered how she and her father would respond to an unannounced arrival in the middle of the night. Not well, I guessed.

The entrance to the hotel was guarded by a massively built bouncer with chunky rings on every finger. There was no way he was going to let me in. It was interesting to see how the hostile environment of inner-city Manchester club-land, with its menacing platoons of steroid-enhanced doormen guarding every entrance, had spread as far as the outer suburbs. Not so long ago, they'd have only had an elderly man or a youth on duty as night porter.

The bouncer waddled towards me, one hand on the mobile phone at his belt. 'Security,' he announced aggressively.

'I'm expected,' I said. He grunted dismissively and phoned before allowing me in.

Lena was still in her red tracksuit. I don't know

where she'd got the idea of tracksuits from but they didn't suit her at all, especially in the colour she'd chosen. She looked like a bag lady who'd salvaged her kit from an advertising promotion for tomato ketchup.

'Where's Cedric?' I asked.

'He's getting his beauty sleep. I don't think he's recovered from all that vodka he had on Thursday.'

She listened to the tapes of the interviews while I made myself a cup of coffee.

'They'll fill in the background,' was her verdict. 'What you've got here's all very well for a bit of contrast with what he eventually became. That's not what the public wants. The public wants to know what turned Fox into a demon and that's what we're going to give them.'

'Really,' I said, 'I didn't think you and Cedric were that commercial.'

'For £500,000 we can be very commercial,' she answered.

'But that's not the impression Cedric gives,' I pressed. We both listened for a moment to the sound of his steady snoring coming from next door.

'You don't have to worry about what little Lord Fauntleroy in there thinks,' said his mother with a nod towards the bedroom. 'You just get me the material I need and I'll do the thinking about the ethics for all of us. We don't mind paying you well. I might find you a bonus for a nice piece on why Billy turned out the way he did. I've been in touch with our accountant. It's all tax deductible.'

I looked at her for a long time, then I spoke. 'Lena, I wondered, has Sinclair or anyone else given you a hint of what sort of spin they'd like Cedric to put on the Corpseless Head Murders?'

'Who's been putting ideas into your pretty head?' she said after a roguish chuckle.

'No, seriously, have you been asked to discredit psychological profiling?'

'The only thing we've been asked is to produce another bestseller. That's why we're paying you to help us, not for a load of daft questions.'

'How were you and Cedric thinking of dealing with the racial issue?' I persisted.

Her eyes narrowed. My heart began to beat a bit faster. 'What do you mean, "the racial issue"? Billy was black and most of his victims were white. That it?'

I nodded.

'Well. We're not bigots if that's what's worrying you, so you can cut out that frowning. Billy certainly had no racial prejudices either. He didn't care whomever he killed. Blacks, whites, Muslims or Jews, he didn't give a toss. Cedric established that before he even started writing. We don't want anyone pointing a finger at us.'

'Did he say anything about race when he was being questioned?' I persisted.

'Not in the way you mean. That psychologist was on at him for a whole day to make him admit that there was a racial side to his killing rage but Billy didn't understand what she was getting at. It's women, without distinction, that he likes killing.'

'Not quite without distinction. They were all carefully selected,' I said.

Lena gave her odd cackling laugh. 'Eee, it'd be funny, if it weren't so sad. Here we are congratulating ourselves because this murdering shite-hawk killed black girls as well as white ones. Do you know when I was young in Bradford the only black or brown face I ever saw was an Indian doctor and he was married to a white woman. Kids used to come from miles around and wait at his gate for a gawp at him.'

'That was before you married the farmer,' I said to keep conversation flowing.

'What farmer?' she asked. 'You're getting me mixed up with someone else. My husband was a lighthouse keeper. He kept the light off Flamborough Head.' This silenced me completely. I sat back in my chair. The woman was as crazy as a screech owl. Looking at the tracksuit it crossed my mind that this was the unisex garment favoured by certain psychiatric hospitals for the elderly. I stirred and she withdrew from the clinch she'd had me in.

'You're going to have to find some of the people who knew Billy Fox when he was practising his trade,' she said, all businesslike again.

'There's the social worker, his landlady, this property repairer who found the heads,' I said. 'Most of the rest are under contract or negotiating with the tabloids.' I kept quiet about Horatio Bostick and Lurlene Barnacle. They might come in handy on another occasion. I looked at her closely.

'I suppose you want the weekend off to go and see your lady friend?' Lena said.

'Most people would think two-thirty on a Saturday morning *is* the weekend,' I said. 'I thought I might go and see Billy's old landlady. She's in an old folk's home near where Kath's father lives.'

'There's a pile of papers that the police left over there. Information about the victims. There's nothing that they haven't released to the press but you might like to look through it.' She indicated a mound of files about three feet high leaning against the wall by the door.

It took me two trips to load the car. I felt light-hearted when I drove off.

A few years ago I would have headed down into central Manchester looking for some action but the place had been taken over by teenagers with their shirts flapping outside their trousers. I headed back to the flat to resume my interrupted slumbers. I left the heavy files in the boot of the car. If the GMP were so careless with their files as to entrust them to a loopy old lady why should I bust my back hauling them upstairs?

I woke at seven. When I opened the living room curtains the sky was ashen. The trees were motionless. There wasn't a ripple of breeze in the air. Even the birds were silent. I didn't need to stand looking at the scene for more than a couple of seconds before deciding that a quick departure from Manchester was the best plan for a Saturday like this one. I decided to head north and see if Kath's half-hearted invitation to share her weekend had been seriously intended. I could use the excuse that I had to interview old Mrs Colquhuon in her nursing home at Grange-over-Sands as a cover story if my reception at Hawkshead was unfavourable.

I'd promised to give Jay Anderson a lift to my parents' rural retreat on the moors north of Bolton. When I pulled up at his home off Lloyd Street in Moss Side I couldn't help noticing that someone had daubed the words 'PIGS OUT' in indelible red paint across the brickwork. Despite somebody's futile attempt to erase the screed it glowed like a neon hoarding.

'Charming,' I said as Jay slung his bag onto the back seat. He was embarrassed and made that odd gesture of swivelling his wrists that I knew so well.

'Don't get heavy, Dave,' he cautioned, as if he expected me to start tracking down the culprit immediately.

'What's his name, Jay? Don't tell me you don't know the name of your mural artist. It's this that's bugging you, not the red-neck policemen.

'Partly . . . It's both. I don't want any fuss.'

He turned the radio on and tuned it to some loud jungle music. We drove through Manchester and I waited until we were on the motorway before I switched the radio off.

'Who is it?'

'I don't know who did it but I know who put them up to it. It's this guy I was mixed up with years ago, before I came to work with you. He's called Everald Mallick. He's leaning on me to resign from the police. He wants to make a big incident out of it. I keep tying to tell him that I want to stay with the job but he won't listen to me.'

I drove in silence for some time while I digested this information. 'If you could see him, maybe you could talk to him,' Jay suggested hopefully.

'You're one of his own, Jay. If he won't listen to you . . .'

'You're a better talker than I am,' he said.

'I don't know about talking, Jay. It sounds as if the guy could do with a knuckle sandwich.'

We left it there. When this Mallick saw how determined Jay was he'd drop his petty persecution, I hoped. I turned off the motorway and drove to the West Pennine Moors. Jay didn't turn the radio on again.

I had no intention of calling on the aged parents, but when I neared the point where I was due to drop Jay, I caught sight of a familiar figure. My father was sitting on a concrete milk churn stand, leftover from the days when farms in the area still bothered to produce milk. I gave him a thin smile as Jay got out of the car and made to drive off immediately, but he raised his hand.

'I may have been a bit hasty in what I said to you about exploiting the Billy Fox case. It's up to you, Dave. A little bird tells me that everything's not quite as it seems on that case. You want to watch that it doesn't blow up in your face.' He waved me on. Paddy was no more anxious for a gushing reconciliation than I was. I suppressed a smile.

Despite my rebellious disposition, I felt oddly pleased at this belated paternal benediction. I headed back towards the motorway and points north. Thinking over what Paddy had said, I realised that he was still in contact with Sinclair and one or two other grizzle-headed veterans still in the force.

I stopped at Forton Services for a coffee and doughnut and bought a copy of the *Times*. There was an article about Billy in the magazine section called 'Fox on the Rampage', churning out the same old stuff. The public were obviously insatiable when it came to serial killers. Maybe Headstone Press hadn't misjudged the market in offering Cedric half a million for his scribblings.

When I arrived in the village of Hawkshead I had to park the car in the public car park on the outskirts. There was no access by vehicle to Commander Headlam's home. The leaden skies and motionless air of Manchester had given way to sheeting rain and cold winds in the Lake District. As I got out of the car shivering I realised why the Herdwick sheep up here had evolved a specially tough kind of wool.

The car park stood behind a massive clothing store that provided the main activity in the little town. It was opposite the grammar school where a very different Billy from the one who interested me, Billy Wordsworth, had passed his school days. The public showed little interest in the earlier Billy. There were no queues waiting to visit the school. Even so, at ten on a wet Saturday morning, the narrow streets all around Headlam's house heaved with tourists. They were scouring the sheepskin coat and cagoule shops for bargains. I didn't spot a single romantic schoolboy heading off into the hills for intense experiences with nature. The only intense experience available in Hawkshead nowadays was buying sturdy outerwear and then heading back to the car park and the big city with it.

Fortunately, when I arrived the submariner was out on patrol.

'Brought your Barbour with you?' Kath joked, when she released me from a very friendly embrace. 'You look a bit peaky, Dave. A nice long walk over Dungeon Gill will do you good . . . Get some of that city air out of your lungs.'

'Actually Kath, I really came up to see Billy Fox's landlady. She's living a few miles away from here,' I said, tentatively launching into my prepared cover story.

'Oh, Dave! You must stay with us. Daddy will be furious if you clear off. I think he's looking forward to a spot of male bonding. He gets bored with all these earnest middle-aged women he meets on his committees.'

I filled her in on what had been happening since she made an early start to the weekend. She was looking well. Her face had lost the tension it had assumed over the last week. When I finished, she leaned over and kissed me on the lips.

'Let's just have a nice weekend,' she said. 'You know you don't really need to be so inhibited by Daddy. He's not as narrow-minded as you think and what's more he won't be back for a long time,' she added rather breathlessly. Then she led me from my seat and up the rickety stairs to her bedroom, an upper room where generations of weavers had toiled at the loom. When Commander Headlam bought the cottage from a naval colleague it was at a bargain price because terminal death-watch beetle had set in. True to his love of authenticity, he had spent a fortune on oak timbers even where he could have used steel and concrete for internal repairs. This had certain drawbacks, as Kath and I discovered when she peeled her pullover and jeans off and led me to her narrow little bed. It wasn't just the bed that creaked. Images of marching soldiers wrecking bridges flitted through my mind as we achieved our own simple harmonic motion.

An hour later, when he returned, we were downstairs decorously drinking tea in the cramped and dark little living room.

If you took all the naval officers who ever lived, boiled them up together, concentrated the resulting juice and pumped it into one person's veins something like Commander Hugo Headlam would be the result. His eyes were sharp but not piercing. His manner was slightly suspicious. At least, his habit of snatching a quick glance over his shoulder at frequent intervals reminded me of shoplifters I'd known. I put it down to some sort of naval tradition. He wasn't a big man. His physique was slender. He gave an impression of always being alert, like a rare bird ready to fly away quickly. He shared with his daughter the habit of displaying his teeth before speaking.

Somehow, as a natural lower-deck type, I knew that I would never be at ease with him.

'Ah, Cunane, er . . . Dave, . . . you've come,' he said unnecessarily, as he hung his soaking duffel coat behind the door. 'Did you find your way up here all right?' he asked, also, I thought, unnecessarily. He regarded locating Hawkshead by car from Manchester as a feat comparable with reaching Kathmandu or Karakorum by mule train. 'Rough sort of a day, but I like it like this. Doesn't suit us all, though, eh?'

I knew that the last remark was intended to imply that I was the sort of cove who preferred lolling about indoors, trifling with his daughter, to taking a manly stroll up Coniston Old Man. I didn't rise to his bait. Kath had extracted a promise that I would be nice to him. I trotted out the cover story about Mrs Colquhuon with practised ease. He looked me in the eye. It went without saying that he had a very accurate idea about what had preceded his arrival.

'At Wildboar Bank Hall is she? Know it well. The committee visited to vet some alterations to the out-buildings that they'd planned. I, er . . . that is to say we, soon put a stop to those. They wanted to replace stone roofs with corrugated iron. Categorically forbidden,' he said.

The object of the Commander's ceaseless patrolling of the Lakeland moors and fells was to detect any alterations to farm buildings or properties that violated the ultra-strict local planning regulations.

'Yes, I quite fancy a run out in that direction. I could guide you down there if you like.'

I stared back at him with a flinty gaze that matched his own. If I'd needed a sherpa he was the last one I'd have chosen. A small man, he radiated a kind of imperious officiousness. I knew he was absolutely merciless to any culprits he found breaking the decrees about buildings. However, I had promised, and he was the father of my beloved so I smiled agreeably.

In the end it was decided that after lunch we'd all take a trip down to Grange to check out the old lady's story.

Motoring round the narrow, walled-in roads of the Lake District on a wet Saturday afternoon when half thre population of England has decided to do the same thing is an unrepeatable experience at best. Doing it in the only car I owned, with Commander Headlam at the wheel, was a foretaste of the tortures of hell. He was constantly trying to pass slower-moving vehicles, caravans especially, flashing his lights and revving up steep hills. All this was accompanied by a nautical commentary that would have made a pirate's blood freeze.

At least he did know his way there directly. The quaintly named Wildboar Bank Hall turned out to be a Victorian millionaire's idea of a cosy little weekend retreat, built on a hillside above Kent's Bank to catch the best possible view of Morecambe Bay. Unlike the listed buildings under the Commander's care, the colossal red-brick pile was not maintained to the highest standard. There were signs of neglect here and there, weeds and even little trees growing out of drainpipes in out-of-the-way corners of the roof. When these places were built an artisan's wages were hardly considered. It needed an army of carers to keep it going now, though.

Mrs Ethel Colquhuon was quite unlike my vision of a Fallowfield landlady. Veteran of many a brush with lodging keepers in South Manchester, I was expecting some belligerent old hyena. Instead, she was a pleasant, stately person of seventy with rosy cheeks and intelligent eyes. Her hair still had some natural dark colour in it.

'Shame about the weather,' she said as we looked out over the wide curving coastline from the immense bay window of the residents' lounge. 'You can see Blackpool Tower and even the Isle of Man on a fine day.'

Kath and I listened respectfully as she pointed out the sights. It was the Commander who was most anxious to focus on the reason for our visit. He coughed impatiently while the old lady courteously showed us round her temporary accommodation.

'Well,' she said at last, 'I don't expect you've come here for a guided tour. You've found me out, haven't you? I came here to get away from all that fuss over poor Billy.'

I explained that Assistant Chief Constable Sinclair had given us her address and that anything she told us wasn't for immediate publication. She was taken with the idea of a book and TV series and she led us to a quiet corner of the lounge for an interview over a cup of tea.

From her point of view Billy had been the ideal tenant. He'd always paid the rent punctually, had very few visitors, was clean and tidy.

'He had the top floor to himself. Very poky that attic bedroom, but he did have a little kitchen and the bathroom. He had everything he needed. He was my tenant for over ten years and never a word of complaint.'

'Didn't you have any idea what he was up to?' Kath probed gently.

Mrs Colquhuon took out a neat little handkerchief trimmed with lace and dabbed her eyes. 'That's what the police kept asking. I think some of them thought I was some sort of accomplice. There were seven other residents in the house most of the time and never a one mentioned anything funny about Billy. I noticed the smell of formaldehyde occasionally when I cleaned the landing but he said it came in on his clothes and after I'd mentioned it, it would go away for a while.'

The Commander favoured us with another of his thunderous coughs at this point. We all looked at him for a moment and then judiciously sipped our tea.

'I know it's incredible,' she continued when his volcanic rumblings had subsided, 'but I've been thinking it over and if he did kill all those girls in my house he must have been fiendishly cunning. He must have done it at times when most of the other residents were out. There was only old Mr Jones who was solitary like Billy and never left the place. He's half deaf and blind. The rest used to go off at Bank Holidays, and Christmas and so on. I did myself. Many's the time when I left

Billy with my keys so he could let the meter reader in. That's when he had the opportunity.'

'Mrs Colquhuon,' I said delicately, 'you say "poor" Billy and "if" he killed the girls. So you don't entirely accept that he did. Why not?'

'He was such a gentle soul. So helpful. He'd pull the wheelie bins out for me. Once my cat got stuck up a tree. He had it down before I could call the fire brigade.' The memory must have struck a chord because she started crying again. 'Very kind to animals, was Billy. That was one of the few things he ever went out of the house for. He worked for an animal shelter in Moss Side and used to visit an animal refuge somewhere in the Pennines. That's how he met the Summergills. Ever so nice they were. I gave them the contract to do the property repairs on all my buildings.'

The Commander could restrain himself no longer. 'It sounds as if you're proposing to give the chap the MBE or something, woman! The ruddy man's a serial killer!' They may not have been able to hear the roar in the Isle of Man but no one in Wildboar Bank Hall, including the deaf or senile, could have missed it.

I hurriedly turned the tape off, but the damage was done. Mrs Colquhuon swept up her knitting into the large bag by her side and made a dignified exit without another word.

'Nice one, Daddy!' said Kath.

'No, he's right,' I muttered as the three of us walked out under the hostile stares of the other elderly residents. 'This is crap,' I said, tapping the tape recorder. 'According to her and every other witness I've interviewed so far, Billy was the most charming and helpful fellow you could meet in a long day's walk. Yet we know he killed fourteen young women.

The Commander favoured me with a glimpse of his teeth. 'I expect Dr Crippen was charming enough when he wanted to be, but that didn't stop them hanging him. This little swine should get what's coming to him. Do you know that the Royal Navy maintains the only functioning gallows in the UK?'

'The index of similarity between the killing of the unknown female near Mauldeth Road and the killings of Yvonne Clutterbuck and Stacey Shawcross appears to be 100% at this stage. Even the unknown victim's approximate age appears to be the same as theirs and she was definitely using illegal substances. The killing of the male victim does break the pattern. The assumption is that this was an "accidental" killing and that the male intervened after witnessing the assault on the female.'
GMP Internal Memo

9

Saturday evening

The rain continued to lash down for the remainder of Saturday. Even the Commander was sufficiently intimidated by the weather not to take up his daughter's humorous suggestion that he and I should head off for a spot of bonding in Grizedale Forest. Kath had her head stuck into the police papers I'd lugged up from Manchester, so the pair of us were thrown together. Remarkably enough, the Commander and I were beginning to develop a tenuous affinity. He even instructed me to call him by his first name, Hugo, a significant advance. By evening his upper lip had unstiffened sufficiently for him to call me Dave without that half-furtive, half-mocking manner the English upper-middle classes reserve for addressing their assumed social inferiors.

Amusements, apart from conversation and drink, were scarce in the Headlam homestead. Hugo included radio, TV and newspapers in his merciless disapproval of things modern, so we were thrown back on traditional sources of entertainment.

When Kath and I went to bed the gusting wind and buffeting rain was quite loud enough to mask our less than strenuous lovemaking. There was hardly a creak out of the bed.

'Dave, we've got to have conflict in this script. If we can't supply it from Billy's background we'll have to concentrate on the sinister side of the actual killings themselves,' Kath said, as we drifted towards sleep. 'These girls who went up to his flat must have been like Mrs Colquhuon. They must have thought he was a charming, loveable character.'

'He gives a whole new meaning to the words charm offensive,' I said drowsily. It had been a long day.

'I'm going to spend tomorrow going through the rest of the files. I think those poor girls must have been specially susceptible to someone like Billy. Maybe some of them were pregnant by him, there must be medical records . . .'

'You could be right,' I murmured. 'Like father, like son.'

'Has it ever been established how he cut their heads off?' she persisted. 'Perhaps he made them bend over the bath for some reason and then whacked their heads off with his machete.'

'We don't know that he had a machete,' I said. 'Go to sleep, love.'

'A samurai sword then,' she insisted. 'You can send off for them. I've seen the adverts.'

I drifted off to sleep with visions of Kath directing a scene in her TV series . . . *A glittering sword was flashing through the air towards the nape of a young woman's neck.*

I was woken at half seven by the sound of the

Commander, as I still thought of him, bellowing through his window to someone in the street.

'Get that bloody car out of here! Can't you read, man? "No vehicles".'

I cautiously pulled the curtains to one side for a peek down at the narrow street. A familiar blue Sierra was jammed into the narrow cul-de-sac, its wipers battling against the torrential rain as two faces peered up at us. Detective Sergeant Cullen of the GMP and his sidekick, Gobbo, got out. Cullen was clad in his purple shell suit and trainers. It didn't look as if he was up here for the fresh air. Gobbo looked as sullen and silent as ever. Cullen was flashing a provocative, proletarian grin up at the Commander.

I decided to dress. My clothes lay where they'd been cast in the heat of the moment, and my frantic gropings for them woke Kath. As she sat up in alarm, her father was charging down the rickety stairs to confront his uninvited visitors. For a moment there was the sound of fierce argument. Yet, by the time I finally pulled my jeans on, the voices had diminished to a faint murmur.

When I entered the cramped living room Hugo Headlam favoured me with a fierce glare. 'These gentlemen want a word with you,' he muttered between clenched teeth and then pushed past me on his way back upstairs. From his expression I judged that the brief period of probation that he had allowed me last night was at an end.

'Morning, squire,' said Cullen genially, adding, 'Who the hell was that? I thought he was going to slot me.'

I stared at him with stunned incomprehension.

'Sorry to roust you out on your weekend, mate. Mrs Liptrot put us onto you. There's only one Headlam in the Hawkshead phone book.'

Gobbo, who was looking very official in a neat

business suit, ground his teeth at this display of friendly repartee.

Cullen ignored him.

'It's a bit awkward like. Look, Mr Cunane, there were another two killings in Manchester on Friday night and we've had Mr Liptrot in for a chat about them – an official chat. Now Mr Sinclair wants to talk to you as well.'

I tried to get my brain to work. 'Do you mean "talk" to him in the sense of give him advice about the case?' I asked hopefully.

Gobbo wrenched his gaze away from Kath, who had arrived downstairs dressed only in a skimpy silk kimono, and faced Cullen. He gave him a meaningful look. As if taking a cue, Cullen started again. 'Well, technically speaking, it's a bit stronger than that. You have to come with us to help us in our enquiries or we're under orders to arrest you.' Cullen spoke apologetically, but his opposite was fingering the handcuffs at his waist. Slapping them on me would make his day.

I looked from one copper to the other as the meaning of what Cullen was saying dawned on me.

'Do you mean you've arrested Cedric Liptrot on suspicion of actually doing these murders?' I asked. I was unable to keep the incredulity out of my voice.

'There's no one else in the frame at the moment, cocker,' Cullen said. It wasn't quite an answer to the question but it was as much as I was going to get. However, I took him to mean that I wasn't a suspect. Gobbo had the handcuffs out now. Cullen, with a flick of his head, motioned me to get a move on.

'Always happy to help the GMP,' I said with a confidence I didn't feel.

'Dave, you're going nowhere until you've had a decent breakfast,' Kath asserted.

'Yeah, that's all right, Miss. There's no need for us to rush back. We made good time getting here,' Cullen said. 'Make him his breakfast, and crack a couple of eggs for me if you don't mind.' His sidekick snorted in disgust at the weakness of his senior officer.

It was an hour before we departed. I went in the blue Sierra and Kath followed us, driving my car because it had a phone fitted. Gobbo had made it very clear that I was not to be trusted to drive my own vehicle. The Commander gave his daughter a testy farewell, pointedly ignoring me. So much for bonding! His reaction to a visit from the police couldn't have been more frosty if they'd called to arrest me for torching Beatrix Potter's cottage.

When we reached Manchester things were buzzing. The temperature had risen too. It felt hot, almost airless. Jackson's Row, the narrow little street alongside Bootle Street Police Station, was jammed with TV crews and reporters. They crowded forward as we swung towards the car park only clearing a path for us when they saw that no one was under arrest.

I had to metaphorically shake myself as the pair scurried me into the building. It all seemed so unreal. That soon changed. As Cullen led me up the winding stairs and along the corridors of the former City of Manchester Police Headquarters, my father's old stamping ground, I could sense an air of expectancy. Cullen received many knowing glances and nods. Something was definitely up.

Geoff Bartle was standing at the head of the corridor by the upper-floor offices, looking as smooth as ever. Amazingly, when he saw me his eyes lit up with a pleased-looking glow. He grabbed me by the sleeve. 'It's Cedric Liptrot. As you may know, they've interviewed him in connection with the killings.' I looked at him in surprise. 'I'm acting for him,' he said slowly, mistaking my surprise for obtuseness. Bartle wouldn't have been my first choice of solicitor. 'You've been named as his alibi witness. We're all relying on you.'

It took me a moment to join up all the dots.

Cullen took me by the arm and bustled me along. 'This way, sir,' he said, ushering me into the presence of Pinnock and Sinclair. In deference to the warm day, Pinnock, his thick dark hair slicked back, was wearing a new-looking linen suit. Just looking at him made me feel hot and bothered. Sinclair gave me his usual hungry predator's smile. The office wasn't a normal interview room and there was no recorder on the desk.

'You stay,' Pinnock ordered Cullen, as Gobbo took his leave.

'Tell me about Friday night,' Pinnock said to me, without preamble. Sinclair was loading his pipe.

'Isn't that against the new regulations?' I asked pettishly, determined to get my retaliation in first.

'Don't be like that, Davie,' Sinclair said, continuing to shred up his tobacco. 'Just tell DCS Pinnock what he wants to know.'

'Sorry, I'm saying nothing until I know what's going on,' I said.

'Don't you keep up with the news?' Pinnock murmured as he handed me a piece of paper. It was a summary for internal release, marked 'For Force Use Only'. I was still trusted to some extent.

The body of a white female was found under a bridge on the disused Midland Railway line where it crosses Mauldeth Road, Chorlton at 22.00 hrs, Saturday, by a man walking his dog. Preliminary findings indicate that the female, probably an indigent and drug abuser (paraphernalia found) was killed by a single blow to the head with a blunt instrument. An effort had been made to cover the body with rusty corrugated sheeting found nearby.

Further search by officers revealed a second body, that of an Afro-Caribbean male, also probably an indigent and drug abuser. He had suffered multiple blows and appeared to have put up a fierce struggle with his killer. Current speculation is that the male witnessed the killing of the female and then intervened, only to be killed himself.

Neither victim has so far been identified. Forensic have not found traces of skin under the fingernails of the female deceased. Hence, DNA matching or blood sampling are not possible. There was no trace of a struggle. The female may have been asleep when struck. The wound to her head, at the left occiput, is square shaped, about 3.5 cms across, suggesting use of a club hammer. In contrast to her, the male victim has severe fracture injuries to his forearms. These defence injuries imply that he tried to shield himself before receiving six blows to the head, any of which could have proved fatal. The shape of the wounds are less clear than in the female victim but they are consistent with the same type of hammer. Traces of a dark, short-length, woollen fibre were found underneath his fingernails. Preliminary study suggests this is consistent with the assailant wearing a black coat of the type known as a donkey jacket, often used by construction workers.

Research is proceeding to match the wool fibres to known fabrics. All manufacturers and suppliers of donkey jackets are being contacted. All known suppliers of club hammers are being questioned. Very faint traces of oil that may have been present on the murder weapon have been detected and are being traced. Further forensic tests are being undertaken on the wounds to determine physical characteristics of the killer.

I studied it for a long time trying to make sense of what was happening. I could taste the breakfast that Kath had so kindly prepared rising to the back of my throat as I tried to control my emotions. It wouldn't do to throw up in the Detective Chief Superintendent's nice office.

'The time of death was probably between midnight Friday and 3 a.m.,' Sinclair said, sending the first blue cloud of smoke in my direction, no help on the nausea control front. 'The crime wasn't discovered until late on Saturday and this investigation didn't get underway until the small hours of this morning. We're told that you were with Liptrot at the time the deaths occurred,' he added.

'Liptrot?' I repeated. 'I still don't know what the hell you're on about. They weren't battered to death with copies of *A Son To Us All* were they?'

Pinnock pushed another piece of paper at me. 'This is a copy of the register of the Churchill Hotel for 14th August. You will note the names of your client and his mother. At 04.00 hrs on 15th August the body of Yvonne Clutterbuck was recovered from a cardboard box at the rear of the hotel. She had been killed by a single massive blow. Cunane, I know from ACC Sinclair that you have a low idea of the Force's powers of deduction –'

'And a high idea of your own,' broke in Sinclair.

'But even you must admit there's something a little odd going on. An author who's written a study of the Basher killings arrives in Manchester and within a few hours there's an identical killing . . .'

'You obviously don't know Cedric,' I said.

'Oh, but we do,' Pinnock said. 'We know for example that his name appears on a list of judges for a play writing competition sponsored by Northern Arts in September last year. You'll be very interested to hear where the venue was for that competition, Cunane.' He paused for me to ask him, but I already knew what he was going to say. 'It was held in the National Cycling Centre,' he said, with a little sigh of satisfaction. 'Odd place for it, but apparently the acoustics are perfect for dramatic performances as you so recently discovered for yourself.'

'That was last year. There must be hundreds of thousands of people who know their way round the Velodrome. It doesn't prove a thing.'

'Except that Liptrot's more familiar with Manchester than he's led us to believe,' chipped in Sinclair.

'He fits the profile supplied by his rival, Dr Caulfield,' chimed in Pinnock. 'Surely you remember, Cunane. Dr Caulfield suggested that the murders could have been revenge killings by a man who had been castrated. Well, what is Cedric if not a man who has been completely emasculated by his own mother? Psychologically speaking, of course.'

'So that's where all this profiling gets us,' I said bitterly. 'It can be twisted to fit anyone . . . psychologically speaking.' I imagined the e-mail messages that must have been flashing between Lauren Caulfield and Philip Pinnock.

'Listen Cunane,' Pinnock said, 'two killings at places where Liptrot had access strains the laws of probability too much for me to ignore. But a third, with a well-paid private detective and his mother as the only witnesses . . .' There was any amount of venom in his words. I got a strong whiff of personal malice. God knows what his girlfriend had told him about me.

'Obviously the real killer is trying to implicate Cedric. A child could grasp that,' I said heatedly.

'Mr Pinnock isn't saying that Liptrot committed the latest murders, just that the possibility exists,' Sinclair said in his most reasonable voice. 'He's the only suspect we have at the moment, Davie boy. We've rounded up every known sex offender in Greater Manchester, some of them for the third time. No joy. We've got to look at anyone who might be in the frame.'

'You suspected him right from the start, didn't you?' I said to Sinclair. 'That's why you bent over backwards to help him.'

'That's a bit strong, Davie. I offered him co-operation before ever he set foot in Manchester or there were any murders, but in view of the similarity to the Basher cases I'd be foolish not to consider him.'

I didn't know how to handle Sinclair. This situation was so different from my normal confrontations with him. Usually I was trying to keep my own nefarious activities hidden from his prying. Now I wasn't sure whose side I was supposed to be on.

'Did you see him on Friday night?' Pinnock asked, ignoring my objections. If he knew where his ex-lady friend had spent most of that particular evening he'd be less keen to have me go into details, I was sure.

'I paid a visit on his mother. I didn't actually see Cedric but I heard him snoring in the next room.' Cedric was paying me well but I wasn't tempted to strengthen the evidence on his behalf. Sinclair knew me well enough to sniff out a lie.

My interrogators exchanged significant glances. For some reason I felt infuriated.

'Look, Cedric was asleep in the next room. I could tell he was there but I was hardly likely to go in and wake him up, was I? He's paying me for research, not to stand over him whether he's awake or asleep.' This produced no response from either of them. 'Don't tell me you haven't had him under constant surveillance,' I said angrily. 'I spotted your grey van. You know it isn't him.'

'True enough, Davie, I've had him watched,' Sinclair said. 'But we know that psychopathic killers will go to extraordinary lengths to evade even the most complete police surveillance, and by the way, our vans are white not grey.'

I felt a twinge of something at this. It wasn't guilt, maybe it was fear. Lena Liptrot had shown great facility with a tape recorder. Had she recorded the snores and then invited me round to hear them while Cedric prowled the streets for a victim? Then there was the grey van. I'd definitely seen one. Something of the puzzlement I felt must have shown because Sinclair gave me a sympathetic grin.

'There's more than a possibility, isn't there, Davie? He could have slipped out of that hotel in disguise at any time. We don't expect you to spy on him, but we want to be the first to know if you suspect anything. For some reason he and his mother appear to trust you. We've questioned him but he believes it was just a routine interview. He's going to stay in Manchester until the research for the Billy book is done.'

'OK. Can I go?' I said.

'What's the rush, Cunane? Don't you want us to catch this murderer?' Pinnock asked sharply.

'That's what I love about our police force,' I said. 'You drag me down from the Lake District to ask questions that I could have answered over the phone and then add insult to injury by implying that I would shield a murderer.'

'Don't fly off the handle, Davie,' Sinclair interjected. 'Mr Pinnock is only concerned with saving lives. We want to know immediately if you spot anything suspicious going on. I don't want to hear that the son of Paddy Cunane has been trying to get himself a bit of free publicity by upstaging the police.'

So that was it. Sinclair couldn't have been more direct. If anyone was going to get credit for an arrest it had to be the GMP. I nodded my head to signify agreement and got up. Pinnock glanced at Sinclair and then waved his hand to the uniformed officer at the door. I was free to go. Cullen escorted me out, an incongruous figure in his shell suit and trainers after the elegance of his bosses.

He pushed a piece of paper with two phone numbers

on it into my hand. 'That's my office and Vodaphone numbers there, Dave,' he said in his pally way. 'If you need a chat with anyone, I'll be ready to listen.' I tucked the numbers in my wallet.

He gave me a lift back to my office. He tried to be matey all the way across town but I responded to his chat with a series of monosyllabic grunts. 'Cheer up, mate. It might never happen!' he said infuriatingly as he dropped me off.

Kath was waiting for me, wading through the large pile of papers Lena had given me. I told her about the police suspicions while she made me a cup of coffee.

'There's no way, Dave. Cedric just doesn't give out the vibrations,' she said.

'Oh, it's as simple as that with you, is it? Just a matter of vibrations.' I was astonished at the casual way she received the news that her employer might be a serial killer.

'Dave, I know you've got hang-ups about poor old Cedric but believe me he's harmless,' she said calmly.

'I don't suppose Billy's victims thought he would hurt a fly either,' I reminded her.

'I think I've found an angle,' she said, changing the subject. 'You know I was looking for a hook to work the script round. Well, what about love of animals? According to those profiles of Billy's victims they were all either actual or potential pet lovers. I think that's how he got to meet them . . . through his work with the Animal Shelter. We could contrast the love shown to the animals with the brutality of the kilings . . .'

I shook my head dubiously. 'Nobody's mentioned this before. Are you saying the police missed it?'

'Dave, it didn't come out at the trial because the prosecution didn't need it. They had Billy's confession and a mass of circumstantial evidence, but this must be how Billy linked up with his victims.'

'But the press haven't brought it out either. Are you sure?'

'Listen kiddo! Since when have the press been interested in victims? I'm telling you that I've found a new angle here and you might at least listen.'

'Sorry . . . I thought I was the investigator.'

'You shouldn't be so lazy. You let me plough through these papers. So – victim number one – Sharon Mulligan. The approximate date of her murder was January 1990. She was into animal rights.'

'So?'

'So, who do you think she might have met at some indignation meeting? Billy, right? Now, victim number two, Heather Wainwright. She was a helper at the People's Dispensary for Sick Animals in Withington.'

'Impressive,' I said.

'Number three, Shani Tarbutt, was a drug addict from Liverpool. She hadn't been in Manchester long so she wasn't into any organised animal loving, but still, what would be more natural for a lonely girl than to try and find a pet? And whom might she have met? Billy.'

'That one's pure supposition.'

'I'll give you that, but look at number four – Chantelle Clough. Her special interest was the Animal Shelter in Withington. It goes on. Pauline Rimmer, number five, she owned two dogs.'

'Are you saying every victim was an animal lover? I just can't believe the police missed this.'

'I'm not saying they were all connected with animals. Just that too many of them were for it to be a coincidence. And don't forget, Mrs Colquhuon told us that Billy went to an animal shelter in Moss Side. I could hit Daddy. He shut her up just as she was telling us about this refuge in the Pennines where he met the property repairer who brought about his downfall. What was his name?'

'Dennis Summergill,' I supplied. 'He has a son called Dean. But it was Dennis who found the heads when he came to repair the roof above Billy's flat.'

'I want to see him right away,' she said.

'What about the Liptrots? Don't you think we should check in with them?'

'Dave, I should have thought you'd want to get this enquiry over with. Don't forget we're only trying to put a viable script together. No one's ever going to uncover all the details of Billy Fox's life. Find out where the Summergills live and we can invite them out for a drink or something.'

I did as I was bid. A quick phone call to Sergeant Cullen provided me with their phone number. They lived in Withington, handy for property repairing in Fallowfield.

I still felt uneasy about the sudden summons back to Manchester. The police must have something more to base their suspicions on than a series of coincidences Kath was happy to go on working for the Liptrots because she felt that a spot of publicity would help her TV series but I wasn't so sure that it would do me any good.

'Do you think we should go swanning off to Withington before we're sure what's going on here? Why don't I call Geoff Bartle and find out what I can from him?'

'Getting cold feet again, Dave?' Kath said with a curl of her lip. 'We're going to have to see the Summergills at some stage. They're absolutely vital as far as my script is concerned. If you're too chicken I'll go on my own while you're agonising with this lawyer.'

I felt an unpleasant emotion stir. It took me a second to realise that it was jealousy. I suppressed it by asking myself how safe was it for her to wander about making enquiries. It wasn't as if Withington was Britain's version of the Bronx; it was more like Queens. I'd often thought it was gloomy with its avenues lined by overgrown trees. She should be safe enough visiting this animal-loving carpenter or whatever he was.

I passed her the number that Cullen had supplied me. She dialled without another word. It didn't take her long to get in touch. Summergill Senior was delighted to hear from her. It had been a month since he'd last told his story to the press. He asked for a fee but when Kath told him that there was the chance of an extended TV appearance he agreed to do a freebie – 'Just as a one-off, like.'

He provided her with complicated instructions to reach his home.

'See you later, investigator!' was Kath's jaunty comment as she left. The little pang of jealousy that I'd momentarily suppressed stirred again.

When I tried Bartle's number all I got was the answering machine. I needed to know more. In frustration I phoned Cullen again. He suggested that I meet him outside the Café Uno in Albert Square.

It was after two when I arrived. Cullen had sloughed off the shell suit when I met him at the end of the little colonnade opposite the Town Hall. He was wearing a jacket and looked almost normal. I was in a savage mood. I get that way when I feel that people are manipulating me.

'Do you mind telling me what that bloody old fox you work for is up to,' I demanded.

'Got you up too early, didn't we?' he replied. 'Sorry about that, mate. Actually, if you hadn't phoned just now I was going to pay you a visit anyway. Something's come up. You mentioned a grey van.' He looked at me expectantly.

I nodded.

'Now there was low-level surveillance on Liptrot's

hotel right from the time he checked in. A couple of detective constables photographing people coming in and out just in case Chummy turned up.'

'Chummy?' I asked angrily.

'The killer of Yvonne Clutterbuck.'

'So you know who he is,' I said.

'Of course not, the photos were being checked against files of known sex offenders, just in case this crazy tried to get in touch with Cedric. It was obvious the killer was using the MO set out in *A Son To Us All* and we thought he might try and pay Cedric a visit. It was me doing the checking. Five years on the Vice Squad,' he said proudly. 'We got a lovely shot of you coming out on Thursday. You looked like a bitterly disappointed man.'

'Yeah, well I wasn't so disappointed that I failed to clock your surveillance van,' I said, wondering where all this was leading to.

'That's just it. The van wasn't ours. Our unit was in the groundsman's hut adjacent to the entrance. Sinclair's worried. Did you clock the driver? We want you to come in and look through the files.'

I explained that I'd only formed the briefest impression of the van and hadn't seen the driver on either of the two occasions I'd noticed the van. Nevertheless, Cullen insisted that I go and look through the files. 'Me pervert albums,' as he called them.

Back in Bootle Street, but on a lower floor this time, I wasted almost an hour going through the photos. Most of the men were completely innocuous looking, not an obvious monster among them, though some were surprisingly young. The afternoon was slipping away.

'Well, you win some, you lose some,' Cullen muttered. 'Fancy a pint?' Against my better judgement I agreed and he led me across Albert Square to a small pub in the back streets behind Tibb Street.

'You've got to think how it will all read in the papers,' he explained as we settled round a table in the corner of the lounge bar. 'This is the third unexplained murder this month and we've got no clues and no suspects apart from your boss.'

'Yeah, but if the papers print one word about him . . . think of how much Cedric would sue for,' I said.

'Personally speaking, I think you're right. It's not our Cedric. Hasn't got the bottle. But we've got to come up with something. Sinclair's feeling the heat. This takes the pressure off him, even if only for a day or two.'

'I see,' I said bitterly. 'Another media-led investigation with the police half an hour behind yesterday's headlines.'

'What's your problem? Liptrot's publishers are paying you enough, aren't they? Daily rate plus as much again in expenses, hell of a lot more than I get!' Cullen sounded more amused than bitter. The guy was really laid back. I felt tempted to say something to needle him.

'You know there are always wheels within wheels in these high profile cases,' I said. 'Somebody gets banged up. The police responsible bask in publicity and promotion for a while and then years later the Appeal Court unravels everything because somebody didn't do their job right.' I mentioned half a dozen cases that had come unstuck in the nastiest possible way.

Cullen's reply was to crack open a packet of peanuts and smile at me. 'You know, I do believe that you think there's something wrong with the Billy Fox conviction.' Cullen waited for an answer. I shrugged my shoulders and looked away. No one was paying me to set the world to rights.

'I'll grant you that Pinnock got promotion right after Billy was banged up. It's also true that people in high places were pleased that everything had been wrapped up so tidily. They were happy that there weren't race riots and all,' Cullen said. 'Even so, quick though the whole job was, Fox's own brief agrees that there are no grounds for an appeal and I haven't heard that Billy's started claiming that he's innocent.'

'Bugger off, Cullen!' I growled. I was really irritated. He was speaking to me as if I was an idiot.

'Well, what is your problem then?' he said reasonably.

I looked at his bland and innocent expression. He knew something that I didn't and he was having fun by mocking me. I decided to try to probe a little further.

'Fine, Detective Sergeant,' I said cantankerously, 'I wonder what the press would make of the way the investigation into the recent murders has been handled. A detective sergeant has gone out of his way to set me up as an enemy of first Lauren Caulfield and then of her lover, Philip Pinnock . . .'

'What are you talking about?' Cullen asked. His bland expression was showing signs of slipping.

'Oh yes. Don't say that you weren't falling over yourself to get me to take out a summons against Caulfield.'

Cullen grinned.

'Now it seems that Pinnock is trying to frame Cedric Liptrot who so conveniently fits the profile supplied by Caulfield.'

'Going a bit far there, aren't you, mate?' he asked, smiling again. 'I mean Pinnock's a shit, but banging up a totally innocent man's too strong even for him.'

He looked so pleased with himself that I could have kicked the table over in frustration. Obviously I was wide of the mark. There was a complicated game going on and I was playing the part of a pawn, though in whose hand still wasn't clear.

'OK. So you don't mind if I tell a few journalist friends about your little quarrel with Pinnock.'

'Hold on,' Cullen said, with an anxious look in his eye again.

'Well, do you and Sinclair suspect that Pinnock and his lady friend have covered something up about the Billy Fox case? Do you think Pinnock's in the process of cocking up the present investigation? I'm entitled to know. If you think I'm going to allow myself or Cedric Liptrot, who, as you reminded me is paying me good money, to be staked out as a Judas goat while some nutter stalks us –'

'God! You're firing on all cylinders aren't you! Steady on. All that's happened is that some perfectly normal, routine enquiries have been made about your employer.'

'Yes, and what about your employer? Suppose Pinnock's so frightened that negligence is going to be revealed in the Fox case that he sent his girlfriend round to throw me off the track. That failed. So now he's trying to frame Liptrot so I'll be taken off the case. Do you think one of the Sunday papers might find that plausible? Do you think that Pinnock might have killed these girls himself just to ruin Liptrot?'

Cullen laughed. 'You've got a hell of an imagination, Cunane! Keep taking the medicine!' He chuckled to himself for some minutes as he supped his ale. The idea of a senior officer being a killer was amusing. I found it hard to believe myself but Lauren Caulfield was certainly very nervous about something and my wild surmise was as plausible as the idea that Cedric Liptrot was a serial killer.

As he finished his drink Cullen lost the amused expression. 'There is one thing though. Pinnock does have a grey van,' he said seriously.

'Where every prospect pleases and only man seems vile . . .'
From 'The Son of God goes forth to War', *Missionary Hymns*, Reginald Heber

10

Sunday, 16th September, afternoon

I stayed with Cullen longer than I should have done and felt irritated about the waste of time when I came away. It was obvious that Sinclair had instructed Cullen to pump me for any little extra titbits about Cedric. I knew he was on duty because he kept the racial and sexual jokes to a minimum. Even so, it was a relief to get away from him and the crowded little pub.

I hadn't been back in the office for more than ten minutes when my pager bleeped. It was the familiar summons from the Liptrots. For once I tried to put off the meeting. Kath had the car, we could both see them when she came back.

'I want you to come right away. Get a taxi,' Lena ordered.

'No way. It's Sunday and I thought I had the weekend off.' I was abrupt, but I didn't put the phone down quickly enough.

'We're paying you very well. We're entitled . . . We need help,' she said, on a very shrill note.

'All right, all right!' I surrendered without further struggle. 'I'll come, but I'm waiting until my partner gets back. She's been to see the man who discovered the heads and she'll have some more information to pass on.'

Lena slammed the phone down by way of answer. It really hadn't been a very good day for the Liptrots. Nor for me either. I felt tired, my exertions of yesterday and the early start this morning were taking their toll. I felt as if I was standing at the head of a long slope that went downhill all the way. I paced up and down the office for a while, mildly anxious about how Kath had got on, but then gave up the soul searching, lay down on the sofa and slept soundly.

It was well after four when Kath roused me.

She took the recorder out of her bag and slapped it down on the desk with an air of triumph. 'They're an amazing pair. Honestly the whole house is like the Natural History Museum, bursting at the seams with stuffed animals,' she said. I looked at her in surprise. According to Mrs Clquhuon the Summergills were animal lovers. A passion for taxidermy wasn't in character.

'They had this fascinating formicary as well,' Kath added. 'That's a live ant hill in a glass case. We could get a terrific shot of it for the opening sequence.'

'You'll have to save the story. I promised our dear employers that we'd go down there and deliver it in person,' I said.

'Fine time this is!' Lena said grudgingly when we arrived in the now familiar hotel suite. She was dressed in clashing colours as usual, not the tracksuit this time but a green, sick-coloured dress with an orange pullover.

'See this,' I pinched my arm. 'I'm pinching myself to see if I'm dreaming I'm here. I remember someone telling me to take the weekend off –'

'All right, you don't need to go on,' Cedric interrupted.

He looked even seedier than usual. 'They were only eliminating me from their enquiries. It wasn't us that brought you back but now you are here I want you to tell me what's going on. That solicitor we had spent more time with the police than with us.'

'Geoff Bartle!' I snorted. 'What did you pick him for? You do know he represented Billy Fox?'

'His name was the only one I could think of when Sinclair said I ought to get a solicitor,' Cedric explained lamely.

'Well he didn't do Billy much good, did he?'

Cedric had begun to look very nervous. Sweat was leaking out from under the wig-like mass of hair. His mother leaned over and patted his hand.

'So you think we've cause to worry?' she asked.

I looked at her and raised my eyebrows.

'Right, well we'll change that solicitor right away,' she said firmly. 'Lend me your mobile, they've probably got the hotel phone bugged.' I handed her my phone. 'Don't look at me like that, Mr Cunane,' she said sedately. 'I'm not so green as I'm cabbage looking.'

Kath and I sat back while Lena robustly booted Geoff Bartle into touch. It was very satisfactory to hear his squawks of protest being rudely cut off. Then Lena phoned her own solicitor in Bradford and got him to recommend someone in Manchester.

When she'd finished speaking I gave her my own potted version of recent occurrences.

'What you've got to realise is that Cedric here's got himself mixed up in the politics of the Greater Manchester Police. They've banged Billy up for the Corpseless Head Murders, almost certainly correctly, but they can't come up with the substantiating evidence, namely the missing torsos. So they're under pressure for that. Their profiler, Caulfield, is going mad because she thinks Cedric's about to tear her profile of

Billy to shreds and now they've got another mass murderer on the loose. Putting pressure on Cedric takes some of the heat off them.'

'Fine, but it won't bring the bacon home, will it?' Lena asked in her most matter-of-fact, *Bratfurt* tones. 'If Cedric doesn't shift himself and get this book produced we'll all end up in Carey Street.'

I smiled at her. She was completely round the loop, but there was character there.

'Right,' said Kath, equally businesslike. 'I taped an interview with Dennis Summergill and his son, Dean. They're a pair of absolutely fabulous characters and I think they gave us a completely new way of looking at Billy that'll make really great material for the TV . . . Sorry, I mean for Cedric's book,' she said, correcting herself with an awkward glance at Lena. It took me a moment to remember that this was the first time she'd been with the Liptrots since the unpleasant interview on Thursday. I was so familiar with the pair by now that they felt like blood relatives.

'Give me some background first,' Cedric ordered, shutting his eyes and sinking back into his chair. He steepled his fingers, I supposed to signify that he was passing from victim mode into creative-thinker mode.

'OK,' Kath drew in her breath slowly. I could see that she needed a fag, but we all have to make sacrifices for our careers. 'They live in this rambling old house in Hamer Lane, Withington. Dennis is a former military type, you know, short hair and moustache. Good bearing. I should say he's about fifty-five. He couldn't have been more charming and helpful. Dean's very much another kettle of fish, unfortunately. He's about thirty and he's been reared on an exclusive diet of takeaway curries. He was eating one when I got there and there were the remains of about a dozen others down the front of his sweater.' She gave an involuntary shudder. 'He's rather surly. I can't stand that type, you know . . . he's prematurely bald, rather short, with a beer belly, dirty sweater and jeans. Oh yes, and halitosis.'

'Sounds like the standard type of *Homo Mancuniensis*,' Cedric said spitefully.

'Go on,' Lena urged. 'What about Mrs Summergill?'

'Hmmm. I rather gathered she'd decamped some years ago and that they were embarrassed about it.'

'Has either of them got a female in tow?' I asked.

'I don't think so. You'd be hard pressed to find a home that showed less of a feminine touch. As I said, the son feeds off takeaways and he drops the packaging wherever he last browsed, and the house itself is like a junk dealer's warehouse. Not so much the furniture, but these dusty glass cases everywhere with beady eyed animals peering out. I could hardly get in the front door for them. The whole hallway's lined with them. You name it, they've got it; the whole furry kingdom from moles to marmosets and also our feathered friends. Not to mention the live ants in the living room.

Cedric ambled over to the table and started clicking away at his portable computer. Had inspiration struck, I wondered? The three of us kept a respectful silence. Finally he spoke. 'This material's all very colourful, I'm sure, but do you think there's much relevance? According to my notes, Summergill was barely acquainted with Billy before he discovered the cache of severed heads.'

'That's not what Mrs Colquhuon said,' I sprung to my partner's defence. 'She claims that Billy used to go to an animal shelter up in the Pennines with them. Not very often, because Billy didn't leave his den very often, but he was definitely acquainted with them and it was Billy who introduced them to her when she needed property repairs doing. I've got it all on tape.'

'Carry on then, Ms Headlam,' Cedric said, for all the world like a High Court judge after chiding a junior counsel.

For answer Kath switched the tape on.

'We met Billy at the People's Crusade for Animals office in Moss Side. He had this barn owl with a broken wing that he'd been caring for . . .'

'That's Dennis speaking,' Kath commented. Despite the tinny sound quality on the little recorder, the voice sounded firm, very well spoken, with a Northern accent but the diction was almost that of a trained actor.

'Someone suggested that he take the owl to the Chillgate Animal Sanctuary up near Pateley Bridge. He could release it there and if it didn't fly off they'd be able to look after it until it gained enough strength.'

'Let me get this right. Billy had cared for the owl in his flat?' Kath's voice asked incredulously.

'I suppose so. At any rate, it was the first of many trips we made with him. Dean and I are supporters of the Sanctuary. We spend a lot of time up there caring for cruelly treated animals. There were some fairground donkeys so badly abused that we had to put them down. Nothing we could do for them –'

'Yes,' Kath's voice cut in, *'but to get back to Billy Fox . . .'*

'He were all right, were Billy,' came a third voice, presumably Dean's. *'I don't know what you had to drop him in it for. He were my mate, were Billy. You should never grass your mates up.'*

'Are you saying your father shouldn't have reported what he found in Billy's cupboard?' Kath's voice asked.

'You don't grass your mates up,' came the surly reply. Dean's accent and manner of speaking couldn't have been more different from that of his father.

'Switch off for a moment,' Cedric commanded.

'I would have done anyway. Dennis clipped Dean

round the ear at that point and knocked the recorder off the table,' Kath answered dryly. 'Then he laughed and said something like, "Now you see what I've got to put up with, Miss." He was amused by Dean's attitude.'

'What else is on the tape then?' Cedric asked her.

'There's more about how kind to animals Billy was and then Dennis goes on about what a shock it was when he opened the cupboard and found out what Billy had been up to.'

'Leave it with me,' Cedric said, 'And I'll take the one from Mrs Colquhuon as well. I need to put quite a bit of thought into this. The story's going in an entirely different direction from what I expected.'

Watching him carefully I couldn't help noticing the searching and warm gaze he lavished on my partner. My spine tingled. Was Cedric thinking of finding himself a new source of inspiration, I wondered?

'He'll come up with something. Don't worry,' cackled Lena. 'Did I ever tell you about when I was in Kenya with my first husband? We used to have lots of stuffed animals about the place –'

'Leave it out, Mother,' Cedric cut in sharply. 'I'm sure no one here wants to hear your White Hunter story.' Lena subsided into her chair. We'd been spared another of her trips to fantasy land. 'You're going to have to come up with somebody else who was close to Billy. This Pilatski woman is good in a way, but she only knew him up to the age of seven or eight. Can't you trace the missing father?' he asked irritably.

I shifted uncomfortably in my chair. I didn't wish to disclose my knowledge about Horatio Bostick. 'There is the social worker . . . Angie Mallory,' I said after racking my brain. 'I could see her tomorrow.'

Cedric didn't look too pleased. 'She was the one who was pelted in the streets because she stuck up for him in court, isn't she? Not likely to get much sensational material from her, are you?'

'She might give us a lead on the parents. And then for dirt I've got the address of the girl who complained that Billy was sexually harassing her.'

'That sounds much more promising. Why don't you go round there now,' he said eagerly, handing me the tape recorder back.

'Sunday evenings aren't a very good time for this sort of thing,' I said.

Cedric gave an airy wave of his arm and bent over his computer. He began rattling the keyboard again. We were dismissed. I looked at Mother. She was sitting back in her chair with a glazed expression on her face. A glance at the drinks trolley confirmed that most of the sherry had been consumed. Kath and I left without another word.

All the way back to Manchester I kept my eyes open for grey vans. There were dozens of them on the road. When we parked near the office sure enough there was a grey van at the kerb close by. There was no sign of any owner. I went across and gave it the once-over. Kath followed reluctantly. I wrote down the registration.

'Getting a bit paranoid, aren't you, Dave?' she asked.

I turned to her frowning, 'I want you to note the number of any grey van that you see parked anywhere near us. Understand!. We've got to take this seriously. Sinclair is.' She wasn't convinced. 'Kath, there's more than a remote chance that this killer is interested in Cedric so it stands to reason that he's also going to focus on you and me. After all, Cedric hardly sets foot out of his hotel room without a police escort.'

'All right, but you look strained, Dave. I think we should go back to Hawkshead. I'll make you and Daddy the meal I had planned and we'll treat ourselves to a long lie in on Monday morning. How about that?'

I tried to laugh but it came out rather thinly even to my own ears. 'Kath, your daddy's likely to go for his shotgun when he sees me.'

'Don't be silly, Dave. Daddy doesn't have a gun. He's nice really.'

She looked at me in that appealing and demure way that had enabled her to twist me round her finger before, but I shook my head. 'No way, Kath. I'm sorry.' The Commander's reaction to Cullen's morning visit to Hawkshead still rankled. Headlam had been happy to have his nasty expectations about me confirmed.

In the end I agreed to run Kath up to Hawkshead and drop her off. She'd left her own car, the metallic silver Mazda, there this morning. I couldn't afford to lend her my car. The trip north took me just over one and a half hours. We passed the time discussing how Billy might have been able to lure his victims. There wasn't a scrap of evidence to suggest that Billy had kidnapped his victims from their homes or picked them up at random on the street. It was another of the features of this case that was still shrouded in mystery.

'Assume for the sake of argument that Billy did meet some of his victims at say . . . the People's Crusade for Animals in Moss Side,' she argued, 'wouldn't it have been easy for him to ask them to come and see that owl or whatever it was that he had in his own flat?'

'It would, but he'd have been caught fairly soon after the first couple disappeared,' I said confidently.

'Why?'

'They weren't just random animal lovers as you think, that's why. Each one was carefully chosen. They were women who weren't missed – at least not immediately. Otherwise there'd have been a hue and cry and he'd never have managed to kill fourteen. There was no hint that he was connected with unexplained disappearances until the skull-rack was found in his room. If he'd been in the habit of simply inviting women up to his room you'd have expected some to refuse. We'd have heard from them. Or one, at least, would have mentioned to a friend that she was going to see this stranger's pet.'

'Perhaps he killed all he invited,' Kath said. I could see she was unwilling to discard her animal theory.

'That doesn't wash. You'd have to assume no one ever turned down his invitation. We know he was an occasional visitor to animal shelters in Manchester. You heard Mrs Colquhuon tell us that he didn't go out often. To achieve a one hundred per cent score with his casual pickups on rare visits . . . well it's impossible.'

'OK,' she said thoughtfully. 'Maybe he did only go out very rarely, but on those rare trips he spotted potential victims and then secretly stalked them and found out all he needed to know.'

'That's more likely,' I admitted.

'Anyway, there was a hue and cry about some of the victims. Shani Tarbutt's parents put up hundreds of posters about her.'

'Yes, but in London not Manchester.'

'Well, maybe he was just lucky with most of them. How could he have known that Chantelle Clough's mother would tell her daughter's college that Chantelle had gone to join her father in America?'

'Kath, no one gets lucky fourteen times in a row. Fox must be fiendishly cunning. Some of these psychopaths can sense that their victims haven't got firm ties to anyone . . . a few chance remarks are enough for them.'

'Well, how do you explain that so many of Billy's victims were either animal rights activists or worked in animal shelters? There must be some connection.'

'It is curious,' I agreed. 'But what about Ann Frances Madingly? Her special interest was old churches.'

'There's got to be an exception that proves the rule.'

I looked across at Kath. Her mouth was set in a very determined way. She was certain that she'd found an angle the police had missed. I thought about the unfortunate Ann Frances Madingly for a while. In her case foul play had been suspected immediately. She was a graduate of Cheltenham Ladies College and Oxford, studying in Manchester to complete her Ph.D. in History. Her supervisor raised the alarm when she failed to re-register at the university. A police search discovered her car in a back street in Keswick, Cumbria. Her credit cards had been used after the disappearance but only in big stores and cash dispensers where there was no chance of a description. Goaded by her frantic parents, the police had arranged for Buttermere Tarn to be dragged and for mountain rescue to scour the hillsides but nothing had turned up. That was back in 1992.

Though it had never been stated in so many words, it was obvious that the police had scaled down the search because they believed that Ann was deliberately avoiding discovery. Perhaps she wanted to drop out of the academic life and break with her parents. Her father was a professor. The truly ghoulish feature of her story was that when she was identified as one of Billy's victims her spectacles were still on her face. Billy had taped them onto her severed head.

'You could be right. She could be an exception,' I said. 'How were you thinking of playing this animal issue?'

'I think it's the key to the whole story,' she said enthusiastically.

'Kath, you know I don't like to discourage you but lots of killers have kept pets. Look at Hitler with his dog Blondi and Dennis Nilsen with his spaniel. It's commonplace.'

'There you are!' she said triumphantly. 'And what about Bill Sikes with his dog. Everyone remembers. It proves my point. There's something extra about a human being who'll fix an owl's wing at the same time that he's decapitating women wholesale. It's really creepy. I can see an episode set in this sanctuary in Yorkshire. I bet they've a slogan over the entrance gate, "No Animal Turned Away" just like the sign *"Arbeit Macht Frei"* over the entrance at Auschwitz. I can see it in the background with Billy's face superimposed. I must check it out.'

'That's a bit tasteless, isn't it?' I asked.

'Darling, this is for TV! Not a Jane Austen novel.'

The rest of the journey north was uneventful. There wasn't even a queue at the M61 junction with the M6. We'd chosen the right time of day to head out of Manchester, most of the day-trippers were heading back. Even the weather was improving. I didn't spot a single grey van. Kath was bubbling with ideas for the series all the way. She contentedly chain-smoked her way north, oblivious to my occasional coughs and splutters.

When we arrived in South Lakeland there had been one of those dramatic changes in the weather that the area's famous for. Late evening sun was shining across a cloudless sky. The wooded hillside above Backbarrow was glowing with many different shades of colour – deep greens, russets, browns. It all looked so inviting that for a moment I almost changed my mind and decided to stay. Then I thought of Commander Headlam with his sour face and pursed lips and realised that I'd made the right choice. I left Kath in the car park at Hawkshead.

We parted affectionately. We'd agreed that she'd check out the Animal Shelter at Pateley Bridge while I tried to dig up the dirt about Billy's sex life.

I took my time driving back and had a leisurely meal in a hotel near Hawkshead. Cullen was right about one thing. My expenses on this job were a lot better than his.

'The problem with preconceived ideas is that they very often lead us directly away from the true culprit. How many times has every police officer "known" for certain who the author of a particular crime was only to be horrified later when the true perpetrator, often a complete unknown, steps Into the frame?'

From an article entitled 'Jumping to the Wrong Conclusion,' signed by **'Invigilator'** in the Journal of Contemporary Police Science, Washington DC, 5th issue, 1994.

11

Monday, 17th September

I woke, having enjoyed a restful night's sleep. It was Monday morning, but for once I didn't have that sinking feeling in the pit of the stomach. The prospect of five days of toil ahead didn't seem so bad. There was every chance of my employer scuttling back whence he came, or finding himself incarcerated. It wasn't that I particularly yearned for either eventuality, but the prospect of them didn't fill me with dismay.

Still, arrangements had been made and deadlines set. I was to interview Cynthia Royton and Angie Mallory. Kath was going to work on her script and would come back to Manchester on Tuesday, driving via Pateley Bridge. She had some weird ideas about what an animal sanctuary was like and it would do her no harm to find out for herself.

After breakfast I joined the stream of traffic heading into town. I felt carefree. I found myself whistling 'Born Free' without any conscious choice. 'Born free . . . Free as the wind blows . . . As free as the . . .' It only took a flip of my finger on the car radio switch to change my mood.

Friday night's victims had been identified. The man was Carter Gumbs, an immigrant from the Caribbean island of Anguilla who'd been missing from his home in Slough for some months. The girl was a local, Lisa Dolan. She was a runaway from Middleton who'd taken to the streets of Manchester. She was seventeen, Gumbs was twenty-two. There was no evidence that they had even known each other. Gumbs just happened to be in the wrong place when what the media were now calling 'Son of Basher' or the 'Manchester Basher' had found a victim.

There was an interview with Detective Chief Superintendent Philip Pinnock. He sounded apologetic but hopeful. Measures were being co-ordinated with Social Services departments to get homeless girls into temporary accommodation, but this was a difficult task because, despite the danger, some of the girls wouldn't co-operate with the police. He wasn't confident of an early arrest. The police were doing everything they could, extra men had been drafted in. The well-known author, Cedric Liptrot, had been interviewed. The force wanted any extra information about the Bradford Basher now that an imitator had set up on this side of the Pennines.

The interviewer asked him what he thought about the suggestion by a local MP that crime books that encouraged imitators should be banned. Pinnock thought it wasn't up to him to say anything about that, but he, like any other experienced police officer, knew that certain crimes attract imitators.

Listening to the newsreader close the piece by reciting the list of victims helped me to put my ideas in perspective. As he described it, Manchester was in a state of terror. Another snippet of news was of interest. There had been a demonstration outside GMP Force Headquarters by VICPAC, Victims' Parents Action Committee, demanding that the police put more effort into finding the corpses of Billy Fox's victims. There was an interview with an angry mother, she couldn't get on with her grieving until her daughter's complete remains were returned to her.

Later that afternoon, in my office, I listened to the tapes I'd gleaned from the day's interviews. I'd been lucky to find both women in when I called on them. Cynthia Royton worked afternoons on the bread counter at the Tesco supermarket in Didsbury. A pretty blonde of about eighteen with rather unformed, doll-like features, she was willing to be interviewed about her experience with Billy. When I called her boyfriend was with her and they had an hour or two to kill until she started her shift. She was an Oasis fan. The living room of her parents' home was littered with photos of Liam and Noel.

I explained that nearly everyone who had spoken to me about Billy had given me a favourable account of him. I was almost pleading with her to tell me that he was a monster, but once again I was out of luck. Thinking about it afterwards, I thought that she was deliberately minimising Billy's behaviour for reasons of her own. Some people are perverse like that.

'The police made a lot more out of what I said than I wanted them to,' she complained. 'That psychologist woman went on and on about it. She wanted me to claim that Billy had raped me or something. I thought she was one of those feminists, like. It wasn't like she said at all. Billy was, like, the lab assistant and I were doing biology field work. Usually he didn't talk to us much, but our science teacher was off a lot and other teachers would take the lesson, then Billy would have to do more, like.

'I first noticed he had his eye on me because he used to give me the best specimens. The other kids complained, but he just gave that funny smile of his and went right ahead. I didn't do anything to encourage him except for smiling back a few times. Well, you have to, don't you?' She shrugged her shoulders, favouring me with what I was sure was exactly the same naïve smile she'd tried on Billy.

'Then we had to go up to this nature reserve in Silverdale, that's near Morecambe Bay like, to do our practical. Billy was in one of the two minibuses that we went in. We just stayed up there for two nights you know, and spent the days counting various plants in fields and so on, really thrilling like.' Cynthia gave a sigh and rolled her eyes. She expected me to agree. I gave a little rumble of consent from the back of my throat. After all, it was self-evident that nature study was a waste of valuable time which you could otherwise spend listening to Oasis.

'I think some of the girls were playing tricks on me, she continued. 'I think they told Billy that I was attracted to him because he hardly left my side the whole time. I mentioned it to Miss Hector, she was one of the science teachers who was with us. She was always on about sexual harassment. I thought she'd just have a word with Billy. Tell him to keep his distance, something like that. No such thing! Billy just disappeared. I heard from another girl whose mother was a school secretary that Billy had been transferred to a school in Whalley Range.'

'Is that it?' I asked disbelievingly. 'He made a very mild approach to you that hardly amounted to pestering. I was told he created an unpleasant atmosphere of sexual innuendo around him.'

'Sorry to disappoint you, but it's exactly like I said.'

'Are you saying the police have lied? I mean they must have interviewed you.'

'I told you that psychologist woman was there. She was ten times worse than Miss Hector. Every time I said something that didn't suit her she put it into her own words. It came out as if Billy was a monster and I hardly got a chance to put a word in edgeways. She kept saying, "Yes, dear, I understand. It's the Stockholm effect." I didn't know what she was on about. It was as if she was giving the interview, not me.'

I was unwilling to leave it there. 'Look, Miss Royton . . . er, Cynthia. He was much older than you, wasn't he?' I paused to look at the boyfriend for help. If anything he looked younger and more adolescent than Cynthia. He gave me a puzzled frown. 'Perhaps Billy said things to you that you didn't really understand. Perhaps Miss Hector knew what he was up to a bit better than you did.'

'That frustrated old cow knew nothing!' Cynthia exploded. 'It's like I said, Billy did nothing.' She was adamant.

I felt as if I was battering my head against a sack of cotton wool.

'Can I get you to understand?' I pleaded. 'We know Billy killed all those girls. Some of them were like you, girls from places where he'd worked. There were at least three who were at Albigensian Sixth Form College in Victoria Park when he was there. We think he approached these girls and somehow got their sympathy. He appears to have done something similar with you. Then possibly he asked them to come and see some pets he kept in his room and then –'

'It wasn't like that,' she said firmly. 'You think I'm thick, don't you? I'm not too simple-minded to know when someone wants to have it off with me. I don't want to appear in any TV programme if I have to say

Billy was trying to lure me up to his bedroom to chop my head off.'

'You must stick to the facts,' I said to reassure her. 'I'm sure Mr Liptrot wouldn't want you to make something up.' As I said this, more to encourage her than myself, I wasn't entirely sure that it was true. Despite Kath's idea that his love of animals was a sinister cloak for mass murder, Billy was going to come out of this as the most angelic villain in history. I'd reached an impasse.

'I've been thinking about this a lot since that Dr Caulfield came and told me that I was the luckiest girl in Manchester,' Cynthia said helpfully. 'She was like you, annoyed that I wouldn't say worse. Do you know how many people have been to Albigensian since it opened? Thousands! I mean it can't be much of a coincidence that some girls from Fallowfield, right near the college, were also there at the same time Billy was. Where else would they have gone, like?'

I looked at her for a long time. I've often got some of my best stories just by being a good listener.

'I know Billy's guilty,' she continued. 'But however he got these girls, he wasn't trying his tricks out on me that day. I mean, I'm not stupid! I wouldn't have gone with him anyway, but he never said anything, just acted sad and daft. I think he was just doing what one of my foolish mates put him up to.'

'I don't suppose you'd know if this Miss Hector is still at the school?' I asked. 'Perhaps she could put her side of it.'

'You'll be lucky,' Cynthia said with a rather cruel laugh. It seemed out of character somehow. 'She had a nervous breakdown last year and the last I heard she's still in a psychiatric hospital.'

I switched the tape off and thought about what Cynthia

had said. Despite being told that she was lucky to be alive and despite knowing that Billy had killed many other girls, Cynthia still rejected the idea that Billy had been menacing her that day in Silverdale. Her belief in her personal invulnerability was irritating. I think Cynthia's problem was that she wanted to prove her teacher wrong. Maybe Miss Hector had overreacted, and maybe she hadn't. Cynthia was enough to give anyone a nervous breakdown. Miss Hector could hardly have been less clued up than Cynthia, with her supermarket uniform, her boyfriend and her newly won independence. Well, I was being paid to gather information, not interpret it. Cedric would just have to make what he could out of Cynthia's statement.

I took the tape out of the recorder and inserted the one I'd made in my long interview with Angie Mallory. There was a lot more grist for Cedric's mill in this one.

Ms Mallory was one angry lady. I found her at home earlier in the afternoon because she'd been suspended from her job on full pay, pending an enquiry into her case. The Social Services department felt that she'd brought social work into disrepute by championing Billy at his trial.

She lived in Chorlton in one of an estate of identical box-like homes built off the King's Road. The estate had been put up in the 1920s as part of Manchester's suburban sprawl, handy for the tram and the main roads. Space for tennis and cricket clubs had been allocated for residents with sporting interests. These still survived in the area, although several local churches had been converted into temples and mosques. Cyril and Claude had been replaced by Asif and Sanjay, but, apart from that, the neighbourhood looked much as it must have done in the '20s.

If her home was conventional, Angie Mallory was anything but. She was in her early forties, with a close cropped crew cut and a weight problem. Angie was wearing a bitter expression on her face and a loose, low-cut dress over her tights when I met her. The interior of her home was also not what one would expect in this Northern outpost of Betjeman's Metro-land. Strong gloss colours predominated, blacks, purples and rich greens. There was one completely black wall in her living room against which I was invited to squat on a beanbag while Angie spread herself out on the low sofa opposite me. 'I can't bear having too much furniture around,' she explained. 'I hate the room to be cluttered.'

Cluttered or not, it contained an expresso machine and she offered me a cup. She followed up the coffee by furnishing me with a ham sandwich. She had dark strain lines under her eyes. There was an air of suppressed excitement about her, as if sharing coffee with a man in the middle of the afternoon was an exotic treat. I wondered about her preferences.

'The press have cast me as the villain of the piece,' she said defensively.

'Mr Liptrot's hoping to present a much more balanced picture,' I said. I tried to exert the old Cunane charm, but not too much. 'You'd have the right to check any direct quotation,' I said in as persuasive and friendly a tone as I could manage. I could feel sweat breaking out on my brow. Should I bound over to the sofa and offer a reassuring hug? My crouching posture seemed to rule it out.

'How much do you think he would pay me?' she whispered eventually. I breathed a sigh of relief. It was her bank balance that she wanted me to massage.

'You'd get a hefty fee for the TV interview,' I said. 'Four figures.' I hadn't a clue what, if anything, she would be paid. Bugger all, if Lena Liptrot was the one handing out the dosh.

'My solicitor says we might be able to sell the story to the papers,' she said with a brave smile. 'That's if I lose my job, of course.'

'You'd get far more after a favourable write-up in Cedric Liptrot's book,' I said. 'Don't forget those same papers whipped up a mob to lynch you only a few weeks ago.'

She took her time considering this.

'This is your chance to set the record straight,' I cajoled. 'The treatment in Cedric's book will be much more extensive than any tabloid article and don't forget his last book sold a million.' I could see from the nasty set of her mouth that the prospect of getting her side in had won her over. She patted the sofa to indicate that I was to sit beside her,

'I'm the only person who really knows Billy Fox,' she began. 'He was almost the first child I was put in charge of. It was obvious that the mother, Nancy Fox, couldn't cope. She was old when she had him and unfortunately, although kids arrive in neat little bundles, they don't stay that way. They quicly fill your house up.'

'When you say Nancy couldn't cope . . .' I probed.

'She was ill a lot of the time and when she went into hospital for what proved to be the last time Billy came into care. I was his case worker. I suppose that's when you might say we bonded. He was such a lovely kid, he just cried a lot the first year he was in the home. We tried to trace other relatives, but although there were rumours and we asked around, none came forward.'

'Can we just go back to Nancy? I was told she abused him.'

'No more than the abuse you get in most so-called normal families,' she said. She must have seen me raise my eyebrows at this because she enlarged a little. 'Look, she would knock him around a bit when she thought he'd done something bad. She was very judgmental was Nancy. There was nothing else.'

'So it was in local authority care that he was sexually abused?' I asked.

'That was suspected but never really proven. Billy was so inarticulate. They had the sexually explicit dolls out and everything when they interviewed him, but he never confirmed any accusations.'

'Then why was abuse suspected?' I demanded.

'Oh, we felt that there were too many cases of incontinence, soiling their sheets and things in that particular unit. It's one of the classic signs. Although Billy wouldn't talk, others did. They closed that home down and moved the kids.'

'And the staff?' I prompted, when no further explanation was forthcoming.

'They were moved too . . . They went to other homes, other authorities,' she said awkwardly.

'Great!' I said contemptuously.

'I know. It was difficult. They all belonged to minorities, and there was no real hard evidence against any of them. It wasn't long after that that there were complaints from Billy's school about his behaviour. We'd kept him in the same primary school but a case conference decided to move him to give him a fresh chance. And then when he went to secondary school we put him into one in Didsbury.'

'So he wasn't with any of the kids he might have grown up with in Hulme?' I insinuated.

'It was felt a clean break was best for him. There were still complaints from the school but he responded well to a behaviour-modification programme. He was offered concrete rewards for meeting certain targets.'

'Such as what?' I asked.

'He'd get a new computer game or pair of trainers if there were no complaints for a while.'

'Was no attempt ever made to foster him?' I asked.

Angie gave me a wry look. 'We tried. But whatever the reason, Billy never stayed with a family for long. That's the trouble when kids like Billy get institutionalised. They come to expect things that no normal family can provide.'

'Would you be prepared to give me the names of any of those families?' I asked. 'I'm hoping to develop material that will show that Billy had some normal moments in his life or, failing that, to get evidence about precisely what went wrong. I think that's in the public interest, don't you?'

'You're not angling for another of these attacks on social workers, are you? Because despite the way I've been treated –'

'Look, Ms Mallory. I've every sympathy with social workers . . . all kicks and no ha'penny in your job,' I coaxed. 'But if there turns out to have been some incident which turned Billy Fox into a lethal serial killer I think it's in everybody's interest to find out what that incident was. It'll come out eventually whatever we do, but this is your chance to get your version of events down in black and white.'

I smiled at her warmly. She took a nervous swallow of her coffee. Listening to my words as I spieled away I realised that what I'd said was true, but that her version would be filtered through the imaginations of Cedric Liptrot and Kath Headlam.

At this point the taped interview was suspended for a while. I asked Angie exactly what behaviour of Billy's it was that had needed modifying but she wouldn't elaborate.

'Was it sexual?' I asked bluntly.

From the way she blushed I guessed it was.

'Was there an incident?' I pressed.

'Dave, you're awfully pushy,' she replied. 'I should think you're very good as a detective, but you're going to have to use a bit of intuition on this one.' With that she heaved herself upright and went to the expresso machine for a refill. When she returned to the sofa she leaned against my shoulder in a very cosy way. My intuition was telling me that she'd carried the process of bonding with young Billy to its ultimate conclusion, but there was no way that she was going to let me get that on tape.

I pressed on. 'The police say that Billy exuded a kind of unpleasant sexual aura,' I suggested.

'There was never anything unpleasant about Billy,' she said. 'There was jealousy, that's what there was.' As I tried to work out what this meant she made herself more comfortable alongside me. 'All this talk about sex in the middle of the afternoon is having a very funny effect on me,' she whispered.

'Ms Mallory, I'm only here for an interview,' I cautioned. I've never been able to work out what the cause is but certain middle-aged ladies get over excited in my company. Maybe I ought to give out a warning before I interview them, like a cigarette commercial.

'Oh, surely you can call me Angie, can't you?' she replied.

Obviously my caution was wasted on her. 'Or is that against the private detective's code of practice?' She was making it very clear that her own code of practice didn't exclude very much. Thc low-cut dress had slipped off one shoulder and if she carried on squirming against me a full-frontal revelation couldn't be long postponed.

There comes a point in every private detective's life when he has to decide just how far he is prepared to go to get a result. It looked as if I had reached that point now. I put my arm round Angie's shoulder.

'That's nice,' she said as she loosened my tie.

One hour and much exertion later I was able to fill in

most of the missing pieces. When he was sixteen one of the young girls in the home had accused Billy of interfering with her. Angie had been able to exert influence to get the matter overlooked. She claimed that the girl's complaint had been inspired by jealousy but procedure hadn't been followed. The girl had been blackmailed into silence with threats of ejection from care. It was pretty clear why Angie had been on Billy's side. From the coy hints she'd dropped, it became obvious that sexual relief with a mere teenager was the last thing the lad needed.

Apart from the sexual issue; there had been other complaints about Billy who'd gone ahead with various anti-social activities regardless. If restrained at school for a while, he would break out in the care home and vice versa. He had been into 'tagging' for a while and had covered half of Didsbury with his logo. He'd taken cars. Then there'd been a spot of 'taxing'. The one constant point in his life at this time had been Angie and her defence of him.

When he turned eighteen he was out of her care but he still turned up from time to time. She'd helped to find him a job. She caught occasional glimpses of him. One evening she was stopped at traffic lights in Moss Side and who should she see walking along the pavement towards her but Billy? Nothing odd about that, except that he was wearing dark glasses and tapping his way along the street with a white stick.

'That was typical of Billy. Nearly every time he got in trouble there were other boys or youths egging him on. They'd lie like anything but Billy would own up immediately, even when I knew he hadn't been involved. Have you heard about Munchausen's Syndrome?'

I nodded.

'Well, I think Billy had something like that, or a mild

form of it. Have you ever known anyone to lie so that he could take the blame? That was Billy. When we had the review of Billy just before he was leaving care I suggested that there might be something organically wrong with him. It's more common than people think, brain damage. I wanted him to go for tests, but my supervisor just thought I was trying to keep Billy in care for longer.'

'Is that why you stuck up for him at the trial?' I asked.

'I never knew Billy to really hurt anyone. And as for rape and murder – well, they just weren't in his frame of reference. I hardly ever even saw him start a conversation with a girl . . .' She covered her face with her hands and began to cry at this point. I didn't feel like comforting her. She wasn't that sort of woman. Eventually she dried her eyes.

'That horrible woman, Caulfield, said that Billy's behaviour was absolutely typical of the sort of deep repression turning into savage sexual aggression that she would expect in Billy's case. It's rubbish. It was her more than anything that made me decide to testify on Billy's behalf. She's a horrible woman, so certain that she knows everything there is to know about Billy's life.'

There was more on the tape about the trial and how she found Billy now – no different than he'd ever been – but I turned it off at that point. I made copies for Kath. After arranging for delivery, I faxed the Liptrots to tell them that the tapes would be arriving by express messenger.

Before leaving the office I put the pager on top of the highest cupboard and switched off my mobile. I decided to go home by a different route, not from paranoia about being followed but just for the variety. I drove up Oxford Road. The long slow crawl up Manchester's

'Curry Mile' gave me plenty of time to think. There had to be something else that Angie Mallory was covering up, some other serious incident of bullying or violence that would have pointed to Billy's future career as a decapitator. Had she persuaded the authorities to overlook something indicative? That would explain the vehemence with which she insisted that he was innocent.

As for her idea about Munchausen's Syndrome, I found it a convincing theory. Billy's complaint must have been 'Munchausen's by Proxy', a sick fascination with the suffering of others. I shuddered as I thought of him gloating over girls like Cynthia. She was stupid. She didn't realise how lucky she'd been.

I hadn't been back in my flat for long when Jay Anderson phoned. He'd had a great time with Paddy and invited me round to share his mother's cooking.

'Just what I need,' I said gratefully. 'Someone to cook for me. Kath's not here.'

'What about her horse?' he asked anxiously.

'Don't worry, the stable feed him. No, it's just me who requires looking after.'

I had a shower and dressed. I chose casual clothes but not too casual. Lovena was very formal about meals. I wore a collar and tie with a blue silk blouson and grey slacks. I was looking forward to a good meal when I pulled up outside Bert Gibson Close in Moss Side where Lovena, Jay and his brother, Douglas, lived. She was waiting at the door.

'Come in, Dave. You're looking good, man.' She gave me a friendly hug. 'I hope you're hungry. I've got enough food in to make you as strong as a cow. Douglas isn't here. He's at his college rehearsing for a play.' She led me through into the lounge. The dining table was laid out.

'Someone for you to meet, Dave. This is Everald Mallick, a local youth worker,' she said. The man scowling at me across the living room didn't get up from where he was sitting.

'Good evening, Mr Mallick,' I said levelly. I didn't know what sort of response I was going to get from him but I knew enough to understand that he would prefer a formal greeting. West Indians may live close to the easy-going North American continent but they can be very formal until they get to know you. Mallick gave a grunt by way of reply. He was wearing a little black leather pillbox hat and granny glasses. The specs had apparently fogged up when he saw me because he took them off, elaborately cleaned them with a big red handkerchief and carefully replaced them. Then he stood up and moseyed over to me. Although a small man he carried himself well, like an athlete or a boxer. I shook hands, realising that the scowl was his natural expression, more like a permanent frown really.

Mallick, Jay and myself spent the next twenty minutes struggling to break the ice while Lovena finished her preparations.

'Gambling is dandy but liquor is quicker if you want to get to know people,' I joked. My humour attracted cool looks from both my fellow diners.

Lovena started us off with Jamaican pepperpot soup, served with little dumplings called spinners. Although Lovena wasn't originally from Jamaica herself she'd assimilated to Jamaican culture as well as to British in her time here. She didn't let us eat before we'd said grace. I noticed her glare at Mallick who made some sort of apologetic mumble over his food. Lovena was *deastant* people, a deaconess of her local Pentecostal Church and, as the midwife who'd delivered half the population round here, something of a pillar of the community.

My mouth was too scorched from the soup for me to say much. Lovena brought in the next course, ackee and saltfish served with sweet yams baked in their skins and rice and peas. I was working my way through this when Mallick pounced.

'I've heard about you, man,' he said. 'You think you're some kind of Robin Hood, don't you?'

'If that means, have I robbed the local sheriff, no, I haven't,' I said. When I'd spoken I realised it was a mistake. There wasn't the trace of a smile on Mallick's face. I guessed that Mallick was a heavyweight bore for whom the slightest trace of humour acted as a goad. God knows what he'd heard about me. This was the man who was trying to persuade Jay to throw away his career. Somehow, I kept a smile on my face.

'I hear you're trying to rob us of our good name,' he said. 'You just don't understand the African community, man.'

I said nothing, determined to concentrate on Lovena's cooking.

'Oh, this is turning out to be a gloomy feast,' Lovena wailed as she brought in the next course, a dessert of baked bananas with coconut cream. 'What do you want to be troubling Dave for? He was married to a black girl, a real African. Eat your food. Haven't you heard what they say: *Better belly bus', than good bitle spoil.*'

Mallick was silent.

'That was wonderful, Lovena,' I said sincerely, when I finished stuffing my face.

She laughed with pleasure and said, 'You must let me cook you some fried chicken next time you come. And don't wait so long either.'

I really liked Lovena but what I didn't like was the scowling and moody face looking at me across the dining table. Jay was also looking very tense. I considered making an excuse and leaving right away but that would have been insulting to Lovena. She had other plans too.

We went through into the lounge and she brought out photos of Jay in his police uniform and began talking about him and refused to be deflected. She kept stressing what a good career the police was and how well Jay had done, and how proud she was of him. She thanked me over and over again for the help my father and I had given Jay, teaching him 'to live right' as she put it. I would have squirmed with embarrassment if it hadn't been for the effect all this was having on Everald Mallick. His forehead was stippled with tiny beads of sweat that had nothing to do with the pepperpot soup.

Lovena is a teetotaller so there was no chance of anything stronger than coconut milk, but I think both Mallick and I could have used a stiff drink at this stage. Jay switched the television on and flicked through the channels. A suit was discussing the question of banning true crime books that encouraged imitators.

'Leave it on,' Mallick ordered Jay. He sat on the edge of his seat, whistling through his teeth until the suit was through.

'There!' he said.

I held my hands up in a gesture of surrender. 'I wish that I'd never accepted the commission but I have and that's an end of it. I can't back out.'

'You mean you won't.' Surprisingly, after the glum expression he had worn all through Lovena's wonderful meal, Mallick was now grinning.

'Have you heard of SPROAC?' he demanded, handing me a black, red and green card. 'It's a little group I lead, the Society for the Protection of the African Community. We intend to picket any shops which sell Liptrot's book.'

'How very tolerant and liberal-minded of you,' I

commented. 'Particularly as he hasn't even written it yet. There's going to be a book written about the Billy murders whether you like it or not. Even if you stop Cedric Liptrot, there must be other authors warming up their word processors right now. In any case, Cedric's not into racial stereotyping,' I ended lamely.

'There may be other authors on the case, but they won't be employing a notoriously stupid private detective to rehash the whole story. This case is going to be used against our people. By making an example of you and this Liptrot, SPROAC will be sending a message to the entire white power structure.'

'In what way are you going to make an example?' I asked nervously.

'Wait and see man, but don't sleep too sound.' Turning angrily to Lovena, he added, 'I'm very disappointed by you. You have a reputation in this community.'

This was too much for Lovena. She hadn't delivered hundreds of babies without developing powerful arms. She was out of her seat like a tiger and after grabbing Mallick by the scruff of his neck, froamarched him to the door. Mallick was ejected without ceremony. Picking up the leather cap which had fallen off in the struggle, she slung it after him.

'I've got to hand it to you, Lovena,' I said. 'You take no prisoners.'

'That was a threat, Dave. That man actually threatened you here in my house. And you, my own son,' she said, turning to Jay, 'you begged me to invite him. After all Dave's done for this family, you should be down on your bended knees asking him to forgive you.'

'I'm sorry. I got talking to Everald and I mentioned that I knew someone who was researching a book about Billy. He knew all about you, Dave.'

'My fame is spreading.'

'Oh, man, I just hoped that you could persuade him to leave me alone. I'm sick of all this hassle every time I walk out of the house.'

'Maybe if he tries to carry out his threat against me that will take some of the heat off you,' I said, as I got up to leave.

'You know, it's because of that Mallick that Jay doesn't dare to come home wearing his police uniform,' Lovena explained on the doorstep.

'I guessed there was something like that,' I told her. 'You don't want to take any notice of Mallick. He's just one of these professional windbags.'

From her expression I knew that Lovena intended taking a very great deal of notice of Mallick's threats. I wondered what form his revenge would take – more slogans daubed on Lovena's walls or a beating for Jay. There was little I could do.

On the way home, I kept turning over what Mallick had said, '. . . sending a message to the white power structure.' What puzzled me was, why was he reacting so strongly now? Surely the time to send a message to the power structure was immediately after Billy Fox's trial?

'Whatever structure I belong to, it isn't white power,' I thought, as I wearily made my way to bed.

'And we are here as on a darkling plain
Swept with confused alarms of struggle and flight,
Where ignorant armies clash by night.'
Dover Beach, Matthew Arnold

12

Tuesday, 18th September

Despite Mallick's threat I slept very soundly. I felt sluggish and heavy-limbed when I woke. I staggered into the bathroom and showered, then checked my weight on the scales. I'd put on eight pounds since last month. At this rate I'd be needing to get my clothes altered soon. I decided to give breakfast a miss.

Dressed in cycling shorts and T-shirt, I folded up an old newspaper and wadded it round my back, under the T-shirt, to protect my kidneys against chill. Then I went down for the bike and set off on my long circuit of the Meadows. The air in the river valley was fresh and it was soon whistling through my lungs as I worked up speed through Chorlton Water Park. From there I pedalled on to Sale and over the Mersey towards Urmston. I was pounding along the road towards Carrington Moss when I began to get my 'runner's high' as endorphins flowed into my blood stream. Determined to carry on until I felt real pain, I pressed on until my feet could hardly turn the pedals. Sweat was pouring off me as I turned back.

The rush hour was getting under way at eight o'clock as I wearily pedalled my way along Edge Lane and back to the flat. It took me all my strength to get upstairs but after a long soak in the bath, I felt fitter than I had for weeks and ready to face the day.

When I had put on my suit I checked the store on the mobile for unanswered calls. Sure enough the Liptrots had phoned. I switched it off again, thinking that I would get in touch from the office. By the time I'd crawled into town alongside thousands of other commuters and found somewhere to park it was well after nine. I walked along the cracked pavements past Chorlton Street bus station, almost free of prostitutes and their attendant kerb crawlers at this hour of day.

As I neared the Atwood Building, headquarters of Pimpernel Investigations for so long, the sheet of glass that made up one side of the wedge-shaped building was reflecting the dull sky like a giant mirror. I could see there was some sort of commotion going on and a perplexed little group of my fellow Atwoodites were milling about on the street corner. I quickened my pace, thinking it might be a bomb scare. Then I saw one of the permanent residents coming towards me.

'What's going on, Jimmy?' I asked the ferrety little guy who ran a mail-order health food business from the ground floor. He was a wizened veteran of the trade, always one step ahead of the law. I often came across him lugging his sacks of ispaghula husks into the building. He made them up into exorbitantly expensive slimming aids which he posted all over the country.

'Don't go round there!' he gasped, gesturing to the corner. 'There's a whole gang of them. They won't let us in! They say we're all exploiters! I'm going for the police.' Now Jimmy had some reason to feel guilty. His expensive compounds must have raised hopes of a miracle cure amongst the weight-challenged up and down the country. I guessed that there was some investigative TV crew after him.

I pushed through the crowd of fellow residents and

rounded the corner. Mallick's group from SPROAC were completely blocking the steps. I recoiled as if slapped in the face, but it was too late. They'd seen me and as if on cue they all sat down in the doorway and began singing 'We shall not be moved.' As I took in the scene, open-mouthed, I spotted the slight figure of Everald Mallick. He was grinning at me in triumph. While I watched, a group of youths chained themselves to the front door.

A grinning girl ran forward with a fly-sheet, which she shoved in my hand. 'Would you care to sign our petition?' she giggled.

I grabbed the paper off her and advanced towards Everald Mallick, intending to see how far down his throat I could shove it. A sharp-featured, middle-aged white individual interposed herself.

'I'll be a witness if there's any brutality,' she said defiantly, for all the world as if I was a Chinese tank charging at a group of unarmed students. Mallick's opaque glasses were reflecting the morning light like a pair of headlights. He was clutching a mobile phone in his hand as if it were the shield of righteousness. One of the group, a tall black youth, was leaning against the canal wall and filming the scene on a camcorder.

'Well, Mr Cunane, do you still think you can ignore the anger of the community?' Mallick asked triumphantly. 'I think you'd better drop your investigation pretty damn quick if you want to stay in business.'

My white-hot rage cooled very quickly as I took the scene in. There were no more than a dozen in Mallick's group and half of them should have been in school. He wanted me to make a scene, then no doubt with a bit of editing the video tape would look like a vicious assault by a white racist. I turned on my heel and scurried back round the corner to Jimmy. A chorus of jeers and catcalls followed me.

'Any joy with the police?' I asked Jimmy.

'They're sending an inspector to assess the situation, but they won't respond quickly. They say it's not their policy to respond provocatively in this sort of situation. The public have a right to demonstrate.'

'But not stop us getting into our building!' one burly resident shouted angrily. There was quite a head of steam building up amongst the Atwoodites. It wouldn't take much to start an ugly brawl.

'Look, I'll come clean,' I shouted. 'It's me they're after.'

'Who the hell are you?' The burly guy was working himself up into a frantic rage.

'Pimpernel Investigations, top floor,' muttered Jimmy.

'I'm a private detective and that crowd round there object to me gathering information for a TV series and book on Billy Fox,' I explained. This produced a collective groan of disbelief.

'Why are they involving us?' someone asked plaintively.

'They want to get their little story onto the TV news tonight. There's only a couple of dozen of them, but if you go charging in you'll give them just the sort of publicity they're after,' I said. I noticed that Jimmy and several other proprietors of fly-by-night businesses blanched at the suggestion of TV publicity. There was one guy I suspected of organising long firm fraud in derelict shops in the area.

'I've got an idea how to get them off our backs. If we can arrange for cabs, I can get thirty or forty people here who, I guarantee, will shift SPROAC faster than a dose of salts,' I announced. They were desperate enough to listen to my idea. As we went into a huddle a police car cruised slowly past our corner but didn't stop.

Forty-five minutes later we returned in nine separate cabs carrying nearly all of VICPAC, twenty-seven assorted parents of Billy's victims and their hangers-on. It had taken some persuading to get them to move from their encampment outside Police Headquarters, but once I assured them that Cedric's work was far more likely to keep their grave-less children in the public eye than anything they could do outside GMP Headquarters they were eager to help. The procession of taxis through town, some of them with VICPAC banners sticking out of the windows, looked like the annual taxi drivers' treat for poor children.

'Eh, Montgomery of Alamein himself couldn't have done better than this,' Jimmy said to me admiringly as the VICPAC demonstrators disembarked and efficiently sorted themselves out on the pavement. As they set off round the corner to confront SPROAC two camera crews arrived in vans from different network television stations and set up their equipment. I decided it was the right moment for me to beat a discreet retreat.

'Going somewhere, Davie?' came the familiar Scottish tones of Assistant Chief Constable Archie 'Jock' Sinclair. The sudden roar of sound which came from the Atwood entrance drowned any further remarks he made. Rival packs of football supporters at each other's throats couldn't have created more row. Pigeons which infested the roof of the building took off in sudden panic. Almost simultaneously the police vans arrived. 'I knew it was you when I heard the words Atwood Building mentioned,' Sinclair yelled above the hubbub. 'Your talent for disruption ought to be harnessed. It's a national asset. How much would it cost us to get you to set up shop in Brussels?'

I shook myself free from his bony grip and joined the throng of happy residents waiting to enter the Atwood building once more.

Strange how comforting and cosy my office looked now I could enter freely. I had accumulated far too much junk in there, but every piece had its significance. I phoned the Liptrots on my mobile and retrieved my pager.

'Oh, it's you. Do you know how long we've been trying to get hold of you?' Lena's voice was peevish.

'What is it?' I asked.

'That doctor wants to have a chat with Cedric. That Caulfield. I'm not letting him see her on his own. You'll have to take him.'

It took me twenty-five minutes to reach the Swiss Chalet in Hale Barns, and then I had the pleasure of another trip back into the town centre to Caulfield's office in the Metropolitan University not half a mile from my own headquarters with a silent Cedric next to me. Police suspicion and the public criticism of his work had obviously cracked his confidence. Caulfield had an office in the Humanities department in the Cavendish Building, a '70s block somehow reminiscent of the Hanging Gardens of Babylon with its rooftop trees and walkways. It took us so long to find a parking space that I thought it would have been better to leave my car at the multistorey in town and walk. I finally slotted into a space vacated by an elderly priest at the back of St Augustine's church.

Having been summoned so urgently, we now had to wait outside Caulfield's room. She was holding a seminar for her post-grad students, the departmental secretary informed us sweetly. It would be over in twenty minutes. I could hear Caulfield's voice booming through the door but couldn't make out what she was saying.

'What do you think Caulfield wants?' I said, breaking the silence. 'She said she has a vital piece of information about Billy,' Cedric muttered, then lapsed back into silence. 'Same trick she pulled on me,' I thought.

Eventually the post-grads filed out of the room. They were a cowed-looking bunch. Some of them were Chinese, talking in muted tones. Caulfield obviously kept them well under.

When we made it into the office at long last it was immediately clear that Caulfield hadn't asked us along for a social visit. She had her solicitor with her, a female in a navy blue trouser suit. The solicitor proceeded to serve the astonished Cedric with notice that any use of theories about Billy Fox which were the intellectual property of Dr Lauren Caulfield would lead to action in the courts.

'Anybody is entitled to develop his own ideas,' spluttered Cedric.

'That isn't the case,' replied the solicitor coldly. She was a thin-faced person in her mid-thirties with lank dark hair. 'We are claiming that you have had sight of papers developed by Dr Caulfield for police use which remain her intellectual property. We further claim that you intend to use these papers as the basis of your book about the Fox murders.' Caulfield herself was sitting quietly in the corner of the room.

As the solicitor relentlessly pounded on, specifying details, listing the pains and penalties he would incur, Cedric began to react. At first he started jerking forward on his chair trying to say something in his own defence, He got nowhere. The lawyer continued to browbeat him.

Cedric started blustering, talking loudly over the opposing flow of words. Nothing happened. There was no response. The woman calmly continued to spout her legal jargon at him. Caulfield remained seated, with her gaze fixed on an invisible spot on the floor about a metre from her feet.

It was my fault. I should have been more alert. Perhaps I was admiring Caulfield's legs. Cedric was becoming more frantic and hysterical by the second but, still, what happened was unexpected and not just by me. Cedric let out a blood-curdling yell and launched himself at Caulfield. For an alleged scholar and writer he was surprisingly quick. I was petrified with astonishment as he sunk his fingers into Caulfield's shoulders. I think he only intended to shake some sense into her.

Caulfield and the solicitor both gave involuntary shrieks of surprise. Caulfield tried to struggle to her feet. She showed no sign of that ready resort to violence that she'd displayed when I first met her. Maybe that only happened when she'd been on the sauce. Her face made a ghastly white contrast with her flame red hair.

Cedric managed to give the psychologist two good shakes before I got my hands on him. I think he was unaware of the violent aspect of what he was doing. He was yelling in Caulfield's face, spittle flying in all directions. He'd really lost it. I had to exert all my strength to prise him off the unresisting female.

Cedric's startling display had finally silenced the lawyer. She looked on open-mouthed as I pulled my client off her client. Points of law were no use in this situation. I grappled with Cedric, trying to force him back into his chair. I was on the point of hitting him when he suddenly snapped out of his fit of rage. He sat down heavily, trembling from the violent effort,

The silence that fell on the tutorial room was only broken by the sound of the breath wheezing from Cedric's lungs. We remained frozen for at least a minute. Caulfield's eyes were brimming but she kept control. The first move she made was towards her heavy shoulder bag. She turned her back on us and I heard the chinking of glass as she rummaged through it. Cedric cradled his head in his hands like a child trying to shut out his naughty deed. It was the solicitor who was the first to find words.

'That will cost you very dear, Mr Liptrot,' she said. Her eyes were blazing with spite, or to give her the benefit of the doubt, perhaps it was righteous anger. 'I am a witness to this disgusting display. I intend to report you to the police –'

'No. Not the police,' Lauren Caulfield said as she whirled round to face us. She crammed the empty whisky miniature back into her bag. 'I don't want them involved under any circumstances.'

'But Dr Caulfield that was assault! I insist –'

'No you don't. I'm not having them involved. I never meant things to go this far. You shouldn't have persuaded me to threaten him.'

The solicitor was flabbergasted, not understanding Lauren Caulfield's personal reasons for not involving the police. She opened and closed her mouth several times but no words came. In the end she ran her hands over her navy blue suit, then picked up her briefcase and left. I stared in surprise at Lauren Caulfield. She said nothing. She was still in shock. Knowing her disposition, I didn't like the way she'd begun fingering a heavy leather-bound Ph.D. thesis that lay on top of her desk. I went forward and took it out of her hand before she was tempted to crash it onto Cedric's head and give him a well-deserved bruise.

As I replaced the book on a shelf I couldn't help noticing the title – *Normal Stranger: the serial killer in the community* by Lauren C. Caulfield. There was a cold feeling in the pit of my stomach. I had a vision of Cedric sailing into action with a club hammer in his hand. He hadn't hesitated for a millisecond before launching an attack against a seated, defenceless woman. He was far from harmless. Admittedly there was provocation, but I'd have to look at Cedric in a new light from now on.

'You'd better get him out of here,' Caulfield gasped in a low tone, indicating her fellow author. 'I might change my mind.'

I seized the chance to leave, escorting the slightly smashed-up writer and dramatist out of the Cavendish Building. No one barred our exit.

On the way back to the hotel Cedric started complaining about the general unfairness of the world and about the shortcomings of Manchester in particular. He didn't stop until I got him up to the hotel room and into the care of his mother. One thing was clear from his confused ramblings: he believed that Caulfield was responsible for the grilling he'd had from the police yesterday. 'If it's the last thing Mother and I ever do, I'll write this book and show that woman up as the charlatan she is,' he vowed before crumpling up into a heap on the sofa.

'Some sort of minder you turned out to be! What did you let that bitch do to him?' Lena said accusingly when she turned from comforting her son. Cedric had told her the story in a way that cast himself as the victim.

'He attacked Caulfield. Not the other way round. There's nothing in my contract about restraining him from assaulting the locals,' I replied. 'Who does he think he is anyway? Norman Mailer or Ernest Hemingway?'

'This reminds me of when his father worked in a fairground boxing booth. Many's the time he'd come home covered in bruises, but nobody ever succeeded in knocking him out. Nobody but me, that is,' Lena said with a chuckle. She drew in breath to elaborate her saga but Cedric forestalled her.

'Not that one, Mother!' he begged weakly. Clearly

Mrs Uptrot's fantasies weren't off-the-cuff jobs, but tales long in gestation.

Cedric headed for the drinks trolley. He had learned the restorative properties of vodka only too well. He was on his second glass when his mother pleaded, 'At least have something to eat with it.'

Over a tuna sandwich, Cedric related the solicitor's legal and other threats to his mother. Businesslike as ever, Lena faxed the information to Felicity Grete at Headstone Press. It wasn't long before the phone rang. Lena sat grim-faced, listening to the response from the publisher. 'She wants to speak to you,' she said after an age.

'Mr Cunane?' Felicity had a rich, fruity voice. 'Is there any chance we can sue this Caulfield person for assault? It would be marvellous publicity for the book.'

'You could, I suppose,' I said dubiously, visions of Caulfield's counter-suit in my mind. 'It may be best to let sleeping dogs lie.'

'Oh well, perhaps not a good idea, but I'm preparing a press release. I've heard that Caulfield has signed up with Murdle and Withers Inc. to do a book on Billy and they say she's got most of her manuscript ready now. We've prepared a statement to say that Mr Liptrot will only be using original material. We're expecting you to keep him to the mark,' she explained brightly.

'I see,' I said woodenly. I didn't see anything.

'And how is Kath? How are the treatments coming on?'

It took me a second to get back onto her wavelength. 'Oh, the scripts,' I said. 'She's got this idea of making Billy more sinister by contrasting his care of animals with his rage against humans. She worked on it all day yesterday and at this moment she's visiting the Animal Sanctuary in Yorkshire where Billy Fox sometimes worked.'

'Sounds promising. Tell her to call me when she gets in,' she concluded briskly.

When I put the phone down Lena looked at me sadly. She had aged in the last two minutes. 'Dear Felicity just reminded me that we won't get the next part of the advance until Cedric delivers the first 50,000 words, so he'd better get busy. He needs to see the houses where these girls lived so he can soak in the atmosphere,' she said.

Atmosphere wasn't the only thing Cedric was soaking in. I snatched the vodka bottle from his hand. 'Let's get going,' I ordered.

We drove round Fallowfield and Withington as the writer tried to familiarise himself with the area and scan the local scene. It was fairly quiet at the moment. The bulk of the students weren't back for term yet but signs of the blight their presence had wrought on the area were everywhere: houses with bulging wheelie bins on the front paths, overgrown gardens, shops turned into flat rental agencies, second-hand clothes and furniture shops. It didn't take a genius to deduce that most students were bumping along at, or below, the breadline. But Billy's victims had mostly not been drawn from what might be described as the intellectual elite of the student body. They'd been locals drawn to the area by the cheap accommodation on offer.

My employer was doing his stuff. From time to time he scribbled something in his notebook. There was plenty of local colour for him. Even now, into autumn with the leaves getting ready to fall, the whole area had a shadowy stain over it. The trees were old and overgrown. They turned the narrow streets into forest paths. There was a stricken look to many of the houses too, as if the inhabitants only dared to creep out under cover of darkness.

It was nearly four o'clock before I dropped Cedric at

the university shopping precinct on Oxford Road. He was most insistent that I leave him on his own. I warned him not to visit Caulfield again. 'No danger of that,' he said with a thin smile. 'I need a new battery for my laptop. Don't hang around. I'll get a taxi back to the hotel.' He said he'd be writing for most of the rest of the week and would get in touch when he needed me.

I was looking forward to seeing Kath again after her excursion to Pateley Bridge, and it was with a certain eagerness that I waved him farewell. I turned back towards Chorlton and passing into the broad roads of South Manchester was like coming out of a long tunnel. Whatever the council thought about turning Billy's house into a memorial garden it would be many years before I'd be able to walk the streets he had stalked without a shiver.

Kath wasn't back when I got home so I made myself a quick snack of beans on toast and settled down in front of the television. There was nothing on the national news but all local TV channels featured the VICPAC demo. I was delighted to see that the commentary was entirely from the VICPAC point of view, there was no interview with Mallick. The line taken was that VICPAC had clashed with a group trying to prevent publication of a book about Billy Fox. Poor Everald must be gnashing his teeth, I thought.

The rest of the news was pretty downbeat; police were still pursuing their enquiries re Manchester's new serial killer and trying to round up females in the target age-group who were sleeping rough . . .

On the subject of missing females, there was still no sign of Kath. I decided that her trip must have taken her longer than she bargained for. I must have dozed for a while because I was woken by the phone ringing insistently. I picked it up expecting to hear from my partner but it was Everald Mallick.

'I expect you think you're pretty clever, but I'm warning you, no one gets away with insulting the African community – I know where you live.'

'Everald, is that meant to be a threat?' I mocked. 'What are you going to do? Boycott the public libraries? Start burning dictionaries? It's only a book.'

'You stop working on it or you'll face the just anger of the people.' With that he hung up.

When I returned to my solitary vigil I felt seriously peeved about Everald Mallick. The more I thought about him though, the more I decided that he was just a big mouth. After the failure of his demo to intimidate me he must be feeling pretty raw. I just hoped that he wouldn't take his frustration out on the Anderson family. They were a far easier target than me for his spiteful tricks.

By nine o'clock, I decided that I couldn't put off trying to find Kath any longer. I phoned Hawkshead, fully expecting her to answer and say that she'd decided to stay an extra day with her father.

'Headlam speaking,' the Commander's voice announced coldly.

'Is Kath there?' I ventured.

'What?' he boomed. 'Has she left you?' He sounded hopeful.

'I haven't seen her,' I explained. 'I was wondering if she was staying on at Hawkshead.'

'No, she left here at ten this morning. She must have called in somewhere on the way. Telephone me when she gets in,' he ordered sharply before putting the phone down. 'No time for small talk then,' I thought.

I spent another hour nervously waiting for Kath to make contact and then set off for Pateley Bridge myself. If Kath had decided to take up residence at the Animal Shelter I wanted to be the first to know. It would be a pity if she'd decided to devote her life to looking after our dumb friends rather than Hugo Headlam or me. The Shelter was in one of the more remote corners of the north of England, about twenty miles due north of Bradford, in Nidderdale. Even using the M66 and M65 motorways, it took me well over two hours to reach Skipton. From there I had a tortuous journey along the winding A59 before coming to the turning for Pateley Bridge.

'At markets in Northern Congo, the headless carcass of a silver-back lowland gorilla is offered for sale for the equivalent of £20 – a small fortune to a local hunter. The gorilla's hand, eaten as a delicacy, sells for £1 In some parts of Central Africa, gorillas' fingers are ground to a powder and sprinkled Into babies' baths to make them grow strong.'

Publicity material from the World Society for the Protection of Animals,1996.

13

Wednesday, 19th September, morning

The Sanctuary was sign-posted well enough, but it was up a rough track. It was a cold night and there was a crescent moon. There wasn't much light because the moon was obscured by fast-moving clouds. After driving with main-beam headlights it would have taken me some time to get my night vision. I didn't bother. I left the car at the bottom of the dark lane and stumbled along hoping to see Kath's Mazda neatly parked in the farmyard. Instead I found nothing but a small noticeboard stating, 'Chillgate Farm Animal Sanctuary, a place of safety for sick, cruelly treated and lost animals. Proprietor E. Maxwell (Mrs).'

Something felt strange. I stood trying to work it out for a moment. It was an uncomfortable feeling. Then I realised it was the quiet. That absolute dead quiet that you sometimes get on a still night in the countryside.

I climbed over a stile beside the barred gate. There was a light gleaming in the farmhouse but it was after one a.m. and I hesitated to bang on the door. As I stood undecided something rammed me in the back. I whirled round to face an indistinct darker patch of blackness in the surrounding gloom that suddenly revealed itself to be a donkey by letting rip a horrendous braying noise. I could feel my hair standing on end. The beast sounded as if it had swallowed a chain saw.

The braying was taken up by other donkeys and in no time at all the hillside was echoing to brays, barks, neighs and other assorted cries of alarm. More lights came on in the farmhouse and then the door was flung open.

'It's all right,' I yelled, feverishly imagining a hail of buckshot blasting in my direction. 'I'm looking for someone. I mean no harm.' I held my hands up. In films the farmers always emerge with a shotgun.

'Step towards the light. Let me look at you,' an elderly female in a nightdress yelled from the doorway.

I moved cautiously forward, blinking in the strong light which now flooded the yard. I was startled to see a little bearded face suddenly pop out beside the woman's thigh. For a second I thought it was an old man crouching on all fours, then I realised that it was a young billy goat.

'Stop there where I can see you,' the woman said when I was within ten yards of the front door. 'I'll phone the police if you come another step.'

I explained that I was looking for Kath.

'There was a young woman here this afternoon but she said nothing about any private detective. Have you any identification?' the woman asked. I tossed my home-made ID card over to her. The goat picked it up before she did, but she forced open the animal's jaws and retrieved it.

An eerie screaming noise suddenly replaced the animal sounds, which had almost died down. I almost leapt out of my skin.

'It's all right. That's only the peacock,' the woman said with a titter. 'It's a good job for you that I read a lot of detective stories because I've always wanted to meet a private detective. You'd better come in.'

No sooner had I crossed her threshold than I wished I hadn't. The kitchen of the farmhouse smelt like a sewage farm on a hot day. It was an indescribable blend of goat, cat pee, sour milk and above all shit. I gagged but she took my arm and drew me in.

'Come on in. Don't be so *mard*. You've smelt a few animals before now,' she said, sweeping a long-haired black cat off a broken-backed chair for me.

There was a stuffed owl peering down at me from under a glass dome resting on the mantelpiece. I noticed that the cat had only three legs and that the goat had a heavily bandaged right foreleg. I looked at my hostess. To outward appearances, all her faculties were intact. Her eyes had the same shrewd look as those of the owl on her mantelpiece. Still, she was a trusting soul to invite a strange man into her house after one a.m. Either she was very eccentric or she was used to visitors at odd hours. Looking at the battered and scratched furniture I realised that there wouldn't be much to tempt a thief here.

'I never get lonely up here with all my friends but it's nice to have someone who can talk back to me, for a change. Will you have a cup of tea?'

Well on into her seventies, she was wearing a dressing gown over an off-white nightie, with a pair of dirty green wellies on her feet. Her grey hair was in plaits, which reached down to her waist. Long white hairs sprouted from her lips and chin and a brown mole flourished on her right temple. She bustled about, twittering to herself, then banged a mug of tea down on the table beside me.

'Do you take milk?' she offered and when I nodded my head she took the rubber teat off a baby's feeding bottle and poured some milk from it into my cup. 'It's all right,' she said when she saw me goggling at this performance. 'I've not started feeding the goat yet.'

She smiled, exposing a row of gaps where most of her teeth should have been. So how was it that I felt a cold shiver run down my spine? 'My name's Enid Maxwell,' she volunteered, 'and this is my animal shelter.'

The cat jumped up on her knee and she fondled it. Hair stood out like a ruff round the animal's neck. 'She's a mongrel like me,' she explained. 'Got some Persian in her, but I don't know what the rest is. Someone found her in Bradford with her leg hanging off and brought her here to me. You'll never believe the vet's bills it took to get her fixed. Now, your lady friend said she might be able to help there.' Her eyes were sparkling with greed. 'Yes, she said if I let them film here they'd pay me a very good fee. They'd have to make a few alterations. She was very keen to put a big sign up over the entrance gate. I don't know why that was. Everyone round here knows that there's only Chillgate Farm on this road.'

Kath had been here all right, I thought. 'What time did she leave?' I asked.

'I lose track of time, though she was here a good while. It was this afternoon, I think. She must have covered every one of the fifty acres on the farm. She checked all the barns and sheds, even the incinerator. I don't know what it was she was looking for but she did a much more thorough job than the RSPCA inspector does.'

I fished a cat hair out of my tea. 'Did she say where she was going next?' I asked.

'She said she was going on to Manchester and I told her the route my Manchester volunteers usually take on their way home from here,' she replied.

'You have a lot of people coming from Manchester?' I queried.

'Oh, yes, and from Bradford and Leeds too. All over really. I couldn't manage up here on my own.'

'I suppose the Summergills come up here quite a lot,' I said, hoping to get some clue as to where Kath had got herself to.

'If you see Dennis, tell him I've stuff for the incinerator. I haven't seen him or that son of his for months. There are some ladies who run a shop for me in Manchester. Didsbury, I think it is,' she said vaguely.

'Haven't you ever been?' I asked.

'No, I never leave here. The committee deal with all that. There are shops in Bradford, Manchester and Leeds where they sell gifts that people bring. The volunteers use the money to maintain the animals and pay all expenses, like.'

'My friend asked you a lot about Billy Fox, I suppose?' I asked.

'I suppose so,' she said absent-mindedly. 'I don't remember him. We get such a lot of people coming and going up here that it's impossible for me to know every helper by name.'

I sat for a moment in silence. The three-legged cat had jumped off her knee and was now rubbing itself against my leg, presumably anxious to share its fleas with me. It was hard to believe what its owner was saying. Surely Billy would have stood out in a crowd?

I got up to go but I wasn't allowed to leave before I'd paid £10 to the Chillgate Co-operators Society.

Kath's was the last name in the membership book, a heavy leather-bound volume. At any rate there was proof positive that Kath had been here. I leafed through the rest of the volume trying to spot Billy Fox's name. It wasn't there, but one name did jump out at me. *A. Clark.* I checked carefully, there was a Bradford address. The Bradford Basher joined in 1984, the year before his arrest. I continued to turn the pages. The names of Dennis and Dean Summergill leapt out at me. They'd joined before A. Clark. My finger traced along the line to their joint address. It was also a Bradford address. They'd been Bradford residents at the same time as A. Clark. Had Kath spotted this too? A chill of fear was beginning to settle in my bones like an old rheumatic ache. Where was she?

It could just be a coincidence, I told myself as I stumbled blindly past the donkey in the farmyard. It might not even be Albert Clark, the Bradford Basher, or even a man. There must be dozens of *A. Clarks* in Bradford.

It was a quarter to two when I got out into the farmyard. My night vision was completely shot again and it took me almost fifteen minutes blundering about on the pitch-dark lane outside Chillgate Farm before I found my way back to the car. I phoned the flat to see if Kath had turned up. There was no reply.

I was tired, hungry and totally baffled. 'What am I doing up here in the wilds of North Yorkshire?' I said to myself wonderingly, raking my thumbs against the steering wheel.

Without conscious thought, I set off again back to Manchester. Although Pateley Bridge is a fairly desolate spot there was only a slight chance that Kath's car could have gone off the road without being noticed. There were tourists and hikers around the whole time, not to mention animal lovers. Still, I kept my eyes peeled. As the distance between myself and the Animal Sanctuary increased so the chilly feeling of unease grew. I'd missed something.

Maybe I was panicking too soon. Maybe Kath had gone to visit some old friend in the area. Maybe she'd decided she'd had enough of me and of Manchester. Maybe Hugo Headlam was lying and she was safely back at Hawkshead.

Maybe. But maybe not.

The word 'Police' flashed across my mind. I could report Kath missing, but would they take me seriously? I looked at my watch. It was now two thirty. I'd been expecting Kath by six yesterday evening, at the latest.

I phoned Sinclair on his home number. The phone rang forever but when he answered he sounded as alert and fresh as always.

'Sinclair.'

'Mr Sinclair. It's Dave Cunane here. I'm sorry to wake you up, but it's Kath Headlam, my partner . . . she's gone missing.'

'Go on, Davie. Tell me more. You've done the right thing.' His voice sounded encouraging, as if I often called him in the middle of the night to report a missing female companion. I explained Kath's enthusiasm to track down the wildlife angle of the Billy Fox story, her visit to the Summergills and her trip to Chillgate Farm.

'That's very interesting, Davie. Certainly it's something we hadn't thought of. So she's gone missing at this farm?'

'There's more . . . there's something that's really scared me. It may be nothing, but –'

'Come on, Davie. Spit it out, man. What is it?'

'You may think I'm crazy, but the old lady who runs the Animal Sanctuary made me join the Co-operators Society . . . you know . . . like the friends of the place. Well, right there in the book for 1984 is the name A. Clark, Bradford, and a couple of pages before that there's the entry for the Summergills but their address is listed as Bradford not Manchester.' I didn't need to say any more to Sinclair. I could almost hear the cogs meshing in his brain even at this distance.

'Right,' he said after a short pause. 'Here's what I want you to do. I want you to come straight in to the Incident Room at Bootle Street. I'll meet you there. And listen, Davie, I want you to come directly. No side trips and no speaking to anyone. Not even Paddy. Have you checked if you're being followed?'

I explained that I was on a winding country lane in the depths of North Yorkshire, with no other vehicle in sight for miles. I gave him all the information about Kath I could think of; description, car registration, father's address, I even told him about the strawberry birthmark on her right breast.

'OK. Well, we'll have done some checking at this end by the time you get to Bootle Street. Now listen, Davie, there may be a perfectly innocent explanation for why Miss Headlam hasn't turned up, so hope for the best.'

For once I was grateful for Sinclair's brevity. At least he'd spared me recriminations about private detectives rushing in where the police fear to tread.

As I drove on through the night, Sinclair's well-meant final words and his brevity gradually took on a sinister meaning. It was a case of the dog that didn't bark in the night. A prolonged tongue-lashing and a demand for an exhaustive explanation would have told me that he thought my fears were stupid or maudlin. But no, here is a woman researching Billy Fox. She finds a tenuous link between Fox, the Basher and the so-helpful Summergills and then goes missing. Very quietly, without any fuss Sinclair had pressed the panic button the instant he got the news. Why else was I to go to the Incident Room at Bootle Street if there wasn't a link in his mind? Somehow Kath had stumbled over a connection between Albert Clark, Billy Fox, the

Summergill family and perhaps the killer currently operating in Manchester. I could only hope against hope, that Kath hadn't paid for her enthusiasm with her life.

Dawn was breaking when I pulled into the tiny car park at Bootle Street. DS Cullen was waiting for me, he took me upstairs to his desk in the empty general CID office. He was wearing a shell suit again, emerald green. 'Perhaps he sleeps in them,' I thought. This time there was no expectant feeling in the old Police Headquarters, no crowd of reporters jamming the doors. There was just that slack early morning calm that you get in hospitals and police stations when the night shift are waiting hopefully for relief to arrive and praying that there are no further incidents.

'She's not at your flat or your office or at her father's,' Cullen said. Then he leant forward and shaded his eyes with his hand. 'We've checked the hospitals . . . nothing.'

'Go on,' I said. I could tell he was holding something back.

'It might not mean anything, but the car, the metallic silver Mazda RX7 with personalised plates. It's turned up in Bradford . . . it was parked right across the entrance of the cemetery where Albert Clark used to work. That's why it was reported so quickly.'

It felt as if I was being dealt one of the hammer blows which Clark had made his trademark.

'I gave Mr Sinclair the address of the Summergills' former home in Bradford.'

'Yes, that's been checked. It's a dead end I'm afraid, Dave. The house is now occupied by a Mr George Hanley, a forty-three-year-old primary school headmaster, his wife Rita and their two teenage sons. There's nothing known against any of them and they're adamant that Kath Headlam did not pay them a visit yesterday. Yes, and they also say that they've never heard of Chillgate Farm. Hanley's threatening to sue the Central Yorkshire Police for rousing him in the middle of the night.'

'She must have gone back to see the Summergills. She was fascinated by them and what she saw at their home. She could easily have called on them yesterday afternoon. Perhaps she just wanted to know if they'd ever met Albert Clark.'

'Now, Dave,' he said cautiously. 'You know it's not yet been confirmed that the A. Clark in the Chillgate Book is the Bradford Basher. Anyone can use a false name and address. The handwriting will have to be compared by a police professional.' From the expression on Cullen's face I could see that, notwithstanding lack of confirmation, he did believe that A. Clark was the Basher.

'What about the Summergills?' I asked.

'The house in Withington is under discreet observation. The Tactical Support Group's on stand-by. Naturally Mr Sinclair thought that your call might be the break in the current murder case. It's a very delicate situation, Dave. We've no sort of evidence against them except that they were rather better acquainted with Billy Fox than they cared to let on and that they supported the same Animal Sanctuary as Albert Clark. A good brief, or even a lousy one –'

'All I want is for them to be asked if they've seen Kath,' I said angrily.

'We can't casually stroll up and ask a pair of possible serial killers have they seen someone who we think just might have been their latest victim. Talk sense!'

I found it hard to breathe for a moment. Cullen's brutal phrasing had made my worst fears concrete.

'Sorry, Dave,' he said, 'but these things need careful handling. Mr Sinclair and DCS Pinnock will do everything they can to ensure Kath's safety, but you've got to see they can't just charge in and alert suspects until they're absolutely certain that . . . well, you know. Kath might turn up at any moment, or they might have her in that house, or they might know where she is.'

'If they've killed her you mean.'

'It may be a hostage situation. They may be holding her.' Even as Cullen spoke we both knew that he was whistling in the dark to keep my spirits up. 'Mr Sinclair and Pinnock are over there now working out what is the best move. We can only wait.'

'I want to go there. I want to see them.'

'No, it's best if you stay here. Mr Sinclair will contact us when he knows anything. Why don't you get some kip? You look shattered. There's a rest room next door where you can lie down. There's nothing you can do.'

His words were like nails driving into Kath's coffin. '*Nothing you can do . . . Nothing you can do.*' A powerful surge of shame swept over me. I should have been the one who uncovered whatever secret it was Kath had found. I tried to tell myself that nothing I could have done would have stopped Kath following up the lead she'd found at Chillgate Farm. Hell! She was a modern woman. She didn't require male protection at all times. Kath had made that abundantly clear on many occasions.

Not that she was capable of defending herself in actuality. That was the trouble. Psychologically, she could rip a man to shreds quickly enough, but she wasn't streetwise. In some ways Kath was a more mature version of naïve Cynthia Royton, the girl who thought Billy was 'nice'. She was equally convinced that she could talk her way out of any danger with a few sharp words.

With an effort I forced myself to stop brooding. If I was to flake out now, it wouldn't do Kath any good.

Cullen shepherded me into the canteen, sat me down and fed me a bacon sandwich and two cups of coffee.

'You've been up all night. Get some kip,' he cajoled. 'Even half an hour'll be a bonus. They might be a while up in Withington yet.'

I slept briefly, slumped in a chair, and woke up with a start as Cullen shook my shoulder.

'They're bringing them in,' he said.

'Who?' I mumbled.

'The Summergills. Dennis and Dean. Your very good friend, Mr Sinclair, persuaded a magistrate that there were sufficient grounds for a search of their property. He acted against the advice of Pinnock. Pinnock's blown his top. Anyway Kath's not there which is good news, but they have a grey van. You'll have to identify it.' Cullen was eager. Good copper that he was, he had the quarry in sight. I could see he was anxious to get involved in the interrogation and quit his duties as my nursemaid. I envied him and sympathised at the same time.

'There's more. The North Yorkshire Police have just raided Chffigate Farm. They had to take a posse of RSPCA people with them to round up the animals . . .' He paused significantly. 'Kath Headlam wasn't there either, but they found her recorder. It's in a leather pouch with her name on. It was hidden in the back of a cupboard. There's nothing on the tape.'

I crushed my fists so tightly that the nails bit into the palms of my hand. 'She'd never leave it. She'd never have forgotten it accidentally. It was like her right hand,' I said vehemently. 'If she'd just dropped it, that bleeding goat the old woman lives with would have chewed it to pieces.'

'That's what we reckoned,' he agreed. 'Christ! What a mess! Listen, there's more, and it's bad news. Look, you'd better just swill your face or something before I tell you.' He thought I was going to faint or turn hysterical on him.

Passively, like a condemned man being told the time fixed for his execution, I took my shirt off and had a really good wash at a basin in the corner. There was a disposable razor and foam there, so I used that as well. Cullen watched my sartorial preparations with a hint of impatience. I straightened up my suit and brushed some of the hairs off the jacket. Long black cat hairs, I noticed. Then I gave my teeth a rub and flicked the dust off my shoes.

'OK. Let's hear the worst,' I said grimly.

'Human remains. They have an incinerator for the dead animals.'

'I know, the old lady told me. She asked me to tell Dennis Summergill that she had stuff for it,' I said.

'Yeah, well, we know why he didn't come and fix it. It looks as if someone's been trying to barbecue half the animal population of England. Most of it's just ash and grease but they've found some partly calcined bones that they think are human. There's a forensic team from Sheffield on its way up there right now. The North Yorkshire Police have set up an incident room in a museum at Pateley Bridge.'

The bacon sandwich felt like a lump of lead in my stomach. Seeing my face turn green, Cullen said quickly, 'They're not fresh bones. The incinerator hasn't been used in months. There's no trace of Kath apart from the recorder.'

I sat down for a moment. All this new information had set my mind racing. Something must have happened to Kath at the Animal Sanctuary. Maybe she'd never gone on to Bradford or Manchester.

She'd had an intuition about that place right from the start with her talk of Auschwitz. Was it a wild fancy to think she'd said something when she visited the Summergills, something that alerted them that she might discover that they had secret links with both the Basher and Fox? Had they been waiting for her there, up at Chillgate?

I said nothing. I realised that my thoughts were racing well ahead of any possible evidence and that it was still far more likely that the Summergills were just the innocent animal lovers that they claimed to be.

'Have a belt of this,' Cullen said, mistaking my silence for shock. He offered me a small bottle of Famous Grouse which he'd fished out of his bum bag. I took a hefty slug. I gagged on it for a moment but then it produced the familiar glow.

'It takes a drinker to know a drinker, eh?' he said, watching me. 'Well, if you're OK, Mr Sinclair and DCS Pinnock want to see you.' He sounded slightly doubtful about the idea, but I knew there was no mileage in further delay, I had to take what was coming on the chin. He led me into the office I'd been interviewed in before. This time there was a recorder on the table, but it was an ordinary tape recorder not the standard twin-deck interview job.

Seeing me looking at it Sinclair commented, 'It's just here to make sure that we don't miss anything from your witness statement, Davie. It's a pretty tangled story.' He shook his head sadly. I knew he didn't expect to see Kath Headlam alive again any more than I did. Pinnock sat next to him, dark and silent. He was radiating hostility.

'That's fine,' I said. The hopeless way I felt at that moment, I wouldn't have given a damn if Sinclair had said I was to be taken to the central courtyard and shot by firing squad.

Sinclair led me through the story. I told them about everything, including Lena Liptrot's fantasies, Kath's ambitions for her scripts, and about her father's little temper tantrum on Sunday morning. When I told them about Everald Mallick and his threats, they sent a uniformed constable running to fetch the file on SPROAC. When I came to the part about Cedric Liptrot's crazy behaviour in Lauren Caulfield's office, Pinnock was particularly interested. I put that down to Caulfield being his lover, or ex-lover according to her. He made a point of demanding to know the exact time we'd entered her room and the time we'd left and the time that Old Mother Liptrot phoned Felicity Grete at the publishers. He made notes and sent them downstairs to the incident room. That should have alerted me to what was going to come next but it didn't.

It took me the best part of an hour to get through everything. It was clear that there was profound disagreement between Sinclair and Pinnock. Pinnock left the room at several points in my story. He had a look of long-suffering exasperation on his face.

'Billy Fox is the key. That old hag at Chillgate clammed up when I asked her about him. She must know all about what the incinerator was used for,' I concluded.

'That's what you think is it, Cunane?' Pinnock said sarcastically. 'Well, Mr Sinclair, unlike you, I don't have the benefit of being a friend of Cunane's family. I'm only able to use normal criteria in assessing the value of Mr Cunane's insights but this is what our colleagues in North Yorkshire have gleaned from Mrs Enid Maxwell so far.' He held up a fax. 'She claims the large incinerator is necessary because of Creutzfeldt-Jakob disease . . . BSE . . . mad cow disease. This thing that's infecting animals. A lot of cats get it and if the corpses weren't destroyed the other animals up there might dig them up and spread it,' Pinnock explained.

'So that's why human bones were found among the rubbish underneath it?' I asked.

'That supposition has yet to be fully established,' Pinnock said, in the manner of one who does not suffer fools gladly. He was not going to let a civilian get the better of him.

'Billy must have persuaded the Summergills to run him up to Chillgate regularly so he could get rid of his "animal remains". Perhaps they didn't know what he was up to,' I argued. I felt that I must provide a provenance for the bones like a dealer trying to sell a suspect Old Master painting. As I heard myself speak I wondered why I was bothering to argue. Pinnock and Sinclair were the police, not me. I was irrational.

'I see,' Pinnock said. 'In that case the Summergills must both be just as guilty as Billy Fox because no human being could be so stupid as to *innocently* dispose of fourteen human torsos. You idiot, Cunane! Do you suppose Fox wrapped them up in brown paper parcels.'

'It's possible that they didn't know,' I said weakly. 'It's also possible that they might be involved with the crimes.'

'Let me tell you that both Dennis and Dean Summergill are responding to our questioning and our search of their home like two very outraged and completely innocent members of the public. There's no sign that they know anything about your fantasies.' When Pinnock said this he was looking at Sinclair, not me.

Sinclair nervously rapped his pipe out into the ashtray. 'You're sure?' he asked Pinnock.

'Detective Inspector Lofthouse is doing the questioning. He's very experienced. He says there's nothing.'

'How do they explain being members up at Chillgate at the same time that both Albert Clark and Billy Fox were?' I said. 'Bit of a coincidence, isn't it? Haven't there always been doubts that Albert Clark committed all those killings on his own?'

'Aside from the fact that Mrs Maxwell is unable to confirm that Fox was a member, simply having their names in the same book as Albert Clark is not evidence. Do you know how many names there are in that book? Over three thousand.'

'There must be some connection or why has Kath disappeared?' I said desperately. 'There's not been a justified suspicion in history that someone couldn't cast cold water on like you're doing.'

'Go on, Davie,' Sinclair said, silencing Pinnock's reply before he could utter it.

'We know Kath went up there. She searched the farm. She asked dozens of questions and Maxwell let something out. Did she say something about Billy using that incinerator? Later she might have got scared when she realised that Kath would put two and two together and guess that the Summergills were helping Billy to dispose of his victims. Don't forget they're good supporters of the Sanctuary. Anyway, Maxwell warned them before Kath left and they, or some other unknown person, perhaps even this so-called Manchester Basher, intercepted Kath on her way back.'

'I'm glad you're keeping an open mind about the Summergills,' Pinnock said dryly. 'Perhaps the Assistant Chief Constable will excuse me while I knock one or two holes in your theory. You're saying that Fox was somehow in league with all these people, the Summergills, Albert Clark, Mrs Maxwell, even the new killer?'

I nodded my head. I knew what was coming next.

'How do you explain that it was Dennis Summergill who turned Fox in? Surely if Summergill had ratted on him the first thing Fox would have done is to have shopped the whole lot of them?'

I shook my head. I couldn't explain it but then why did I have to? Kath's disappearance was mysterious. She was researching the Fox story and it was because of that story that the police themselves had involved us in the most recent killings. It was up to know-all Pinnock to find the connection, wasn't it? If Kath had been employed by the police instead of by Headstone Press there would have been no question about a search.

I said just that, producing an angry snort from Pinnock. I could feel the veins in my neck swelling. What did the guy need? I knew he'd have acted rapidly enough if Lauren Caulfield had gone missing.

'We've been told that Billy suffers from some odd but genuine form of amnesia,' I said, speaking slowly and trying to curb my temper. Pinnock gave me a strange, almost nervous, look when I said that. My intuition told me that he and his girlfriend knew something about Billy Fox that they didn't want revealed. I wasn't worrying about the ins-and-outs of the Fox case at that moment. I pressed on.

'You've got to get Billy up there. God, having another look at that incinerator should jog his memory. He might even tell us who this new Basher is,' I pleaded. I knew I was clutching at straws but it made sense to me just as the idea of getting Billy back to Manchester made sense to all those grieving parents in VICPAC.

'It's up to you, Assistant Chief Constable,' Pinnock said huffily. 'You know what my advice is. We've got to concentrate on the task in hand . . . catching the man responsible for four murders in this city in the last few weeks. I must say, Mr Sinclair, and I'll be completely frank here and tell you that I intend to repeat this conversation to the Chief Constable. I have very grave suspicions about Cunane's motives.'

I drew in my breath sharply. Sinclair looked taken aback for a second but his face quickly resumed its normal bland and benign expression.

'Tell us more, Mr Pinnock,' he invited.

'Cunane's fooled you. You think of him as a private detective, son of a much-respected former senior officer,' he said.

Sinclair nodded.

'He's nothing of the sort. He's a paid publicity agent for a London publisher. I think you'll find that the genesis of the extraordinary disappearance of Ms Headlam is in the meeting between Cedric Liptrot and Lauren Caulfield. When the publishers heard that Lauren is going to produce a far more authentic and readable book than anything the eccentric recluse Liptrot could come up with, they panicked. After all we're not talking about peanuts here. They've already invested tens of thousands. Ms Headlam, according to Cunane's own story, is desperate to use Liptrot's book to make her way back into television. So they all stand to lose a lot.'

Sinclair shook his head at this point. It wasn't clear if this was because of shock at the revelation of my villainy or if he didn't believe a word he was hearing.

'They decided to stage this perverted publicity stunt for Liptrot's book,' Pinnock continued. 'Isn't it strange that Mrs Maxwell only found Headlam's recorder after Cunane's visit.'

Pinnock began gathering up his papers.

'We've got to come at this from every possible angle. If there is some tie-up between Fox and Clark and our current murderer, I want it out in the open,' Sinclair said decisively.

Pinnock's silence was eloquent as he left the room.

'I'm sorry if I'm causing trouble,' I said to Sinclair. He

threw up his hands, as if to say, 'When have you caused anything else?'

'You've got to realise that Detective Chief Superintendent Philip Pinnock and myself, and indeed every copper in the force, are under intense media pressure at the moment,' he explained. 'How many camera teams are out there now?' he asked Cullen.

'There's BBC, ITN, Sky, Australian Channel 7, West Deutscher Rundfunk, CNN and Dutch TV at the last count, sir, and more arriving all the time. They've set up satellite communication links in Albert Square. Also radio and print media,' Cullen said with a sigh. 'Some of the lads are running a book on it.'

'Just leave the room for a moment, would you?' Sinclair asked Cullen politely. 'You might bring us some coffee.'

When Cullen had gone Sinclair extinguished his pipe and took out a whisky bottle from the top drawer of a filing cabinet. 'Life's very complicated these days, Davie. When I started work with your father the press left us to get on with our job. Of course, we always had the legal establishment and the politicians looking over our shoulders, but that was a given. We're much more on our own now. The politicians are very quick to pass the buck back to us if there's any slip-up, and perhaps we're a bit more defensive and scared to admit an honest mistake as a result. We've lost confidence in lots of ways. Look at this profiling. I've never believed in it. Philip backed Caulfield's theories to the hilt, but in my opinion she's more of a "psycho-forensicologist" than a forensic psychologist. We might as well go back to reading tea leaves like my old granny used to.'

I think he was trying to take my mind off my troubles and he succeeded to the extent that I managed a smile.

'I want you to look at this,' he said. He handed me a file, marked 'Restricted Circulation'.

'This is highly confidential, senior officers only. It's a critique of the Central Yorkshire force's handling of the Albert Clark case prepared by a unit at the Home Office. It makes an interesting study in the light of your current job. Have a look through it, but it mustn't leave this room.'

The classified Home Office report made sombre reading. It had actually taken the CYP years to accept that the killings were linked, and the force had been far too quick to discount the possibility that Clark had had an accomplice. Factors pointing in that direction included: the speed with which corpses had been moved, the number of footprints found, and Clark's hair's breadth escapes from the scenes of some of his murders. Taken together, these implied either he'd had exceptional luck, or that someone had been helping him. The report concluded by hinting that Cedric Liptrot's book had been a very successful pro-police smoke screen in covering up these awkward issues. None of which was of much comfort to me as I thought of what might have happened to Kath. Sinclair was doing his best to prepare me for bad news.

After Sinclair had left, Cullen came back with the coffee. 'Gone has he?' he said. 'You don't want to let Pinnock get you down. We all have trouble pronouncing that bugger's name.

'The main function of the Missing Persons Bureau of the Metropolitan Policeis the matching of descriptions of missing persons with dead bodies which have been found. In the year April 1992 to March 1993, 30,475 missing persons were reported in London alone.'
Police Gazette

14

Wednesday – 10 a.m.

I didn't want Cullen sniffing round my flat so I insisted on him taking me to the Atwood Building. I had a suspicion that he intended to get me rat-arsed. There was nothing much to drink in the office and, more significantly, it didn't hold the same memories. Kath's tenancy of the outer office had been brief. No demonstrators barred our way into the building today, it was quiet and my attic room was cool and shaded.

Life has to go on, or at least it does go on. Time still has duration. Although I wanted it to run backwards to Sunday evening when I'd agreed to Kath's solo mission, it was ticking towards the moment when I would be asked to identify her body. It crossed my mind to wonder what Hugo Headlam was going through. I phoned him from Kath's desk while Cullen sprawled over the sofa in my office.

'Have you heard anything?' Headlam's voice was shaky.

'No, the police are checking every possibility. I'm just waiting,' I said. I suppose my drift must have conveyed hopelessness because he picked me up straight away.

'Cunane, er . . . Dave, can't you do something? You're supposed to be a detective, aren't you?' His voice held a pleading note that I found disturbing. Coming from him it meant things were really bad.

'It's knowing where to start,' I said, more forcefully than I should have done. 'I've already retraced her steps to Chillgate Farm, of course.'

'There must be something,' he insisted. 'Something someone said. Something you've missed. I feel so helpless just waiting.' Then he rang off abruptly. I knew that if Kath had been missing on the fells, he'd have combed the entire Lake District by now.

Tracing missing persons has always been part of my job. The commander was right. I ought to be able to do something more than just sitting around feeling sorry or deciding that people I'd never met had abducted Kath. Where to start, though, that was the problem. I'd conducted many searches for errant teenagers and runaway spouses but in those cases there was always something more to go on than I had now. Though I say it myself, the police are infinitely better equipped for this than any private detective agency, however intuitive and brilliant the personnel may be. It's a matter of having the numbers to run down all the possibilities quickly. They say Britain's a small island, but when you have to start looking under every stone it expands until it's as big as a galaxy.

I went back into my office and looked at Cullen. He seemed amiable enough. He was stretching his arms and yawning.

'Do you believe this is all a publicity stunt?' I asked.

'I believe in Jock Sinclair's nose,' he said. 'Your feet wouldn't have touched the ground if he'd thought you were wasting police time. So, although I don't know you very well personally, I trust Mr Sinclair's instincts. Yeah, she's missing all right.'

'OK, then you know that I won't be able to sit on my hands and wait for Kath to turn up. I can't believe that she's involved in some sort of publicity game. Anyway there's no way she could have known that Pinnock's girlfriend was going to produce a rival book to Liptrot's. You can check that yourself.'

'I told you I believe you.'

'And I insist. Phone Felicity Grete at Headstone and ask if Kath knew about Caulfield's book. Do it in your professional capacity and then I'll have one little verified fact to throw in Pinnock's face.'

He looked doubtful for a moment and I wondered if, despite his assurances, he was afraid to go up against Pinnock. He hauled himself upright on the sofa, shaking his head dubiously.

'What they say about you is true, isn't it?' he said. 'You never stop stirring. Well, I can't say I blame you. You know I had to sit with the mother of Maeve Aldritt, Billy's last victim, while we grilled the poor girl's fiancé. It was absolute hell, trying to give the woman hope. Of course, we didn't know anything about Billy Fox at that time.'

Whether I looked interested or just to remind me that other people had their troubles too, Cullen went on to tell me that he'd shared many a tragic wait with bereaved relatives. I was patient with him because I hoped he was psyching himself up for some independent action, always difficult for a copper.

The Maeve Aldritt case was relevant to my troubles. Billy's fourteenth victim was a nurse, very well thought of at St Mary's. It was the hospital that reported her missing. Then it was discovered that all her personal gear was also missing from the house she shared with other nurses. Suspicion fell on her fiancé, Joseph Talbot, when it was found that no money had been taken from her substantial bank balance. This suggested that she hadn't done a runner. Talbot was questioned for days. The poor guy came up with the story of a black Peeping Tom hanging round the house in Rusholme. He wasn't believed until it was too late. The police had to release Talbot after questioning but they did nothing to dispel the officially inspired cloud of suspicion hanging over him. In despair, he eventually committed suicide. That confirmed all suspicions. The police put Maeve's disappearance down to him, until the fine day she turned up on the skull-rack, second bottle from the left on the middle row. Her head was one of Billy's better pickling jobs.

Grunting curiously to himself, DS Cullen phoned Felicity Grete in his official capacity. She denied any knowledge of a publicity stunt and threatened legal action against the GMP if they persisted with the story.

'I didn't need to be convinced, but your friend with the plum in her mouth sounded pretty convincing to me,' he said when he finished the call.

'I'll give you odds of ten to one that the story of Kath's disappearance is in the London tabloids tomorrow,' I said. 'Felicity won't keep such a juicy titbit to herself. Meanwhile, what are you going to do?'

'There's not much I can do. You know the situation. I don't mind making a few phone calls. I can't get in any worse with Pinnock than I am now.'

We spent the next four hours phoning as many of Kath's contacts as we could. Cullen used the office phone and I used my mobile until the battery ran out. There were far too many names in Kath's Filofax for even a horde of telephonists to contact. We confined ourselves to those numbers listed on the very long itemised phone bill we found in her desk drawer. I knew Kath had been job hunting, but it was a surprise to find just how many calls she'd made.

It seemed that Kath's friends, and they were mostly

television people that she'd worked with at one time or another, were willing to do anything for her except give her a job. None of them knew where she was. I wasn't totally disappointed. By widening the hunt we were eliminating the possibility that Kath had just swanned off somewhere for a joke.

It was Pinnock who terminated our search. He phoned the office and I answered.

'What are you up to, little man?' he asked in a contemptuous voice. 'You are pathetic. If you think that I'm going to change my mind because Headlam's friends are ready to back up your story . . .'

'Rubbish, Mr Pinnock,' I said bravely, interrupting his polemic to tell him that Felicity Grete denied any knowledge of a publicity stunt.

'Well, she would say that wouldn't she? You seem to have organised a round-robin between you and if you think that some sort of phone-in campaign is going to make me divert police resources from far more pressing matters you can think again. I'm going to need cast-iron evidence before I accept that Ms Headlam has come to harm. You've already wasted enough police manpower with your fairy story. Is Cullen with you?'

'He was for a short time,' I lied.

Pinnock gave a long exhalation of breath over the phone, which came out as a mixture of contempt and disbelief. 'If you should see him, tell him that if he puts me to the trouble of sending someone round to fetch him it'll be the worse for him.' He slammed the phone down.

I relayed the tidings to Cullen. He didn't seem too concerned.

'If Kath's body turns up on some moor in Yorkshire would you give odds who Pinnock will select as chief suspect?' I asked angrily.

'You're a racing certainty, mate,' Cullen answered.

There was just a glimmering of another idea in the back of my mind. I got out the large-scale map of central Manchester and spread it on the floor. Using a Chinagraph pencil, I circled the places where the recent murders had taken place – the Churchill Hotel, the Velodrome, the disused railway cutting at Mauldeth Road. Then I put an X against the Summergills' house in Withington. I looked at it for a long while. There wasn't the slightest shred of proof that the Summergills were involved in the Manchester killings but what if they were? If . . .? If . . .? Too many damned ifs. But still, their home was equidistant between the Velodrome and Mauldeth Road killing grounds, connected by main roads. So were tens of thousands of others.

I made myself hypothesise that they must be involved. In the face of official scepticism I felt justified in taking a short cut. The alternative was so much worse. If Kath had been stalked by a complete unknown, Caulfield's 'Stranger Killer', I had no chance. It could be months before Pinnock was willing to accept that Kath's disappearance at Chillgate wasn't a publicity stunt. I felt a shiver of fear again. Suppose the Manchester Killer was some complete unknown from Bradford – the possible accomplice mentioned in the Home Office report, someone who'd cheekily dumped Kath's car near his old partner-in-crime's workplace? I willed myself to reject such a possibility.

There was just the faintest chance that the Summergills were keeping Kath alive in some hideout. Their home had already been searched. That left . . . what?

With a shaky hand I marked all the places where Billy's victims had lived. Cullen watched in silence. Again these were mostly in Fallowfleld and Withington, and the Summergill home was slap bang in the centre of the area.

Billy had no van or car, he didn't drive – so one of the Summergills must have helped him shift those torsos up to Chillgate. Suppose the connection Kath had stumbled across was that the Summergills had helped Billy to dispose of his victims?

Then there were all the material effects. Most of those women had just disappeared. Vanished. Left, with no forwarding addresses. Although some of Billy's victims were dropouts none of them were actual bag ladies. They all had possessions, and in some cases the possessions had disappeared when they did. At the trial, the prosecuting counsel had claimed that this showed Billy's cunning, his determination to mislead the police. What it showed me was that he must have had some help so he could shift the stuff.

Cullen tapped me on the shoulder. 'What's up, cocker? You're looking a bit flushed. First time today I've seen you with any colour in your face.'

'What would you need to dispose of things?' I asked him. 'Awkward things you don't want anyone to find out about, like bodies, a young woman's clothing, souvenirs, personal effects? You know, all the little things people accumulate?'

'Christ! I don't know about the bodies,' he said genially, 'but my oldest daughter's studying medicine at Liverpool University and I have to shift her out of her digs regularly. If it was just little things there'd be no problem but I can't get everything in the car. The audio equipment and computer alone make one load, then there's all the clothes and books. You wouldn't believe it. A ten-tonne truck would just about be comfortable.'

I went over to the white memo board behind Kath's desk and wrote down *Transport*. Cullen smiled as if to humour me.

'Well, what else?' I asked.

'Eh, come on, Dave,' he said. 'Just try and relax,

you're going to damage your brain going on like this.'

'So, Pinnock says "Get lost", and I just sit here, do I? And then, next week, when the pathologist tells us that Kath wasn't killed until tomorrow or Friday or whenever, I explain to her father I was sitting on my backside here the whole time.' He seemed inclined to humour me, so I continued, 'When you're disposing of things, what else do you need besides transport?'

'A depot, I suppose,' he said doubtfully. 'You like rubbishing the police force don't you? The prime reason why there was no intensive investigation into these missing girls was the evidence that they had simply upped sticks and gone.'

'There was never an intensive investigation into the victims and you know it. There was a perfunctory enquiry after the murders were discovered,' I said. 'I'm not going to let history repeat itelf in Kath's case.'

'Hmmm,' he said thoughtfully. 'But surely they'd have taken all these chattels back to their home. If we're talking about a body, I suppose on your theory that would go straight to Chillgate.'

'Which would leave them in the frame if there was a little accident,' I said. 'Suppose their van broke down? Don't forget how Albert Clark was caught, a routine check by an alert special constable. Presumably they'd be aware of that danger. No, I'm assuming that they had some kind of storeroom somewhere –,

'Hoping, more like, you mean,' he interrupted. 'You're expecting that if we find this invented storeroom Kath will be there, aren't you?'

'Maybe,' I said uncertainly, writing the word <u>Depot</u> down on the board. One of the big mysteries to me is why the boys in blue are so unwilling to accept that a cunning criminal with everything to lose from chance discovery would have secret places. Albert Clark was a stone mason and these Summergills were handymen.

Why shouldn't they have hiding places? Certainly the Summergills if not Clark. I didn't say any of that. Cullen was my sole ally and I didn't want to offend him.

'Dave, listen mate. Just because Billy Fox hadn't got a driving licence didn't mean he couldn't hot-wire something and shift any amount of stuff in it.'

'Humour me. Suppose he didn't,' I said wearily. Reasoning with Cullen was like trying to get superglue off your fingers. Police theory demanded that killers were not only stupid, but cunning and lucky to the nth degree as well. Otherwise how could they get away with it?

'Right,' he said slowly and dubiously. 'Dave, man, his brief would have brought all this out at the trial.'

'What trial?' I sneered. 'He confessed to everything. Geoff Bartle saw to that.'

Cullen shook his head, 'All right, just for the sake of argument. What next?'

'Disposal, obviously,' I muttered. 'Has the great Pinnock got a team out scouring the second-hand and charity shops for anything that might be traceable back to the missing girls?'

'Hold on,' Cullen ordered. 'You're way ahead of me.'

'Eleven out of fourteen of Billy's victims had personal effects missing. Maeve Aldritt had clothing and souvenirs missing. Every item belonging to Julie Anne Goodchild disappeared. In some cases even the furniture went. Every room in Tara Belling's flat was stripped. All that stuff was worth something. Shouldn't someone have checked if it was sold, and if so who by?'

'It'll be long gone.'

'Not if Billy had cautious accomplices, slowly releasing the goods,' I explained. 'The Summergills are the best fund-raisers for dear, sweet old Mrs Maxwell's animal sanctuary. OK. After Billy's added another head to his collection he tells them where to go to pick up the victim's belongings. Or maybe they picked them up before he topped her, I don't know Anyway they take the stuff to their secret storeroom and then gradually sell it through the shop in Didsbury. It stands to reason that there's someone out there who can say, "that belonged to Miss X," and another person who can say, "Yeah it was brought into the shop by Dennis or Dean Summergill." After all, not all of these girls were without friends or relatives.'

'I know that. I've had to walk past a VICPAC demo every day. It still sounds like a ten thousand to one shot to me,' Cullen said sceptically.

'There were fourteen victims,' I persisted in a reasonable tone. 'One of them must have owned some article that was unique to her, a family heirloom, something distinctive.'

'Granted all that,' he said, 'I still don't see why Dennis and Dean Summergill would want to help Billy Fox or Albert Clark either, for that matter.'

'I'm guessing,' I admitted. 'To my mind they're the most obvious because Kath visited them. Also because they are involved with Chillgate and with Billy, but if we found some complete unknown I'd be happy because I think he'd know why Kath's come to harm.'

'What do you mean by harm? If you're right she's got to be dead,' he said slowly.

'What you don't see is that Kath's sudden disappearance is a break in the pattern. This was a kidnapping and, as long as her body hasn't turned up, I've got to believe she's alive somewhere.'

'You know you're a headcase, you are, Cunane,' Cullen said gently, with a weary shake of the head. 'Mr Sinclair sent me round here to keep an eye on you and in no time you come up with a plan requiring almost the entire manpower of the GMP. There's something in what you say, but I don't see how it helps you to find

Kath. They haven't got her in the house in Withington. If they had had Pinnock wouldn't be riding so high.'

'If we establish that the Summergills are linked to the Billy murders then Sinclair and Pinnock will have to bring Billy back to Manchester. He might "remember" where this storeroom is and then we might find Kath.'

I didn't say that I felt we were more likely to find her dead than alive, but he'd grasped that.

'All right, you win,' he agreed. 'Give me the phone. You go in there,' he said, indicating the inner office. 'I don't want your ears flapping while I get yet another bollocking from Pinnock.'

I lay on the sofa and yawned despite myself. I was dog tired but as far from sleep as I'd ever be. My mind was racing. It all made sense to me. The later Albert Clark killings had been careless and he'd been caught. Super careful Billy Fox had done better but had eventually been caught because he kept trophies in jars. This new man was going one better. He'd already killed four and he was selecting his targets not from prostitutes like Clark, or lonely women like Fox, but from the poorest of the poor – drugs addicts living in cardboard boxes. It beat me how anyone could not believe that the crimes were all linked in some way.

I switched on the radio for the GMR local news.

The two men the police were holding in connection with the recent spate of murders here in Manchester were released from custody half an hour ago. DCS Philip Pinnock, the officer heading the case, discounted rumours that they were being questioned in connection with a fourth missing woman. Mr Pinnock made the following statement, 'We are convinced that in this case we are looking for a man who has serious psychosexual problems. We think he's a loner, possibly someone who has suffered a humiliating sexual injury recently. There is someone sheltering him, very likely a wife or mother, and we appeal to them to turn him in before he strikes again. Any young woman who needs a place of safety should phone our hot-line 0161 406 1213 and an experienced female officer will accommodate her in complete confidence. If you are a drug abuser, don't worry. We're only interested in your safety.'

'Chief Superintendent, have you anything to say about reports that you were interviewing two men about the disappearance of a woman connected with this case?' the interviewer asked.

'We've interviewed many people and we will interview many more, but sadly, none of the victims in this case had been previously reported missing. The victims have all been found in some public place where they had taken shelter. That is why we are appealing for any females living rough to report to us and we will find temporary accommodation for them. Remember, phone the hot-line 0161 406 1213, any time, day or night.'

When he spoke it all sounded so sensible and reasonable. Protecting the potential targets sounded like a good idea except for two things. Drug addicts would never go far from their suppliers and the more girls Pinnock gathered in, the greater was the risk to those remaining on the streets. Even if he did round up every potential target in Greater Manchester that didn't bring him any nearer to catching the killer. Still, what he'd done would look good in the papers. It was action of a sort . . . action that denied any hope that Kath would survive.

A moment later Cullen appeared at the door. 'You've heard then?' he said. 'Mr Pinnock wants a word with you.'

I went through and picked up the receiver with a fair idea of what Pinnock was going to say already in my mind.

'Cunane,' he snapped. 'I'm on the point of having you arrested. Say the wrong thing and I'll order Cullen to bring you in with handcuffs on. Your lady love's either done a bunk, and I can't say I blame her, or she's deliberately trying to hype this book you and Liptrot are dreaming up.'

'You think so, do you?' I said. 'What does Mr Sinclair have to say about that?'

'Mr Sinclair is with the Chief Constable at this very moment discussing the manpower implications of this case,' he replied acidly. There was something about the way he said it that suggested that Sinclair wasn't with the Chief for a jolly little chat about how many bobbies they could shake out of the bushes.

'But what about the bones up at Chillgate Farm?' I persevered. I could feel Kath's life slipping away between my fingers.

'There is nothing to connect them with Ms Headlam's disappearance or anybody else's disappearance. They're just old bones, very old bones!' he said angrily.

'Listen, you're making a tragic mistake,' I said, but he cut me off. 'I'm sorry, Cunane,' Cullen said sympathetically. He'd caught the gist. 'I've to report back to Bootle Street where he'll find me some nice job like counting up the paperclips on his desk. The Chief Constable's leaning more in Pinnock's direction than Sinc;air's. Belt me in the mouth if it makes you feel any better. I don't mind. For what it's worth, I think there's something in your theory. It's never made sense to me that Billy committed those murders on his own.'

'It's not your fault,' I agreed. The last thing I needed was to alienate a police officer who, however lowly his position, was still in the force and might be of use in the future. It looked as if I'd already landed Sinclair in the doghouse with the Chief Constable.

'Let me know right away if Kath does turn up,' he said as he left.

'For your sake I hope Pinnock's right and that she's just gone off somewhere with a touch of the moodies.'

I sat at Kath's desk not thinking anything at all for a long time. I was beaten. Pinnock was obviously backing Caulfield in her theories of a random killer and who was to blame him? He was hoping that his purge of the streets would force the killer into making a mistake. Perhaps the 'sexually damaged' perpetrator would home in on one of the 'places of safety'.

There was a strong temptation to go round to Dennis Summergill's and force him to tell me what he knew. It didn't take me long to reject that idea. He'd be under surveillance, with either a uniform on his doorstep or CID watching him discreetly from across the street. Even Pinnock wasn't daft enough to neglect that little precaution.

I turned to the memo board behind me. Picking up the marker, I added the words shops, and then Kath. After a moment I added the word Billy??? He was the key somehow. I put the marker down. It was hopeless. Even with the services of a fully co-operative police force the gathering of evidence was an insuperable task.

There was another way. I go through the motions and hope that whoever had taken Kath might take me. Then I stretched my legs out under the desk and inadvertently kicked one of the boxes in which Kath had stowed the victim profiles Sinclair had supplied when the GMP was in a more helpful mood.

I pulled them out. Cullen had said he thought my idea had possibilities. It was my only lead to finding Kath. What else had I to do? I began sorting through the statements for any mention of distinctive possessions which might give me some definite grounds for demanding that Pinnock lean on the Summergills again. That is, if I could trace them back through a junk shop to the property repairer and his son.

It took me hours. Labour that Lauren Caulfield claimed she'd already done. Why hadn't I accepted the offer of a peek at her database when I had thc chance? Putting regrets to one side, I toiled away. I was so absorbed that I didn't notice that the office had become quite dismal. When I stood up to turn the light on my stomach rumbled loudly. I looked at my watch. It was eight thirty. I hadn't eaten anything all day apart from the bacon sandwich supplied by Cullen in the police canteen at dawn. I was torn. The list I'd compiled wasn't extensive but if I went on I might collapse from hunger and fatigue.

I let myself out of the office heading for Piccadilly Station' and a quick meal. Scrawled on the wall of the Atwood Building was *Liptrot + Cunane = Racism.* I smiled thinly.

The station was busy as usual, the concourse thronged with people. They all had destinations in their minds, loved ones to meet, appointments to keep. 'Don't start revelling in self pity,' I said to myself, as I mechanically chewed my way through a flame-grilled burger.

Walking back through the gloomy and almost deserted early evening streets I began to feel uneasy. I stood on the corner of Aytoun Street and scanned the vicinity. There was nothing out of the ordinary, a couple of young prostitutes trying to drum up trade by the kerbside. Nevertheless, I quickened my pace.

Back at the office I resumed my task. I looked at the pile of papers on the table. A sense of futility swept over me but I continued to compile the list of possessions. There was a long list, but it included a lot of consumable items – nobody was likely to be still wearing the hand-knitted pullover with the name

Carmel on it that had belonged to one of Billy's earliest victims.

Compiling the list did at least give me the satisfaction of knowing that what I'd said to Cullen about transport must be right. There was a massive load of material. So much that it was incredible now that anyone could have even implied that Billy Fox had merely stalked his victims off the street. The trouble was that the trial had been so hurried. There hadn't been time for all these issues to be ventilated. The process of murder must have involved identification of a likely target, then luring her to the killing ground, disposing of her and sifting through her worldly goods and stealing whatever he wanted. A furniture van was definitely indicated. Those little showy trifles that he'd hung onto had made his conviction doubly certain, as if the heads themselves weren't enough.

Curiously, when Billy had assembled his collection of mementoes from his victims he hadn't chosen them for their value. There were fourteen items and the total value of the lot of them wasn't more than £10 – plastic gonks, trolls and worn-out teddy bears of no value to anyone, bits of jewellery that he'd been wearing when arrested. There was the cup marked Julie, a particularly damning piece of evidence for the Prosecution. Julie Goodchild had owned some good things. She'd had a hand-painted blue pottery spaghetti set that had been a present from a holiday in Italy. There couldn't be too many of them drifting round Manchester. There was also a Royal Doulton bibelot, again a comparative rarity. It depicted a polar bear poised above a frozen ice pool and was one of a limited number made in 1922.

Another of her possessions was a broken Meissen figurine of a little girl having a tug of war with a dog for her doll. It sounded very distinctive. Altogether I had ten highly distinctive items listed, mainly antiques and *objets d'art*. It still wasn't quite enough. In the current climate of mistrust Pinnock would just deny that they were the same objects even if I found any of them. I needed one of the decapitated girl's parents to make positive identification. The parents addresses had all been carefully inked over in the files. Fair enough, they had the right to have their identities protected. It wouldn't have taken me long to find their addresses or even pay a call on VICPAC and ask straight out for them, but time was the one thing I didn't have.

That left me with Jay Anderson's acquaintance – Julie Goodchild's mum. It all boiled down to looking for Julie's things, just seven separate items. It wasn't much to go on. Cullen had been optimistic when he said it was a ten thousand to one shot.

It was almost eleven. There had to be action I could take now, this minute, something that might alter the outcome.

I wandered downstairs in a frenzy of indecision. I was the last one in the building and had to lock the outer door. It was raining, that fine Manchester drizzle that soaks you to the skin in a few minutes. I got in the car and found myself heading for Withington and the Summergill house. I turned down Mauldeth Road, then into Hamer Lane. Was this the heart of darkness? The lights were on in the big crumbling detached house. The front door and ground floor windows were screened by overgrown rhododendron bushes so I slowed to a halt outside the house next door, hoping for a closer view. There was somebody moving through the bushes towards the gate. My heart missed a beat. It was a uniformed police officer. She was bidding farewell to a colleague standing in the shadows by the imposing entrance.

I gently accelerated away. She didn't look across at me. I breathed again, thankful that I was driving a

Nissan Bluebird, the same make as half the cabs in the city. Partly satisfied by my peek at the suspect's home, I went to check out the windows of the Chillgate Sanctuary Gift Shop located in School Lane, Didsbury. I ought to have gone there first and not taken a chance of being arrested. I couldn't help noticing just how many charity shops there were. Julie Goodchild's stuff might have ended up in any of them – even an antique shop.

The School Lane shop was a disappointment. Nothing but old frocks and bedroom slippers. It was no surprise Maxwell had never visited. I started searching more methodically as the night wore on. There were blocks of shops scattered throughout the suburbs but in various places they were crumbling. Along Stockport Road and in Burnage a lot of the once high-quality shops were now boarded up. Here and there, an Asian newsagent survived as the sole remnant, like a healthy tooth in a blackened gum. Still, it was incredible how many shop windows there were. It was almost four a.m. before I got lucky.

I was heading back into town, bleary eyed and disappointed, when I noticed a parade of shops set back from the road just past the drive-in McDonalds on Wilmslow Road. There was an antique and *objets d'art* shop next to the post office. I wearily walked over and scanned the window, by now attuned to disappointment. Nothing caught my eye in the front of the shop. However, set back from the window was a glass cabinet containing curios and on the second shelf there was the polar bear poised above the icy pool. There was no mistake. It sat next to a Doulton figure of a balloon-seller.

There was no feeling of vindication or triumph. It was just a start. The early morning was quiet. No birds sang. A dim morning light crept along from the east.

The sky was dappled with shades of grey. An occasional private car sped along, bearing a returning adulterer or early-morning worker at well above the speed limit. A council streetsweeping vehicle nudged along the traffic-free kerbs, pointlessly spraying as it brushed.

I sat in the car for a while trying to think what to do until a milk float pulled up behind me and roused me from a doze. I'd slept for several hours. It was nearly eight and there was the sound of children shouting in the street. I set off for Moss Side and the pale morning sun was just beginning to gleam on the wet roads when I turned into the close where Lovena Anderson lived.

By chance, Jay was just returning from night shift – dressed in civvies. He threw his arms up in mock surrender when he saw me. I raised my eyebrows but I wasn't in the mood for jokes.

'I've come for Mrs Goodchild's address.'

'Difficult, Boss, difficult,' he murmured.

'Jay, you owe me. You know what happened to Mallick, don't you?'

He laughed, then leaned over and told me the address in a theatrical whisper.

When I got to the Goodchild home I was in luck for once. Mrs Goodchild, a wasted and wan-looking bottle blonde who appeared to have trouble standing upright at nine o'clock in the morning, was one of those who'd been demonstrating with the VICPAC group. She recognised me right away. She bared her yellowish teeth in a feeble smile of greeting.

'I've come about your daughter,' I said, getting to the point right away. The poor woman recoiled in fright.

'You're not press are you?' she asked. 'I couldn't stand any more questions. Did you see what it said in the Sun about me? I'm a negligent parent.' She looked ready to howl so I hurriedly reassured her.

'All I want you to do is to identity something that might have belonged to her.'

When I told her about the bibelot she was as eager to get to the shop in Wilmslow Road as I was.

The shopkeeper, James McTavish, a Scot with an attitude, made a big performance about opening the shop and letting us in with much rattling of keys and switching off of alarms. Mrs Goodchild identified the bibelot right away. She'd bought it at an antiques fair at G-Mex. She reeled off the number and told us that there were the initials MB faintly scratched on the bottom before McTavish had it out of the case.

'They would be the artist's initials,' the Scot muttered, raising his eyebrows as he turned the figure over to reveal that the letters were indeed scratched on the base.

'I know because my late husband spent a lot of time checking up on it,' Goodchild explained.

McTavish passed the piece to me. He completely misread the situation. He thought he was making a sale. 'Sentimental value is it? You can see it's the same one all right. Those are the initials, and the Royal Doulton Battersea stamp, all right. Made as a curiosity and registered by Doulton. It's a rare piece – there weren't many polar bears manufactured. The number is a factory code, this was only the twenty-fifth and there weren't many more than that made. Perhaps a hundred. I can look all the details up for you if you like. £170,' he said as I looked to confirm his identification.

It took me five minutes to beat him down to £120 and even then I guessed from his self-satisfied expression that he'd got the better of the bargain. Mrs Goodchild was weeping silently when we came to the main part of the proceedings. McTavish claimed that he didn't remember from whom he'd bought it or when. It took several moments of concentrated glare on my part before he cracked.

'Oh well, they do bring me things from time to time. A father and son. I don't like to enquire too closely. The son's rather surly,' he explained. That was enough identification for me but the police could arrange a line-up if they wanted. He had another piece in the back. He brought that out. It was the broken Meissen figure of the girl having a tug of war with her dog. He'd obviously been trying to repair it. There was some kind of white filler stuck on it, but there was no doubt as to whom it had belonged. I paid him £20 for it.

I dropped Mrs Goodchild off at her home after explaining that she could have the pieces as keepsakes after the police had finished with them.

As she got out of the car, she said, 'I think she knew her killer, you know. That Fox! She phoned me the week before she disappeared to say she'd met someone who was going to improve her life. Those were her exact words.' This reflection produced a flood of tears. I walked with her to the door but there were no further revelations.

It was only when I got to Bootle Street that I realised that the whole expedition was a waste of time. I got no further than the enquiry desk. The sergeant on duty smiled and shook his head. Cullen wasn't available. DCS Pinnock wasn't available. ACC (Crime) Sinclair wasn't available. The word had gone out.

Outside in the street the press contingent had dwindled to almost nothing. I took out my mobile and tried both the numbers Cullen had given me, as well as GMP Force HQ to raise Sinclair. No luck. In desperation I rang the number of the phone that I'd noted yesterday on Pinnock's desk.

He snarled, when I got through. 'I'm going to have you arrested for wasting police time. You shouldn't be using this number.'

'But, I've got a definite link between Billy's victims and the Summergills,' I said desperately.

'What?'

I told him about the bibelot and the Meissen fragment.

'She knew the number?' he asked incredulously. 'What is it?'

'Ten thousand, four hundred and twenty five,' I replied, confident that I was getting somewhere at last. 'Mrs Goodchild has documentary proof –'

'You bloody idiot!' he snapped. 'How could you possibly identify something of which so many were made. And the other thing is broken, that wouldn't stand up for a moment.'

He slammed the phone down before I had a chance to explain that the number was a serial number and didn't mean that 10,425 objects had been made.

I think if I'd dug up the missing remains of all fourteen girls from the Summergills' garden, loaded them on a fork-lift truck and dumped them on his doorstep he'd have said the same. He was determined not to give an inch.

Pinnock had gained rapid promotion for his speedy handling of the Billy Fox case. Any suggestion that all was not as it should be was as welcome to him as a kick in the face from a hobnailed boot. I felt despair creep over me.

Customs Seize Taxidermist's Illegal Hoard
Customs Officers, believed to have been tipped off by animal rights activists, raided a remote barn on the Welsh Borders. There is a racket in smuggling remains of protected species into Britain from third world countries. Private collectors will pay tens of thousands of pounds for well-mounted specimens.

Animals found included the rare Pacific eagle, red pandas, chimpanzees and a komodo dragon from Indonesia. They were being presented either by freezing or by pickling in formalin.'

News report, 1995

15

Thursday, 20th September, morning

Walking back across Albert Square towards the Atwood Building, I couldn't help noticing that the street people had gone from their customary perches. Pinnock's purge must be having its effect.

I was carrying my mobile and it chose that precise moment of despair to remind me that I was still employed.

'Mr Cunane, I'd like you to come and see Cedric right away . . . He's got one of his blockages,' Lena barked.

'Look Lena, send for Dynorod or get him a good proctologist but I'm occupied just now,' I snapped.

'That's enough of your lip! I want you out here to go over the story with him, give him some ideas. Bring your lady friend with you.' I switched the phone off without replying. I was irrationally angry with her for not knowing what had happened. I quickened my pace. A path opened for me along the crowded street. With my unshaven face and fierce expression, I must have been a frightening sight . . . a psychotic, low on medication.

Once at home, I washed and changed. Then I spent over an hour working in the kitchen. It had been weeks since I'd given it a really good clean and various strangers had had the run of it since then. As usual, I found that thoughts came best while scouring out my pans and the cooker hob.

I went in the bedroom and selected a blue denim jacket. With matching jeans it looked something like a van driver's outfit. I then went back into the kitchen and made up a parcel out of one of Kath's Next bags. She liked to get her underwear from their catalogue. There'd been a delivery only last week and the jiffy bag it had come in was still around. Altering the label was the tricky bit but after playing around with Kath's Apple Mac a bit I managed to produce a passable imitation of the Next address label. For want of anything better I put three dishcloths inside the parcel and resealed it.

When I reached Withington it was a fair morning, still early. There were little soggy heaps of fallen leaves on the pavements but the sun was shining for once. Only the elderly, the unemployed and the young mums were on the streets. I parked round the corner from Hamer Lane and walked briskly towards the house, whistling 'I Did it My Way'. Sure enough, there was a police car parked outside, manned by two sour-looking uniformed officers. When I reached the gate they gave me the once over and I obliged by turning to face them.

'Is it all right to go in? . . . Delivery,' I said. I got a nod and a grunt by way of answer, but I could feel their eyes following me up the path.

The house was in its original Victorian condition. There was no car space at the front and no sign of the grey van, only a footpath to the imposing front entrance. Most of the houses of this type in the area had had the garden ripped out and had been converted into flats, but this was still under single ownership. As I climbed the steps to the entrance porch, I noted that the house had a cellar as well as an attic. These places had been built by wealthy professionals when Withington was a charming village. They had been intended to house half a dozen servants as well as a large Victorian family.

Drawing a deep breath, I rang the bell. There was no reply so I rang again. There must be someone in or else why the police presence? Eventually, I heard a loo flushing somewhere above me and then a heavy body charging down stairs. The door was flung open by an ugly-looking young man still in the process of tucking his shirt into his jeans.

'What the fucking hell is it this time?' he demanded.

'Delivery from Next.'

'What?' he stared at me blankly and furrowed his low brows. I noted that as well as a sloping forehead he had black bushy eyebrows that met in the middle. His gelled-down hair was receding up the slope of his skull.

He thrust out his hand for the parcel. The hands were stubby and the fingers fat and blunt. Dirt was deeply engrained under the nails and in the wrinkles. A hammer would fit into those hands quite comfortably.

'We don't get anything from Next,' he said, stating the obvious. He certainly didn't qualify as a fully paid-up member of the *Now Generation* in his filthy pullover and dirty jeans. He had short legs and a muscular torso and his head fitted directly onto his shoulders. He had no neck. The guy was a real hangman's nightmare. The way he was positioned blocked my view into the interior. Looking over his shoulder I could just make out the dusty display cases, which filled the hallway.

'What is it, Dean?' a voice called from somewhere in the back of the house.

'Delivery. He say's it's for us,' he replied, squinting short-sightedly at the label. I snatched the parcel back.

'This is 13 Bramah Lane?' I asked.

Dean frowned. I studied him closely. Although clean shaven, his skin was marked by about a dozen small abscesses caused by ingrowing hairs and raw-looking razor cuts. It wasn't a mug you would forget. With the gelled hair and the low brow, he looked like the missing link between man and the seals. The front of his pullover was as Kath had described it, covered in reminders of his previous menus.

'Fuck off, you dickhead! This is 13 Hamer Lane,' he said slowly.

I backed down the steps just as a man I took to be his father appeared at the door. He was very different from his son; a tall erect figure with a friendly, humorous-looking face. Summergill Senior was neatly dressed in dark trousers with razor-sharp creases, a shortsleeved beige pullover and an open-necked check shirt with the cuffs rolled up.

'Sorry, wrong address,' I explained, holding up the parcel as I retreated to the corner of the path. 'Is it all right if I take a short cut through the back?' I indicated the path along the side of the house. At the end of the wide, long garden I could see a two-storey building that must have been the stable block.

'I'm afraid you can't go that way,' said the older Summergill. 'It's private, and anyway the back gate is padlocked.' He spoke firmly but politely, making it clear that there was to be no argument.

Dean advanced down the steps with a scowl on his

face to show me off the premises. He was muttering under his breath. I hurried off down the path, pausing only to give them a friendly wave as I went.

When I got to the car I drove slowly round to the back lane. I wasn't worried about being seen. Overhanging bushes screened the area. There were no police at this side and I stopped and got out. The mews at the back of number 13 still retained the tall, Victorian stable gates with windows about two feet above my eyelevel. I jumped up for a look but could only catch a glimpse of the roof of the van. I heard footsteps approaching and decided to clear off before one of the Summergills emerged. They were obviously nervous about their property, but that didn't prove anything. Half the residents of this area are on permanent watch to guard their belongings from the other half.

I tried to evaluate my reactions to the ill-matched duo as I drove to the Swiss Chalet Hotel. They gave out no vibrations whatever. Dean didn't have the appearance of an intellectual high flyer, but appearances meant nothing. There was a thuggishness about him but no more so than dozens of men I met every day. Dennis, however, was different. He looked like the steady, reliable type a lost traveller would pick out from a bus queue to ask for directions, an obvious animal lover and friend to the poor.

All of which got me precisely nowhere.

I wasn't in the best of moods when I reached the suite where the Liptrots had now been immured for a week.

'Where've you been?' Lena accused when I put my head round the door.

'Don't start,' I snapped. 'Kath's missing.'

It took me ten minutes to explain what had happened.

'So what it boils down to is that you think she's come to some harm and the police won't do anything about it although human remains have been discovered at this animal sanctuary,' Cedric said when I'd concluded.

'Eeeh, as if we'd do something like that for publicity,' Lena moaned.

'It's a power struggle at the GMP between Sinclair and Pinnock. Sinclair wasn't happy about the Billy investigation, you could see that when he took us to see Billy's room,' I told them. 'Pinnock shot to the top like a rocket after banging Billy up so quickly and now he wants the fame of solving these new cases all for himself. Doubts about the Headless Corpse Murders are the last thing he wants to hear.'

'You know, Cunane,' Cedric said thoughtfully. 'What you've said has given me a whole new outlook on this case. I think I can write something now.'

I eyed him in consternation. This was just a literary opportunity to him. His face didn't register any particular expression.

'I hope I've given you more than that,' I said. 'I'm looking for ideas on how to get my partner back.'

'Hmmm, yes,' he muttered casually. 'Perhaps Billy will be able to shed a little light when we see him.'

'What?' I exploded angrily.

'Haven't you heard? Billy's asked to see us. They can't prevent him having visitors and the publishers have put pressure on the Prison Service but the thing is . . . He specially wants to see me. You see he *has* read my book.'

I went over to the drinks trolley and poured myself a stiff whisky.

'Pour me a sherry while you're there,' Lena invited.

'Cunane, I'm expecting you to drive me over to Greenash this afternoon,' Cedric warned. I gulped the whisky down, regardless.

I had to get out. There must be something I could be doing. I looked at Cedric. That mass of dark hair looked more than ever like a helmet clamped onto a bald head.

Mrs Goodchild's comments about her daughter's last words to her had been rattling round in my head. It was a strange way to talk about finding a boyfriend – she'd 'met someone who was going to improve her life'.

'I'll be back in an hour,' I said as I left.

'We leave at two,' Cedric replied without looking up from his work.

I drove back into town, to Upper Chorlton Road and the home of Mrs Goodchild.

'Julie was a good girl,' she wailed. 'She just insisted on getting a flat. Me and her father argued for hours but it was no good. She wanted to be on her own. It wasn't even a proper flat. Just a furnished room.'

'Why do you think she was so keen to get away?' I pressed.

Goodchild covered her face with her hands and sobbed. 'He wasn't her father . . . Julie's real dad died when she was two. She said Henry kept looking at her, you know, in a funny way. I didn't like to say anything to him and in the end we just agreed that it was best that she should go. She'd just turned seventeen when she left. She had a job at Safeway and with housing benefit and a bit of help from me she could just manage the rent.'

'Didn't you keep in touch with her?' I asked. 'The room was only in Fallowfield.' It was hard to keep an accusatory tone out of my voice.

She let out another wail. 'Julie came home one Saturday. I think she wanted me to invite her to come back and live here. She found it hard going on her own. She had no friends. Then the three of us got talking. She said she'd stay if Henry would stop following her into the bathroom and finding excuses to come into her room when she was getting changed. Well, he hit the roof! Cursing, swearing, shouting, you name it. Julie left straight away. I don't think he meant anything by it. She was rather a big girl and you know, some men, they can't keep their eyes to themselves. I think she was too sensitive,' she concluded lamely.

I thought Julie probably had the late Henry Goodchild bang to rights.

'So when did you discover that she was missing?' I asked brutally. I was in no mood to be kind to her.

'Henry didn't want me to go to see her. He said she'd come round when she felt lonely enough. Then she could apologise to him.' Mrs Goodchild had a thin face and deadly white skin with prominent eyes. She'd rubbed them until they stood out like red lamps.

'When did you realise she was missing?' I said more gently this time, but still insistently.

'It was three weeks later. I went round to see her but this man said she'd left with no forwarding address and there was a week's rent owing.'

'So you reported her as a missing person, then?' I said. 'She was under eighteen.'

'No. What was the use? Henry said she'd come home when she was ready,' she blubbered. The wailing started at full volume again. 'The next time I saw her was when they made me go and identify that horrible head in the bottle. Henry wouldn't come with me. He said it would set off his angina. It did anyway. He died three weeks later.'

'Right, get your coat on,' I said briskly, cheered by the news of Henry's demise. 'I want you to take me to the bedsit.'

'Why, what good will it do now?' she lamented. 'I don't like going out like this.'

I guessed it was useless to appeal to her finer feelings. 'Lady,' I said, 'you know you won't rest easy until

Julie's body is reunited with her head and given a proper burial. That's why you're a member of VICPAC, right?' She reluctanfly nodded agreement. She knew and I knew that she was in VICPAC in the hope of financial compensation. 'The police aren't going to find the corpse, not if they dig up every school playground in Manchester, but if you help me I swear that I'll find out what happened to her. I'm seeing Billy Fox this afternoon.'

She gasped in surprise, then headed for the hallway and her coat.

Julie's ex-room was in an Edwardian house at Paradise Street in Fallowfield. There was a postcard saying 'No DSS' in a corner of the window'. I kicked, banged and rattled on the door for almost five minutes before a hard-faced, stockily built woman in her fifties finally opened it. She folded her arms across her chest and shouted aggressively, 'What do you think you're doing? Go to the rental agency if you're looking for a vacancy.'

I put my hand into my inside pocket and a sly smile briefly flickered across her forbidding features. I took a £20 note out of my wallet and waved it at her. 'I want to see Julie Goodchild's room,' I said.

'You're in luck,' she replied, snatching the money off me. 'There's no one in there at the moment.' She turned and led us down the narrow hall and up the stairs. The cheap linoleum and the characteristic sour smell I associated with these places were equally apparent. I think it was years of living in such dumps that had caused me to develop my own fetish about cleanliness. I caught a glimpse of her living quarters on the ground floor. Julie's former room was on the second floor. There was an attic flat above it, just like the one Billy Fox had lived in for all those years.

The room was bare. A coin-operated gas fire, an

electric ring on an asbestos sheet and a chipped sink surrounded by a surrealist sculpture of pipework in one corner were the limit of the facilities. The furnishings consisted of a narrow bed, broken sofa and two chairs, folding card table and an antique wardrobe with a cracked mirror.

'How much do you charge for this?' I demanded.

'Forty pounds a week, with a month's rent in advance,' the landlady said without a trace of a blush.

'Forty pounds. That was the price of independence and an early death for poor Julie,' I thought. Behind me Goodchild had commenced snivelling again, reminding me of my purpose.

'This is Julie's mum,' I said. 'She'd like to know what happened to Julie here before her death.'

'Don't start on me,' the landlady said. 'If you're from the press I shall want a lot more than twenty pounds to talk to you.'

I could see the cash registers flashing in her little piggy eyes. I opened my wallet under her nose. Fortunately, I was carrying a lot of cash.

'So, you were Julie's landlady,' I said.

'The police have already questioned me, you know. Billy Fox never set foot in this house but the girl did belong to the Adult Education evening centre at Hoggett's Wood. They reckon that's where she met him.'

'I know about that,' I conceded. 'What I want to know is, who called on Julie when she lived here?'

'Nobody. She had no visitors,' she replied.

'Think!' I shouted. 'There must have been someone.

She backed away from me into a corner of the room. 'I don't know what you're carrying on for. They've caught Billy Fox haven't they?'

'Did anyone else come into this room apart from yourself and . . . Who was this man who demanded the extra week's rent off you?' I said, turning to Mrs Goodchild.

'That sounds like Arthur, he's my husband,' the landlady said. 'Did he do that?' I asked, pointing to the patch of fresh plaster above the window.

'No. The agency send round their own repairman when something needs doing.'

'So the repairman would have visited the room when Julie was here?' I questioned. She nodded. 'What was his name?'

'I don't know, there are dozens of them,' she said with a shrug of her shoulders.

I felt I was getting somewhere at last. I gave her another £10 just to make sure that she didn't get on the phone to the police. The last thing I wanted was Pinnock on my back again.

The flat agency was on the corner of Ladybarn Lane. There was a new BMW on the pavement, jammed up against the doorway. 'Someone's doing well out of property,' I thought. 'A twenty pound bung will get me nowhere fast here.'

I flung open the door and pushed the weeping, red-faced Mrs Goodchild into the shop in front of me. She didn't need me to instruct her to act the part of the aggrieved mother.

'I'm going to sue you for every penny you've got and I'm going to the police,' I shouted to the startled young woman behind the counter. Just to add emphasis to my words I crashed my fist down on her desk. 'Where's the manager? I want him now,' I said forcefully.

'Mr Starling,' she shouted, as if this was an everyday occurrence. 'Angry customer!'

A dark-suited individual emerged from an inner office flashing a pearly smile above his Day-Glo red tie. He kept his distance as I glared at him angrily.

'That bloody repairman of yours,' I said, jabbing my

finger at him to show that I held him responsible. 'He's had his way with our daughter. Practically raped her he has. Now she's up the spout.'

'Really! Well, I'm not responsible for my employees extra-curricular activities,' Starling said with a smile.

'He knocked her up in your time. Come round to repair the window frame when she was asleep and the next thing she knew he was in bed with her. Harvey Fotheringay, he said his name was and I'm not leaving this shop until you give me his address.'

Starling gave his assistant a bemused glance and she took a list out of a drawer. Mrs Goodchild lent credulity to my ploy by throwing her head back and howling. Her cries must have been audible three streets away. At the same time the assistant was rapidly scanning through the list and shaking her head at Starling.

'I want to see that,' I said menacingly. Starling slapped the paper into my hand. 'No Fotheringays there, see! Fancy name for a repairman, if you ask me.'

I went down the column of names slowly, breathing as heavily as any outraged parent would. The names of Dennis and Dean Summergill were on the list. I gave the sheet back. 'He's given her the wrong name but I'll be back and I'll smash this place up if I find you're sheltering the git.'

I drove back to Upper Chorlton Road in a hurry to dump Mrs Goodchild before she inflicted permanent damage on my ears.

'*Was* that what happened to her?' she asked frantically as I left her at her doorstep.

'No. I was only saying that so they'd show me the list of employees,' I said reassuringly. I patted her on the shoulder. She wiped her streaming eyes for the hundredth time and went in.

Driving back to the hotel, though, I wasn't so sure that it might not have happened that way. At least I'd established that the Summergills could have had contact with one of Billy's victims quite independently of him. Was Billy the killer and the Summergills his assistants, or was it the other way round?

This theory didn't impress Cedric when I put it to him. 'I'm being paid to write a book about Billy, not some unknown repairman,' he complained. 'And don't forget that I've already written a bestseller about Albert Clark. I'd look just as big a fool as the police if, as you say, there were others involved in the Bradford killings.

'You could always say you'd decided to revise your previous theories on Clark,' Lena commented.

The arrival of an unexpected visitor postponed further discussion. It was Assistant Chief Constable Sinclair in person. As he entered the room he looked more uncomfortable than I'd ever seen him. The often practised, genial smile looked distinctly fragile. I decided to listen to what he had to say before demanding to know when he was going to make Pinnock start looking for Kath. It took him some time to come to the purpose of his visit. Lena ordered tea from room service and it wasn't until he'd drained two cups that he opened up.

'Things are very difficult at the moment,' he said with his usual gift for the obvious. 'Proceedings are at a very delicate stage. As you know, I welcomed you here to our city, Mr Liptrot. Indeed, some would say I championed you. I invited you to give your views. I showed you round the culprit's flat. I even hinted at some of my own reservations about the handling of the case . . .'

Lena and Cedric exchanged glances.

'Now I find myself in rather an awkward position. I know it sounds ridiculous,' he continued with a shake of his head. 'Some people are saying that I'm letting you talk to Fox in the hope that he'll discredit the officers responsible for the original inquiry.'

I knew what was coming next – he was going to ask us not to go. I decided to put my oar in. 'Force politics strike again,' I said. 'Any chance some of your lads might spare the time from battling for their own careers to catch a few villains?'

'You're asking us not to go then?' Cedric asked.

'A postponement only. The next few days may see developments, which will render these perverse criticisms redundant,' he said, as usual, coyly refraining from the specific.

However, I didn't need to worry. It was not easy to blow Lena Liptrot off course. 'See here,' she said trenchantly, 'Cedric is being paid good money to do this interview. It'll make his book. This is what the public want to read, the actual killer's own words.'

'Yes, and what about Kath Headlam,' I burst in. 'You were anxious enough to help the other night, but now her disappearance is part of a cheap publicity stunt.' I must have sounded hysterical because Sinclair gave me a gentle calming wave, like a pared down Presbyterian version of a papal blessing.

'Davie, all this wild casting about won't help Kath. You're damaging your cause. Things are coming to light all the time. Things that you aren't aware . . . You remember the cases of stuffed animals belonging to the Summergills that Kath commented on?'

I nodded.

'They aren't all antiques. Dennis Summergill practises taxidermy as a little sideline. As it happens none of the stuffed animals in the house belonged to protected species, or we'd have nicked him by now. We've been in contact with the RSPB and the World Wide Fund for Nature. They inform us that they have long suspected the existence of a well-organised illegal taxidermy ring in the North of England. The animals involved include chimpanzees, red pandas, rare breeds of eagle and so on. Animals from overseas, rare protected species, which are killed so they can be stuffed and sold – high scarcity value. So it may be that your theory of a secret workroom or store is not all that far-fetched. Now you can see why we don't want you blundering about, alerting them to our suspicions. We think Dennis Summergill is extremely crafty. He will make no move towards that storeroom until he is absolutely certain that he's not under surveillance.'

I felt sick. The man had no sense of urgency. 'Where does that leave Kath?' I asked. 'He might be holding her captive somewhere, like that guy in Nottingham, Sams.'

Sinclair nodded his head sadly. 'It's possible,' he admitted. 'But unfortunately, putting pressure on him until he decides to talk is not permissible. Moreover, there may be others involved, people in Bradford and Leeds using the Chillgate Animal Sanctuary as a cover for their illegal activities.'

Shame was driving out the anger and fear that I'd been able to use to motivate myself into action. I was the one who had pointed Kath Headlam in the direction of Chillgate and blithely sent her on her way.

'And there's more, I'm afraid.' Lena's eyes were starting from her head by this time. I think she was working out how she could convert all this information into hard cash.

Sinclair continued. 'The younger man, Dean Summergill, he is of rather distinctive appearance. He answers the description of an individual seen in the vicinity during some rather nasty incidents involving the wanton killing of animals.' He took a computer printout from his inside pocket. 'This is an extract from a report describing one case early last year. You can thank your friend DS Cullen for ferreting this out –' He handed me the flimsy strip of paper.

May 23 1994, Heaton Park Children's Zoo – 16 rabbits had their heads torn off. 5 chickens and a cockerel were also decapitated. The heads were apparently removed as 'trophies', for the next morning only the remaining untouched carcasses were discovered – neatly arranged in a line on the bloody sanctuary floor. 'I have never seen anything like it – someone obviously got a great deal of pleasure out of this,' said Mandy Bullinger, an attendant at the zoo. Three days before the massacre Mandy discovered four rabbits had been killed. Thomas Mitchell, the Park Manager said: 'I have known dogs rip heads off then leave the bodies but I have never known one to unbolt a cage and they certainly don't wring necks or leave their prey in a nice, neat line.'

'The witness, Mandy Bullinger, had noted a man answering the description of Dean Summergill pushing children out of the way so he could get close to the animals. She'd had to speak to him twice. Cullen has also discovered that an individual answering Dean's description was seen in the vicinity before an attack on the animals at Buile Hill Park, Sallord in April 1991. This was simllar to the Heaton Park attack in that animals were decapitated although in this case more animals were removed and some never recovered, including two donkeys. He gets frisky in the spring.'

It was enough to freeze the blood, but there was more. 'Cullen has since run a computer check. Attacks on animals in the GMP area have been running at three times the national average since 1984. Before that the record was held by the Central Yorkshire Police area. Dennis and Dean Summergill moved to Manchester from Bradford in 1984.'

'That's where Billy got his injured animals from,' I said.

Sinclair nodded his head. 'It's possible,' he admitted.

'Well, for God's sake, where else would he find them?' I asked. 'How many owls are there roaming loose in Fallowfield?'

'Look, Cunane . . . er, Dave, would you leave us for a moment?' Cedric requested politely.

I did as I was told, but with a very poor grace. Who did he think he was sending me out of the room like a schoolboy? I went down to the Tyrolean bar in the reception area and bought a pint of lager off the Irish barman. The price matched the mountainous terrain depicted in the murals. I was so preoccupied wondering what quid pro quo the Liptrots were extracting from Sinclair in return for staying away from Billy that I hardly noticed the figure waving to me from the corner.

It was the roly-poly shape of Detective Sergeant Cullen. He was nursing a drink. 'Tomato juice and sauce,' he said with a smile when he saw the direction of my glance. I picked up the glass and took a sip.

'Double vodka, more like.'

'Sent you out while they have grown-up's talk?' he asked glumly. 'Same thing keeps happening to me.'

None of which was Cullen's fault.

'Nice bit of work, that, about the animals,' I said.

'It was you that put me on it,' he said with a shrug. 'All that talk about Kath's ideas . . . Do you know we've checked the ownership of all garages and lock-ups within a one mile radius of the Summergills' house?'

'And?' I asked.

'Nothing.'

'I didn't expect they'd have a sign over it saying "Corpses stored by request – Rare animals stuffed to order",' I said.

'No need to get sarcastic,' he muttered. 'Christ! I'd like to slot those two bastards. But we haven't got a shred of evidence that would stand up for a minute.'

'We'd get proof from Billy Fox. I'm certain he's ready to blab.'

My gloomy prognostications were interrupted by Sinclair himself. He tapped me on the shoulder on his way out. 'Cheer up Davie,' he said. 'There may be a perfectly innocent explanation for your partner's disappearance.'

'What would the world be, once bereft
Of wet and of wildness? Let them be left,
O let them be left, wildness and wet;
Long live the weeds and the wilderness yet.'
Inversnaid, Gerard Manley Hopkins

16

Thursday afternoon

I was so angry about Cedric's private conference with Sinclair that I decided to jack the job in. What good was it doing Kath for me to carry on working for Cedric now? Nobody gave a damn about her.

But Lena, a believer in getting her blow in first, challenged me as soon as I set foot in her room. 'What have you got a face on you like that for? Sinclair's not getting what he wants. A two-day postponement is all we agreed to,' she said. 'He's going to allow us access to Chillgate Farm as a little consolation prize, so we'll want you to drive us there.'

'Sorry Lena, I'm through with ferrying you two around. Kath's missing and neither of you care. Surely you don't think she vanished as a publicity stunt?' I demanded.

'I don't know what I think,' Lena said spitefully, 'but she'll not be the first woman who's cleared off when she found herself a new bloke. She looked like that sort to me.'

'Mother! I won't have this! Ms Headlam wouldn't have just walked out leaving the project up in the air,' Cedric clucked. He sounded like a turkey who's just been told about Christmas. 'She was far too professional and far too involved in producing those scripts.' The guy was tugging at the point of his beard, changing hand over hand, as if he hoped to shape it into a dagger-like point that he could plunge into his mother's heart. Sweat was pouring from under his cap of hair and his glasses were steaming up. If he'd been anything like a man he'd have kicked the old termagant off the balcony but he was paralysed by indecision.

Some emotion equivalent to sympathy for him stirred in my heart. 'Right, Lena,' I sighed, 'get your coat on, there's a cold wind on those hills round Pateley Bridge.'

I made a few more preparations for the trip than I had last time. We were able to hire a Toyota Land-Cruiser from the hotel, which, being so close to the airport, ran an extensive car-hire business. I intended to drive right into the farmyard at Chillgate this time. I also made sure we had some supplies with us, two large flasks of coffee and a hamper of Cedric's favourite tuna sandwiches.

We were well on our way out of Manchester, seated in the big four-wheel-drive vehicle, before Lena found her voice again.

'I thought you were the type of man who would love 'em and leave 'em, Dave. You've got that devil-may-care look about you,' she said coyly. I made no reply, but that didn't discourage her. 'You might not believe it, but Cedric's father was like that.'

I waited for Cedric to respond angrily to this but he didn't speak. He just wound his window down to let some air in and mopped his brow with his handkerchief.

'Yes, I met him during the war, in 1944. An American airman he was. I met him at this do organised by the American Red Cross near the base in Suffolk where he was stationed. I was a land girl on a local farm. I volunteered to show him the English countryside and that wasn't all he wanted to see, I can tell you. He called me his little English rosebud . . . Well, we felt sorry for them, so many didn't come back from their missions, but he did. He won a row of medals. Then when the war ended he was shipped home. He said he'd send for me, but he never did. I found out later that he had a wife in Albuquerque, and I wasn't his only English rosebud either. Quite a bunch of us he had –'

I couldn't restrain myself from interrupting, 'But if he's Cedric's father that makes Cedric at least fifty.'

'Just listen, I haven't finished yet,' she said crossly. 'He made his career in the air force, he hadn't been much more than a mechanic in a garage before the war and now he was a major and doing very well. In 1950 he was posted back to Britain. He was glad they sent him here and not to Korea, I can tell you. Anyway, he put an advert in the Bradford paper asking me to get in touch and I went to see him in London –'

'Mother, do you need to go on like this?' Cedric butted in.

'Curtis, that was his name,' Lena went on, ignoring her son and heir, 'was a full colonel by this time. His marriage was finished but he said a divorce would hurt his military career. So I lived with him while he was over here and then when he went back to the States he left me Cedric as a keepsake.'

I looked from her to Cedric. His jaw was firmly set and his mouth stayed tightly closed. Did his failure to deny this one mean that it was true, or was he simply so wearied by her constant myth-making that he lacked the energy to contradict her?

The Land-Cruiser ate up the miles to Pateley Bridge

and we arrived at the bumpy road leading to Chiilgate Farm before six. Even so, the night was drawing in and there was more than a hint of dusk approaching. I'd phoned to warn Mrs Maxwell of our arrival and she'd confirmed that Sinclair had rung to tell her that we were on our way.

My suspicion that it was hope of gain rather than fear of the police which had persuaded Maxwell to agree was confirmed as soon as we reached the farmyard. She was the first person I saw, heading towards us with her grey plaits whirling like rotor blades. We were hardly out of the vehicle before she began bargaining for a fee for the interview. The woman looked as eccentric in her day clothes as she had done in night attire. She was wearing a tattered old Barbour and baggy army camouflage trousers tucked into her boots, with a red pom-pom hat on her head.

She wasn't on her own this time either, she had three of her followers with her, armed with forks and brooms. Various denizens of the Sanctuary were on the scene as well; donkeys, pit ponies, and dogs scampered round the farmyard, cats meowed in chorus from an extensive range of cages. A group of pigs with horribly flattened faces were rooting in a pile of muck in one corner. 'Vietnamese potbellies,' Cedric informed me knowledgeably.

Lena shouldered her son out of the vehicle and elbowed her way into the feverish little group surrounding Maxwell. Firmly grasping the oldie by the arm, she whispered something in her ear and then frogmarched her into the farmhouse. When the supporters made as if to follow, she shut the door in their faces.

Cedric and I exchanged bemused glances.

'Mother has a way about her at times,' he said. 'It's best if we keep out of things and leave it to her.'

The three co-workers, presumably Chillgate Co-operators like myself, dispersed to the various sheds and barns scattered about the site. All three were equipped with wellies and looking round the yard it wasn't hard to guess the reason why. The dumb friends had made their presence felt. Not having wellies, it took real fortitude for Cedric and myself to go and locate the incinerator.

It stood in a secluded spot at the back of the main farm building. There was nothing to see. The North Yorkshire Police had carefully removed all the ash and charred bone. We could see a tide mark along the wall which indicated the level it had reached. Cedric tired of the task before I did. After five or ten minutes soaking up the atmosphere he announced that he was going to wait in the car and make some notes. I spent about forty minutes longer scouring the vicinity for scraps of bone that might have been missed and was rewarded eventually with what looked like a piece of human knuckle bone.

My careful search was interrupted by the sound of the Land-Cruiser's horn. Nimbly hopping from stone to stone to avoid the mud and crap, I returned to the main farmyard. When I got to the corner of the farmyard the light had quite gone but I could make out the bulky shape of Lena sitting next to her son in the back seat of the vehicle. She impatiently leaned over and pressed the horn again. Assorted animals replied with cries of their own. Maxwell and her acolytes appeared to have done a bunk. I guessed they must have knocked off for the day.

'Get in the car,' Lena ordered. 'We'll drive down the road and have a picnic.' I was happy enough to escape from the menagerie. Even in the open, the mingled odours of so many different animals created a stomach-heaving reek.

Twenty minutes later, well out of aroma-range from the Sanctuary, we were seated in a lay-by on the road out of Pateley Bridge. After dishing out the picnic, Lena told us how the interview with Maxwell had gone.

'Well, for a start she's terrified that the Sanctuary will be closed down,' Lena explained. 'She says she didn't know who Billy Fox was until you and Kath appeared and started asking questions. He only came up a few times and never joined the Co-operators.'

'Rubbish, she's in it right down to the tip of her plaits,' I said hotly, finding it hard to hold back my impatience. 'I should have questioned her myself.'

'Shut up and listen,' Lena replied curtly. 'Her husband was in the wholesale meat trade in Leeds and he collected rare animals, stuffed ones that is . . .'

I raised my eyebrows in disbelief.

'I know! They don't sound a very well-matched couple!' Lena continued. 'They didn't get on, but she stuck by him. Old-fashioned she is. Anyway when he died she sold the business and bought Chillgate Farm to start an animal sanctuary. She hadn't been there long before Dennis Summergill turned up. He obviously has a hold over her. He claimed that he'd been a close friend of her husband. She wouldn't go into that but I think it's obvious that he supplied the husband with his gruesome stuffed animals. He must have threatened to let the animal-loving fraternity up here know what the late Mr Maxwell had been up to.

'Dennis didn't want much, just a barn where he could keep his animal carcasses in freezers and an incinerator to burn away the innards when he'd done. She thinks her husband used to get rid of them before – put them in his beefburgers.'

Somehow, I didn't feel hungry any more. I looked at her closely. Her expression was identical to the one she wore when telling her tales about Cedric's father. She looked me straight in the eye as if to challenge me. I decided to shut up and reserve judgement.

'According to her Kath's eyes lit up when she saw the incinerator. She offered her all kinds of money if Enid, that's Mrs Maxwell's name, would let them use it on television. She kept going on and on about concentration camps and Enid began to worry that Kath knew about the incinerator being used to dispose of illegal animals. They were at cross purposes. Enid is terrified of being discovered as a dealer in endangered species and as for Kath –'

'Yeah, well Kath was bound to make the connection,' I interrupted. 'I as good as told Sinclair myself that Billy must have used an incinerator to get rid of his victims.'

'Well, you were both wrong!' Lena said triumphantly. 'The incinerator was only ever used by the Summergills. Kept the gas burners locked up, they did. The helpers let the animal corpses pile up for the Summergills to get rid of them. Whether they had their own parcels to dispose of, or whether it was the Sanctuary animals, the Summergills would do it all on their own. Like a nasty little secret it was. They usually came on a weekday morning when there weren't too many people about. All Billy Fox ever did when he came was to muck out the donkeys' stable.'

'So, what happened to Kath?' I asked.

'Kath went off to check out the rest of the farm and Enid went in the house. Dennis Summergill had told her that if anyone ever asked about the incinerator she was to say that it was there because of Creutzfeldt-Jakobs amongst the cats and to phone him immediately. So she did.' We sat in silence for a while after this.

'Did Enid tell this to the police?' I asked.

'Of course not,' Lena replied.

'What about the human bones the police took away?' Cedric asked.

'Oh, they're still studying them. Apparently there's a question mark over them. They've been sent to a veterinary pathologist at Sheffield University. In a way, Enid thinks it would be better for her if he finds that they are human bones rather than rare animals – her helpers would go spare.'

'Did Summergill corner Kath at the farm?' I asked. My voice was shaking.

'She says not.'

'I don't believe her,' I said sceptically.

'Look Dave, lad, if Summergill got her, he'd have had to race up here from Manchester. Enid says your Kath spent less than two hours wandering round the farm after she made her call to Summergill and it takes a lot longer than two hours to get here.'

'He might have flagged her down on the road as she left. He'd at least have had time to reach the A59,' I said argumentatively. 'Anyway, how do you know he was in Manchester? He could have been a lot closer if he has connections in Bradford.'

'Do you think he's nearby now?' Cedric asked nervously.

'Don't worry, she won't be sending for him,' Lena said with a sly chuckle. 'I gave her a cheque for ten thousand pounds for the story. She won't know it's dud until she gets to the bank tomorrow.'

'Mother!' Cedric protested. 'You'll be arrested!'

'I doubt if Maxwell will complain, under the circumstances,' I said. 'Does she think Summergill disposed of Kath somewhere on the farm?' I asked.

'You've got disposing on the brain!' Lena's face was a picture of scepticism.

'They got rid of Kath somewhere,' I said hotly.

'Well, give us a shred of proof and we'll believe you,' Lena said. I felt sick.

I had no proof. I got out of the car for a breath of the

clean moorland air. The sun was sinking behind the hills in the west, the last rays illuminating the tops of the hills opposite; the valleys were in deepest black. All I'd done in this case was to scratch about on the sunlit hilltops, only now was information being dredged up from the darkened valleys. When I took this case on it had looked so straightforward, just dig out a little more information and help Kath to get her scripts straight.

Cedric got out and stood beside me. He was breathing heavily. 'It doesn't look as if you think we've got much of a book about Billy Fox, does it?' he said mildly. 'Why are you certain Kath wouldn't have gone off to meet someone in Bradford? She could have been seeing someone else. After all her car was found in Bradford.'

I didn't reply. I was too disheartened to argue. I'd gone over all this until it had worn grooves inside my head.

'Well, anyway,' he continued, 'Mother and I wanted you to know that we're going to get the publishers to issue a statement that Kath's disappearance isn't part of any publicity stunt.'

'Great,' I said, without the slightest feeling or intonation. Even a rank amateur PR man could have told them that such a denial was the surest way to get maximum exposure. 'Let's get back to Manchester.'

We drove in silence. I gazed across the desolate hillsides. There were ten thousand lonely spots between here and Manchester where the Summergills could have buried Kath without fear of detection. It was in the urban areas, with their armies of dog-walkers, that stealthy grave-digging was risky. I switched on the radio to hear the seven o'clock news.

'I still don't think your lady friend has come to any harm,' Lena said, trying to comfort me. 'Look at this road. It wouldn't have been easy for anyone to make Kath stop and get out of her car.'

'Fake an accident . . . car across the road with someone lying under it . . . distraught onlooker to flag her down. She'd stop all right.'

'There's only one person who can settle all this,' Lena said crossly. 'Billy Fox. He's sure to tell us more than he told that greedy bitch Caulfield when we tell him that we know all about his visits to Chillgate Farm.'

It was at that exact point that the news bulletin came on the radio.

News is just coming in that William Fox has been found dead in his cell in Greenash Secure Hospital near Wrexham, North-east Wales. Fox was convicted of an appalling series of murders in April this year. The Home Secretary is being asked to make a statement.

A cold, sick fear gripped my heart. I spun the heavy vehicle onto the grass verge and slammed on the brakes. We listened to the rest of the bulletin and tried other stations but that was all the news there was.

'Do you think there was some connection between us postponing our visit and him being found dead?' Cedric asked timidly, after a moment's stunned silence. I shook my head, I couldn't think. With Billy gone the last slender thread of hope had been snapped.

'There must have been a connection,' Lena said. 'It looks very suspicious to me. We want to visit, Sinclair persuades us to wait and then Billy turns up dead. You'd better phone him, Dave, and find out just what the hell is going on.'

Numbly, I did as I was told. Sinclair answered his home number at once.

'Oh, it's you, Davie,' he said breathlessly. 'I've been expecting your call . . . Just let me speak before you say anything. It was a complete accident. No one could have predicted it. A mix up over free association. A new nurse-warder on Billy's wing didn't realise that Billy was supposed to be supervised and segregated at all times. Billy left his room and wandered into the common room. Some of the others got at him and battered him to death. There'll have to be a full murder enquiry, of course.'

'I'm sorry, Mr Sinclair, but we're going to have to go public about you postponing our visit. It's just too much of a coincidence,' I began.

'Tell the press what you like!' he interrupted. 'They'll lap up a conspiracy theory. But I'm telling you his death was a pure coincidence. Do you think you were his only visitors? Dr Caulfield and a team of psychologists have been interviewing him on a regular basis for months. Strangely enough, Caulfield was the last person to see him.' He broke the connection.

I was willing to bet that Lauren Caulfield had bullied Fox until he didn't know whether he was coming or going. She had everything to gain from brainwashing Billy until the poor guy fitted the profile she'd made for him.

'So, that's it,' I said. 'Shall I run you home to Bradford? I can send your luggage on tomorrow.'

'What do you mean?' Cedric asked.

'There isn't going to be a book now, is there?' I stated flatly.

'Don't be stupid,' Lena barked. 'Of course there's going to be a book. Interest will be greater than ever now. I expect they'll want Cedric to do some TV interviews. He is the main expert on Billy's life after all. Get us back to the hotel and be quick about it.'

I had the choice of dumping them on the lonely moorland road or obeying.

When we reached the Swiss Chalet Hotel two hours later there were vans from TV news in the car park. Lena yanked Cedric out of the Land-Cruiser almost before I'd braked. I watched as the news crews hustled round them and silhouetted them against the hotel wall with brilliant light. Cedric's shadow was ten feet tall. I determined not to return the Land-Cruiser until the morning.

I decided to head to the Summergills' home in Hamer Street, Withington. I felt that checking it out was the least I could do now, if only to convince myself that Kath wasn't there.

I cautiously drove up the lane behind Hamer Street with the lights out and parked against the large building, once a stable, that now served as a garage. With the advantage of the Land-Cruiser's height I could easily see inside. The grey van was still there. The building looked bigger from the inside than I had expected.

There was a side gate leading into the garden, securely padlocked and topped by a barbed wire entanglement. I backed the Land-Cruiser up to it and by climbing on the roof managed to grab the drainpipe that ran down the corner of the old stable and swing myself over the gate. It was a hefty drop on the other side and I landed heavily on the flagged path and lay winded for a moment. Nothing was stirring. No police rushed from cover to snap the cuffs on me. The back of the house was completely dark. The heavily overgrown trees at either side of the narrow lawn created an oppressive, enclosed feeling. Anything could be lurking among those dark bushes. There was only a faint background glow of light from the distant street.

I crept forward.

The house was as secure as modern technology could make it. All windows were alarme. The window frames themselves were new. The French windows and side door were secured with new locks and steel grilles. There were floodlights on all sides of the house. I went back to the mews. It was just as securely guarded. There was no point in trying to get back over the side gate, without a ladder it was an impossible task. Knowing that Dennis was concealing an illegal business didn't entirely explain the elaboration of his defences in my view. I shivered for a moment and thought what a fool I'd been to rush in.

At that instant my mobile phone began ringing. It sounded like an air-raid siren in that confined space. Mentally cursing Lena Liptrot, because I was certain it could only be her, I hurriedly switched it off and ducked into the bushes.

I crawled forward into the dense screen of rhododendrons looking for an easier fence to scale only to be met by a stout concrete wall topped by razor wire. The Summergills were certainly serious about their personal security. There was only one thing for it. I legged it along the side of the house, scrambled over a high padlocked gate, and escaped via the front entrance. There were no police on duty and no cars in the street. I stood panting for a moment by the garden gate and then looked back to the house. There were no lights on, but there was a new CCTV camera mounted above the door. It was pointing towards me. I instinctively put my arm across my face and dodged away but it was too late.

I'd made a pig's ear of my visit, first the mobile and then I'd got my face on *Candid Camera*.

I ran round the block to the back street, half-expecting to find Dean waiting for me. I don't know what I'd have done if he had been, but there was no one. I sat panting behind the wheel of the Land-Cruiser for a moment, trying to make sense of what I'd seen. The Summergills must be out unless they both had gone to bed early.

The only thing I knew for certain was that I was exhausted. I needed sleep desperately. I drove the massive vehicle into the narrow parking space in front of my own lock-up garage and looked up at the flat. There was a light on in the kitchen.

With my heart in my mouth, I raced up the stairs, flung the door open and ran into the living room. There, sprawled on the sofa, was Lauren Caulfield! I lmost recoiled right back onto the landing in surprise.

'How did you get in?' I spluttered.

Although she was as startled by my sudden arrival as I was to see her, she carefully composed her face into a warm welcoming smile.

'I had to see you,' she said anxiously. 'I didn't know who to turn to. You've heard about Billy Fox . . .'

'How did you get in?' I persisted.

'Listen, this is important,' she continued. She sat up on the sofa. I cautiously sat down opposite her.

'I've got doubts about Billy's guilt. I've had them for some time,' she said.

I stood up sharply, turned my back on her and strode over to the window. When I turned to look at her she was staring at me intently. There were dark circles under her eyes. She didn't seem to be drunk or hysterical, just at the end of her tether.

'What does Pinnock say?' I asked.

'That's just it. He's had me fired as the GMP profiler. He says I'm too erratic and unprofessional.'

'He's dead right!' I snapped. I was tired and angry. 'You have a habit of turning up out of the blue and expecting me to drop everything and sort out your problems.'

'I had to speak to someone who knows about the case,' she said. She sounded desperate.

'What about your publisher? I thought you were being paid thousands to produce a book about Billy.'

'Please listen,' she said. 'Make yourself something to eat if you're hungry, but just listen. I shall go mad if I don't speak to someone.'

'Do you think Billy is innocent?' I asked, relenting a little.

'I don't know. That's what's driving me mad. And now I'll never be certain.'

'It's rather convenient that you've started having doubts just when Pinnock's finally dumped you in all senses of the word,' I said.

'I'm a scientist. That's what Philip can't understand. He just wants to draw a line under Billy and to move on to the next case. He hated it when I told him the Fox case might be much more complicated than I first thought.' Her voice cracked with exhaustion.

'Do you want a drink?' I offered. I poured her a generous slug of Old Grouse and it loosened her tongue. She talked all right, but about Philip Pinnock and how he had used and abused her. After about half an hour I felt myself nodding off. Caulfield was slowing down too.

'I'm tired,' I said.

'I don't want to go,' she muttered. 'I've hardly started and anyway I'm drunk.'

'You take my bed and I'll kip down in here,' I said. I knew I'd never get rid of her now. The spare bedroom was crammed with Kath Headlam's possessions. I'd have agreed to sleep on the floor if she'd only volunteer to shut up. Eventually, I persuaded her that we'd both be better with clear heads in the morning. I installed her in my bedroom and then, after longing backward glances at the comfortable pillows and sheets, retreated to the living room and the sofa.

I think I was asleep before my head hit the cushion, the last thing I remember was switching the mobile off. It did me no good. I was fated to have my sleep interrupted.

About three a.m. I was woken by somebody violently shaking my shoulders. It was Lauren Caulfield. She was looking very unscientific, wearing only a short dark-green T-shirt of mine. The contrast between the green of the shirt and the bright red of her hair was too much for me at that time in the morning.

'Red and green should never be seen, Except on an Irish gypsy queen,' I said, quoting from one of the many politically incorrect bits of folk wisdom I'd learnt on my mother's knee.

She shed the T-shirt with an easy motion of her arms.

'I need you,' she said.

'It is only by following a calm, rational approach to the study of multiple killing that we will be able make this heinous species of crime no more than a dim memory for the human race, just as the eighteenth-century practice of public exposure of the corpses of hanged felons is for us today. The prime method by which this will be achieved is by the steady, patient and above all scientific recording of incidents that could have a significant bearing on this type of crime. This study will bear fruit when we can identify those subjects who may be potential "stranger killers" long before they have struck their first fatal blow.'

From *The Normal Stranger: the serial killer in the community*, an unpublished thesis by Dr L. C. Caulfield B.Sc. Ph.D. page 467.

17

Friday, 21st September, morning

I woke in a tangle of limbs, with the sour taste of betrayal in my mouth. I rolled Lauren Caulfield off and she lay flat on her back snoring lightly.

It was going to be a fine morning. Sunlight flooded the room. I studied the changing patterns the passage of clouds threw across the ceiling. I was supposed to be desperately searching for my partner, but here I was in bed with a stranger.

My gloomy thoughts must have somehow communicated themselves to Caulfield because she half woke and turned to me. 'Phil,' she mumbled drowsily.

Recoiling from her, I shook her shoulder roughly and

she snapped into full wakefulness. As her eyes focused, and she took in with whom she was sleeping, her face changed. There was a flash of disappointment but she artfully recovered from the moment of confusion.

We got up in a welter of embarrassment, avoiding eye contact. I thought it best to steer the conversation away from personal matters and after several awkward moments we managed to resume the discussion of Billy Fox. I was annoyed at myself as much as at her. I could do without her trailing her doubts around. If I was going to save Kath I needed certainties.

'So, if Billy didn't do the murders who did?' I asked as I put the coffee on.

'Dave, there were seven hundred and fifty-six murders in this country last year and in nearly every case the killer was someone well known to the victim, usually a close relative. We can show that Billy was known or had the opportunity to know all his victims.'

'I thought you had doubts,' I said.

'I have. That's partly why Phil's fallen out with me. Everything has got to be cut and dried with him. No shades of grey. I can't bring myself to believe that Billy Fox was solely responsible but I'm not saying that he was completely innocent either.'

For once I sympathised with Pinnock. I was beginning to think that, despite her Ph.D. and her criminology studies, Lauren Caulfield was a confused and stupid woman. She knew something about Billy Fox that wasn't on the record – but what? She hadn't told me yet.

She must have been able to read my body language because she launched into a further explanation of her 'doubts'. 'I can't believe his complete lack of recall of all the major details is simply due to a memory blackout. It's as if he happily parrots so much information that he's been taught, and all that stuff from your friend Cedric's book, then the flow comes to a complete stop.'

'Well, he's certainly come to a complete stop now,' I said. 'Sinclair says you were his last visitor. I expect the CID are camped on your doorstep now.'

She put her head into her hands. I felt like hitting her, but I didn't. Why couldn't she say in so many words that Billy was innocent and that she and her boyfriend had convicted the wrong man? She looked so forlorn, slumped there over my kitchen table feeling sorry for herself, that I took pity on her as I had done last night. I was sure no good could come of it.

'I'll go through the victim database with you,' I offered. 'You must know I believe you. I'm not Phil Pinnock.' I filled her in on my suspicions about the Summergills and in particular about how they had access to Julie Goodchild. This snapped her out of her depression.

'Right, come on,' she said forcefully.

Downing her coffee in a gulp and crashing the cup down with a jarringly loud clatter, she headed for the living room. She rummaged through her capacious hold-all for a suspenseful moment. I thought she might be looking for her whisky miniatures but, to my relief, she fished out her IBM laptop computer.

'You'd better go through on your own first and then we'll have a look at it together,' she said having set up the database. 'There are fourteen files with fifty entries each. The format roughly follows the FBI victim-profiling system. Except that in this case we only had the heads to go on, so the copious entries about clothing and staging of the body and so on were unnecessary. By cross-matching all the features of each killing we can get an idea of what the killer's needs were when he committed the crime and so we can deduce something about him.'

'Yet in this case you thought you knew who the killer was from the start,' I said.

'I know, Phil Pinnock didn't want me to bother with any of this. I thought following procedure would confirm the case against Billy. It does in a way. Just spool through all the entries for "Link with Fox".'

In every case, except that of victim number 12, Janet Wilhelmina Greene, there was a circumstantial link between the victim and Billy. My stomach gave a loud rumble at this point and Lauren volunteered to fix breakfast. I took the computer into the kitchen with me and combined my researches with an attempt to swallow a few mouthfuls of cereal. Lauren was seated opposite, observing me dispassionately.

'It's all a bit back to front, isn't it?' I said provocatively. 'If you disregard the trinkets and odds and ends belonging to each of the victims that were found in Billy's flat, and which could have been planted, what have you got?'

'What could be more incriminating than fourteen human heads in bottles?' she hissed. 'Why should you subtract the other evidence?'

'Pass on the heads for a while, though no one's convincingly shown how Billy did wholesale butchery in a tiny flat in a house occupied by ten other people. It's the evidence that Billy knew all these victims and was some kind of sex freak that's thin and you know it. If he'd had a decent defence at the trial, that's where the prosecution case would have come unstuck.'

'There were problems,' Lauren admitted.

'Such as finding evidence to back up the theory that Billy was sexually disturbed. You certainly tried.'

There was no reply to that.

'Look at this one here,' I said calmly. 'Maeve Patricia Aldritt, the last known victim –'

'Last "known" what are you talking about? She *was* the last,' Lauren interjected.

'ACC Sinclair told me that there are dozens of missing females in the Greater Manchester area who fit a similar profile to these fourteen.'

'Oh, him,' she muttered dismissively.

'I'm just playing devil's advocate, but suppose some malevolent soul left these articles. See what it says about Aldritt . . . *No link known prior to the murder . . . Reports of a black man acting as a Peeping Tom behind her house* . . . Looks lovely there in black and white doesn't it? No mention of the fact that Aldritt's fiancé was the main suspect and that his story of a black Peeping Tom may have been a desperate man's attempt to divert suspicion. Unfortunately we can't ask the guy now. He killed himself because he fitted the profile of a killer too well.'

Lauren blushed. 'I'm not the only one who's made mistakes. Joseph Talbot must have been unstable.'

'Fair enough, but the point is your lot had him down as Maeve's murderer until her head turned up with all the others. Then, with a black male in custody, the police were happy to believe Talbot's report of a black prowler. They didn't look for anyone else.'

Lauren moved on her chair uncomfortably.

'The police were certain Billy was their man. You've got the same circular reasoning in several other cases,' I said, scrolling back the computer pages.

'Heather Joy Wainwright, victim number two – *Fox was a member of the Afro-Caribbean Social Club in Withington at the same time as Heather. Heather complained to her father of the unwelcome attentions of a man answering Fox's description* . . . How many men in that club answered Billy's description? Were others eliminated?'

I noticed that Lauren's hands had bunched into fists. The optimistic side of my nature put it down to tension.

'Here again, Ann Frances Madingly, victim number six. She breaks the pattern in some ways. She was comfortably off, yet she was similar to the other victims in that she was very much a woman on her own. Your profile creates a marvellous picture of her – willowy, five feet eleven inches tall, Cheltenham Ladies College, doing a Ph.D. in history at the university, a special interest in medieval churches, yet it says here, *It is suggested that Fox might have helped her when her poorly maintained car broke down. There is an anonymous tip that Miss Madingly liked intercourse with Afro-Caribbean males. This has not been confirmed.* Then you mention in her medical history that she was using an oral contraceptive, which must prove that she was having it off with Fox. Sorry, all that suggests to me is that she was probably in a steady relationship with a married man, who didn't think it was worth wrecking his marriage to come forward.'

'Aldritt's rosary beads were found in Fox's possession,' Lauren said through gritted teeth. 'Heather Wainwright's necklace was found under his bed, and he was wearing Madingly's locket when arrested.'

'Suppose some naughty person put all those things in Fox's flat. Perhaps even gave them to him. He had a drawer full of trinkets. Suppose –'

'Suppose, suppose, bloody suppose,' she replied, beating her fists on the kitchen table. Then she stopped and put her hands down and began weeping in frustration. 'He must have taken those things himself. What sort of man would let incriminating evidence be planted on him and say nothing about it?'

'You tell me,' I said. 'You knew him.'

She bit her lip and shook her head. For a second I thought she was on the point of admitting something.

'I knew this would happen,' she said, desperately. 'That sloppy bastard Pinnock never did a proper police investigation into Billy. It'll all come out now and I'll be blamed.' She was shaking with misery.

If it hadn't been for her track record as an alcohol abuser and the early hour of the morning, I might have offered her a shot of scotch to calm her nerves. As it was I was on the point of trying to coax her out of the kitchen, my holy of holies, the last place on earth where I wanted a hysterical scene, when my attention was caught by motion in the courtyard outside. I was fated not to get that elusive piece of information about Billy out of her.

'Hold on,' I said. 'It looks as if your boyfriend Pinnock has decided to pay me an early morning call.' Through the net curtain I could see a squad of detectives surreptitiously mustering in the courtyard. One of them was holding a metal battering ram. They say a drowning man's whole life flashes before him. In that instant of surprise, I ran through all possible reasons why the GMP might want to raid my home. It never crossed my mind for a second that they might be after someone else. My thoughts flashed to the CCTV outside the Summergills'. I decided that they'd complained and Pinnock was about to carry out his threat to arrest me.

For her part, Lauren took in the scene below at a glance, then she snatched up my largest kitchen knife. 'The bastard's laying this on for my benefit,' she muttered.

'How could it be you? Pinnock doesn't know you're here, does he?'

She shook her head.

'It's me they're after, not you . . .' I said nervously, noting a worrying gleam in her eye. 'I'm getting out of here.'

'The place must be surrounded by now,' she said. 'Give Phil credit for that much efficiency.'

'I do,' I said, mentally cursing myself. If it hadn't been for Lauren's arrival last night, and she still hadn't explained how she'd got into my flat, I'd have probably gone back to Hamer Lane to observe the return of the Summergills. Or at least I'd have been out somewhere trying to track down Kath. Under no circumstances was I prepared to let myself be arrested. While free there was always a slight chance that I might stumble across some clue.

I hastily grabbed my mobile, my jacket and wallet, half a loaf and a bottle of mineral water.

Lauren looked at me irresolutely for a second and then she crammed the computer back into her hold-all, grabbed the bottle of Old Grouse and bunged it and the kitchen knife in after the computer. I had neither time nor energy to discourage her from coming along. Besides, she might have her own reasons for not wanting Pinnock to know where she had spent the night.

We were out of the flat and onto the corridor ready for flight in not much more than sixty seconds after the first sighting of the forces of law and order. Not quickly enough, unfortunately. Pinnock, if it was him in charge, wasn't hanging about. There was a deafening crash as the downstairs main door was battered. 'God knows what the residents' committee will say!' I thought, as I hustled Lauren up the stairs and onto the top floor.

My heart was in my mouth as we heard the sound of heavy feet coming up the stairs, then the thud of the battering ram in action against my front door followed by a sickening sound of splintering plywood. I looked at Lauren Caulfield, her face had that 'trapped-animal' look that always precedes desperate violence. Her fingers were inching towards the bag with the kitchen knife.

Looking round wildly for the means of escape brought little relief. All the doors were firmly shut and

I had no friends among the top floor residents. There was a skylight above me with some sort of opening lever attached. I jumped for it. It was too high. I couldn't reach but it had given me an idea for further flight.

At the end of the corridor was a fire door with a crash-bar that opened onto a tiny railed off landing. I pushed it open and manoeuvred Lauren out.

'There's no way down,' she said despairingly.

'Not down, but up,' I said with a nod at the roof. I looped my belt round the end of the bar on the fire door, pulled it down and then gently pushed the door to until it was almost closed. I whipped my belt through the narrow crack and at the same time slammed the door for the final half inch. I had the satisfaction of hearing the bar drop into place. We were now stranded on a narrow ledge, fifty feet above the ground.

'Now what, genius?' Caulfield asked.

'Onwards and upwards, darling! Motto of my old school,' I replied, before clambering onto the stout metal railing that enclosed the fire exit. It was a stretch but I could reach over the edge of the flat roof and haul myself up. But could Lauren? I looked back at her. She gave a determined nod, and when I turned to give her a hand, she spurned the offer. 'So that's what being the veteran of a childhood with five brothers and an affair with a senior policeman has taught you,' I thought.

A moment later we were both sprawled on the flat part of the roof listening to the sounds coming from below. My absence from the flat had been detected and the search squad was banging on doors. We couldn't hear what was said. Then the fire door beneath us was flung open. 'He'd never have got out of here, one of the detectives said. 'Anyway, you can't shut it from the outside.' The door was slammed shut again.

'What good does this do us?' Lauren whispered

fiercely. 'I want to go and face that bastard. I've got some questions for him.' I looked at her anxiously.

'The trouble with you is that you've only dealt with the police from the side of authority,' I whispered. 'They can tie you up for days asking all sorts of trivial questions and meanwhile there's a genuine serial killer out there doing what he pleases.'

'Are you trying to make out that there's a link between the most recent killings and the Billy murders?' she asked crossly.

'What do you think?' I said.

Her face coloured but she shut up.

There was silence for a long time after that. It was hell lying on the flat roof, the sharp gravel embedded in tar formed a perfect bed of nails. Eventually, I peered cautiously over the edge. They hadn't gone. A white police van was backing up to the entrance and confused residents were milling about in the courtyard below. Signalling to Lauren for silence, I indicated the massive square shape of the water tank. We tiptoed over to it and squatted against the side, it was a relief just to be able to sit upright.

Comfort was short-lived, however, because we'd barely begun to relax before the sudden clatter of helicopter rotors sent us into a panic. The police helicopter was hovering quite low on the other side of the tank from us. Obviously Pinnock had demanded an aerial search of the highways and byways near the flats. The GMP helicopter, a familiar sight in South Manchester, was garaged at Hough End barely half a mile from my home. It must have only been five minutes from Pinnock ordering the pilot to scramble to the machine's arrival over my flat. Fortunately, the helicopter never went high enough for the crew to see all four sides of the tank at once so we were able to creep round and keep the bulk of the water tank between us and it.

After what seemed like hours of playing 'ring-a-ring-of-roses' with us round the tank, the helicopter finally screamed off towards the Meadows. Possibly someone had told Pinnock that I was in the habit of starting the day with a run or ride in that direction. We resumed our roof-top squat against the side of the tank and Lauren took out her computer, her mobile phone and a notebook.

'I can send him an e-mail message on this,' she offered. 'Put him off the scent.'

'Don't bother,' I said irritably. She still thought that all this was being laid on for her benefit. I was worried. There was no way that even Pinnock would have been able to put on this show just because I'd got my face onto the Summergills' CCTV. I couldn't think what else they might want me for.

I risked a peek into the courtyard again. Another van had arrived and white-overalled scene-of-crime officers were entering the building. It looked as if our stay on the roof was going to be protracted.

I crawled back to Lauren who was slumped against the side of the tank. 'I was just thinking about what you said about someone planting the material evidence on Billy,' she whispered. 'Suppose Billy had a partner? If Billy had a friend still at liberty that might explain why he was so unwilling to remember some of the precise details of the killings.'

'You know something else about Billy don't you?' I said. 'You and Pinnock have known for weeks that he wasn't responsible. That's why you were so worried about me finding anything out. Now Billy's dead you want me to salve your conscience.'

'No, that's rubbish. Billy must have been involved,' she said desperately. She wouldn't look at me. 'Maybe there were others *and* Billy.'

I nodded my head slightly and she took this as signal to proceed with her tutorial.

'Using the hypothesis of two perpetrators helps us over the difficulty with the semen stains,' she said confidentially.

'*What*? I said. I hadn't a clue what she was talking about. All kinds of ideas flashed through my mind. 'Billy was sterile, wasn't he? That's what you've been covering up.'

'No, Dave. We know he was completely normal in that respect, at least. In six of the cases the heads showed faint traces of semen under fluorescent light,' she explained.

'Was it his?'

'There wasn't enough . . . Just traces, insufficient for analysis. I think the semen was on the victims' bodies and the killer washed the dead bodies prior to decapitation and left faint traces on the heads for us to detect. So,' she continued, 'we've definitely got sexual activity in six of the killings and none detectable in the other eight.' She paused and studied my face, searching for the answering glow of comprehension I supposed she was used to seeing when she tried her theories out on friend Pinnock. 'Two groups, two killers,' she said emphatically. 'Don't you see it?'

Remembering the faces of Dennis and Dean Summergill, I could see it all too clearly.

'You mean they took it in turns?' I asked.

'Not necessarily,' she replied, still maintaining her infuriating detachment. 'There is the possibility that the semen-positive victims were kept alive for some time. The surviving tissues on their necks and faces show definite wasting.'

'Put that in English!'

'Well following my hypothesis, if there were two . . . one killed his victims quickly. The other kept them alive for some time, presumably while he indulged in some kind of sexual dominance game.'

'How long?'

'I don't know – weeks or months.' She considered the idea for a while. This time her face softened a little as she thought of the awful consequences of what she was saying. I was ahead of her. She was saying that there was an even chance that Kath, if she'd been taken by the Summergills and if they were the killers, was still alive. Lots of ifs, but I felt hope for the first time. I felt that I could almost reach out and touch her.

'There have been many cases of sadistic killers keeping their victims alive for a considerable time. This whole issue needs reinvestigating. I must let Phil know.' She tried to stand up. I pulled her back. I did not share her faith in Phil.

'Good idea!' I said sarcastically. 'I'm sure Phil will be delighted to uncover the evidence that he made a complete balls-up of the case in the first place, won't he?'

'Surely he'll realise that it's better for him to sort this out, than for someone else to do it?' she asked.

'He had his chance and he blew it,' I said angrily. For the first time I noticed that my teeth were chattering. There was a cold wind whipping across the roof now and we were both chilled to the bone. I tugged out the hall loaf I'd stuffed into my jacket pocket and offered her a piece. She shook her head. I stuffed some into my own mouth before offering her the water. She snorted aggressively before rejecting it. Then she took the Old Grouse out of her satchel and took a long pull. I watched in horror as her throat moved while she swallowed. That made my mind up for me. There was no way I was staying up on this roof with her while she drowned her sorrows in my whisky. It was obvious that Pinnock was still the axis around which her thoughts revolved.

It was some time before I risked another peek down below. It was two hours since we'd fled to the roof. The morning rush hour was well under way, the police had gone and so had most of my neighbours. It was only after some minutes of futile effort trying to prise open the skylight that I realised getting off the roof was going to be a problem. If I banged on the skylight or fire door, law-abiding residents would summon the fuzz. Lauren was watching me out of the corner of her eye whilst pretending to make notes from her database. In desperation I crawled over to the side of the building that was screened from the main road by trees. The drainpipe was accessible if I had the guts for shinning down the full fifty-foot length. I took a look back at Lauren, she was pretending not to notice me while sipping from the whisky bottle.

The worst part was going over the edge crab-wise and swinging my full weight onto the pipe as my legs came down after my arms. My last glimpse of Lauren was of her calmly jotting something down in her notebook. There was a slight groan from the masonry. I scrabbled with my legs for a moment before locking them round the pipe and then I began the long journey downwards.

The last twelve feet of the pipe had been coated with anti-climbing paint and I half fell, half slithered down that distance.

I cautiously made my way to the main entrance where workmen were already replacing the smashed safety glass. They made no fuss about letting me in when I waved my key. I sprinted to the top floor. As I expected, Lauren was already waiting on the little fire escape balcony when I got there.

Took your time, didn't you?' she asked with a sneer. 'Now what?'

I led her down to my flat. The door had been sealed with tape so I knew there was no one inside. I plunged into a scene of chaos. Everything that could be emptied had been emptied. I went from room to room surveying the damage. Worst of all was the kitchen.

'They have been rather thorough,' Lauren said jauntily. There must have been something in my expression because she shut up quickly.

'I don't know what the bloody hell they think they were doing but Pinnock will wish he'd never been born before I'm through with him,' I said. I tried phoning Sinclair on both his office and home numbers. There was no reply. Similarly with Cullen. I hesitated about phoning Pinnock himself. He might react savagely if he thought I was onto his nasty little secret.

I went to the bedroom to change. The pockets of all my clothes were turned inside out but they were otherwise undamaged apart from being thrown in a heap on the floor. The clothes I was wearing were covered in black sticky goo from the drainpipe and my knuckles and knees had shed a layer of skin during the final descent. I undressed and took a shower. The shower head had been unscrewed but I repaired that in a moment. Warmth restored thought and feeling. My thoughts were interrupted by the sudden arrival of Lauren, as she pulled the shower curtain back abruptly. She was nothing if not direct.

'You'd better come and listen to this, Dave,' she said grimly. Grabbing a towel, I followed her. She led me into the living room, where, despite having had its back removed, the television was on. I caught the tail end of the ITN news bulletin. Cedric Liptrot was holding forth.

'I feel that in asking to see me Billy Fox was on the verge of making important revelations about the case.

'There was more. You've missed it.' She flicked over to the BBC.

'It is reliably reported that mass murderer Billy Fox was battered to death with the end of a snooker cue by another inmate shortly before he was due to be visited by the well-

known author, Cedric Liptrot. Mr Liptrot, whose book on Albert Clark provides graphic information on the Bradford Basher murders, has recently been consulted by Manchester police about four apparent copycat killings in Manchester. Greater Manchester Police are currently denying any link between the death of Fox and the murders which have wreaked havoc in Manchester. There is speculation that the murder last niht of Mrs Enid Maxwell, the proprietor of an animal shelter in North Yorkshire follows the pattern of the Manchester murders, She had also been visited by Mr Liptrot.'

The view switched from the newsroom to a shot of my nemesis, Detective Chief Superintendent Pinnock.

'I can confirm that arrests are imminent and that the situation is under control. At the request of the Home Office, a team of detectives led by the most senior detective on the Greater Manchester Force, Assistant Chief Constable Sinclair, is at Greenash Secure Hospital at this moment looking into all aspects of the death of Billy Fox. We are hoping to resolve the situation involving alleged links between people with access to Billy Fox, the spate of recent murders here in Manchester and the dreadful killing of Mrs Maxwell in North Yorkshire.'

There was a clamour from reporters as he finished speaking, demanding names and descriptions of those being sought.

'While it would not be conducive to give out names at this moment, I can confirm that Mr Cedric Liptrot has rendered tremendous assistance in our enquiries to date. Mr Liptrot's views are receiving full consideration. Far reaching enquiries are proceeding and you can be sure you will be informed when arrests are made.'

A horrible suspicion began to dawn on me.

The scene switched to a view of the farmyard at Chillgate. As the camera tracked over the cages, the peacocks, donkeys and pigs a voice-over commentary continued.

'North Yorkshire Police have started a manhunt for the killer who battered harmless old animal lover; Enid Maxwell, 81, to death last night. Her body was found at midnight following an anonymous call to the police. Mrs Maxwell was a noted local character in the Pateley Bridge area where she had devoted her life to the care of animals. The almost four hundred animals at the Sanctuary she ran were unharmed but Mrs Maxwell was the victim of what police sources are describing as a frenzied attack. Robbery has been ruled out as a motive and the police are seeking to contact a man from Manchester who is believed to have been among the last to see Mrs Maxwell alive. They have asked him to come forward so that he can be eliminated from enquiries.'

Next the camera panned in on a policeman identified by caption as Detective ChiefInspector Harry Pickles of the North Yorkshire Constabulary. He was asked if he saw any connection with the recent brutal killings in Manchester.

'We are keeping an open mind at this stage. There are signs that this brave lady struggled fiercely against what must have been a savage attack by a strong and determined man.'

I hurried from the living room into the bedroom. Lauren followed me and watched me anxiously as I rapidly dressed.

'I hope you got the gist of that,' I said. 'It should teach you not to be so trusting of your ex-lover. He knows perfectly well that I had nothing to do with the killing of Enid Maxwell. The Liptrots must have told him that I came back with them but it suits him to push me into the frame as a potential killer. He can tie me up with questioning for days while Sinclair tidies up the loose ends of the Billy case for him. Meanwhile no one's looking for Kath and –'

'Dave, I'm sure if you went and explained,' Lauren interrupted.

'Pinnock can hold me for thirty-six hours merely on suspicion. Kath might not have thirty-six hours. You said yourself, "sexual dominance games". I don't know if she could hold out for long.'

'Well, I'll go. He'll have to listen to me.'

'Come on, Lauren. Grow up. What are you to him now, but a disgruntled ex-employee? He's got us both just where he wants us – me on the run and you completely discredited. Didn't you notice that he's depending on Cedric Liptrot for profiling now? Who's going to believe either of us?'

Lauren looked ill. As she took in what I was saying, her face lost the healthy flush caused by her rooftop exertions and resumed the sickly white shade that contrasted so badly with her red hair. She sat down on the corner of the bed. I donned my best lightweight grey suit, a cream-coloured silk shirt and a red tie. I felt in some obscure way that elegant clothes were some sort of protection against suspicion, not that elegance would survive contact with Pinnock for long. He'd have me in prison kit in no time.

All I could think was that I must get hold of the Liptrots. I had to check just what sort of yarn they'd spun to Pinnock. I'd no reason to believe that they'd have dropped me in it, but with those two anything was possible. I phoned their hotel on the mobile. They'd checked out yesterday evening not long after leaving me. The receptionist asked me to hold for a moment and then the voice of Sergeant Cullen came on the line.

'That you, cocker?' he asked. He took my silence for assent. 'Is your mobile digital? Right, ring off now and I'll phone you back on mine. I'm on a conference call here.'

'You're in a hell of a mess,' were his first comforting words.

'Where does that leave you, then?' I asked. 'Known associate of a suspected killer . . .'

'Yeah, well my career went down the tube some time ago. I was hoping that Sinclair would help me to revive it but he's gone off to Greenash without me, the sad bugger.'

'My heart bleeds for you. Where are the Liptrots and what am I supposed to have done to Mrs Maxwell?'

'Whoa. I can't tell you about the Liptrots, except that they're in another hotel not a million miles from the centre of Manchester and that they're under guard for their own protection.'

'Not from me, I hope?'

'Dave, I just don't know. No one tells me anything but I suspect Pinnock's covering his bets. He's hoping that either the so-called Manchester Basher or you will pay them a visit.'

'What do they say that I've done? You do realise that your workmates completely trashed my flat?'

'Pinnock reckons that Kath's disappearance upset you so much that you returned to question Mrs Maxwell after leaving the Liptrots and that you might have gone over the top in a frenzy.'

I had nothing to say about that.

'You didn't, did you, Dave?'

'Do what?' I said nastily. It was so nice to see how even a fairly normal copper like Cullen could entertain suspicions of me.

'Go back. I mean you were so anxious about Kath. Not that I blame you for that.'

'Thanks, Cullen. With friends like you, who needs enemies? If Pinnock is so anxious to check on my movements tell him to ask Dennis Summergill to play back his CCTV recording for last night. There should be a very good shot of me on it. As for the rest of the night, his ex-lover, Lauren Caulfield will be getting in touch with him. She should be able to give a blow by blow account of my movements.'

I switched the phone off. Lauren Caulfield was looking very angry. She got to her feet unsteadily and walked out of the flat.

'Great!' I thought. 'Not a single friend in the world and now the entire British police force is on maximum alert for me.'

'The clear inference from the data is that at least two perpetrators were involved in the Billy Fox murders. Therefore, the death of Billy Fox should not mark the closure of the case. This is particularly importantin view of the recent spate of murders by the so-called Manchester Basher or Son of Basher. lthough the scientific evidence suggests that they were dlfferent, we must not discount the possibility that the killer may be alert to the possibilities of forensic psychology and may be altering methods accordingly. Certain senior police officers must not tidy away what could be a whole series of linked killings merely to gratify personal ambition.'
Note attached to an anonymous leak of database information to the Press Association.

18

Friday, noon

Fortunately I had transport. The hired Land-Cruiser was still where I'd left it. Pinnock's raiding party mustn't have connected it with me. I'd been sifting through my options, such as they were, and getting out of Manchester came top of the list. I could do nothing for Kath from the inside of a cell. It had occurred to me that Pinnock's idea that I'd gone back to Chillgate to find out more from Mrs Maxwell wasn't so wide of the mark. That's what I should have done if exhaustion hadn't driven me back to my flat in the hope of a few hours sleep.

Sinclair had a lot to answer for. I should never have phoned him about Kath's disappearance in the first place. What good had it done? If I'd been on my own, I'd have tried to retrace Kath's route when she left Chillgate. She must have driven to Bradford, not Manchester. Knowing her, that could only have been in the interests of gleaning more useful material for her script. What was there to interest her in Bradford? I could only think of two things – the addresses of Albert Clark and of the Summergills. She might have thought of somehow weaving a shot of Clark's former home into her story about Chillgate. There was also the home of my revered employer, Cedric Liptrot.

I took a different route out of Manchester than usual. I drove through Salford to the M602 and then joined the M62 heading east. Four solid lanes of traffic were moving over the hill, and progress was slow. I resisted the temptation to turn on the radio. The prospect of hearing the voices of either Cedric Liptrot, now promoted into a world-class expert on serial killers, or the ubiquitous Pinnock, was highly depressing. I brooded for a while on Pinnock's motives, but the job of driving eventually took up all my attention. I wasn't anxious to get booked for speeding and crawled along at seventy. The run from Manchester to Bradford was an easy one, all on motorways. It must have been very convenient for Dennis and Dean Summergill to move to Manchester.

When I finally arrived, I parked in a multistorey near the cathedral and made my way to the land registry office. I intended to do a search for any properties belonging to Clark or Summergill. I had the addresses from the Chillgate Co-operators book in my notes, so I looked them up first. Clark's house in Manningham had changed hands six times since his involuntary departure. It now belonged to Bradford Social Services. The Summergills' former home was also in Manningham. When I looked it up, Dennis Summergill was still the owner.

I asked the clerk if there could be some mistake. He was indignant. 'These files are constantly kept up-to-date. How could anyone do a property search if they weren't?'

I forked out the cash for a search of the computerised index under the name of Summergill. I came up with five more properties, all belonging to Dennis Summergill. I left the office clutching the printout. I now had a good idea what Dennis did with the money he gained from his profession of illegal taxidermy but I hadn't made my job of finding Kath any easier.

I tried to think myself into Kath's shoes. When I'd looked through the Chillgate Co-operators book it was the surprise of seeing Albert Clark's name listed that had struck me forcibly. It must have been the same for Kath. I bought a street map at a newsagent's and marked the various addresses. The former Clark home in Manningham was the nearest and was probably Kath's first choice too, so I went there. It was in the heart of Bradford's red-light district. Even at four o'clock there was trade on the streets.

Unfamiliar as I was with street scenes in the Punjab, this seemed like a reasonable facsimile, except that most of the prostitutes were white. It had been ten years since the Basher cleared the streets – they were certainly out in force again now. The properties on one side of the street were a jumble of Asian shops, food stores and domestic houses. The side I was on consisted of large old houses, mostly in urgent need of repair.

I parked on the road outside Clark's former home and scanned it. The building had a surprisingly half-derelict look about it, considering it now belonged to an official body. Overgrown bushes partly screened it from the road. I don't know what I'd been expecting but the house was much more substantial than a stone mason could have afforded. It was a large, pre-1914, redbrick detached house in its own grounds. Either Clark had inherited it or he, like Summergill, had hidden sources of wealth. My inspection was brief because the expensive-looking vehicle I'd arrived in was beginning to attract interested stares from the working girls and angry glances from the Asian residents of the area. This is where my battered old red Nissan comes into its own. It never attracts a second glance.

I turned into the drive and parked. There was a crumbling, green-painted wooden porch over the entrance to the house. I rang the bell. An Asian woman of about thirty, dressed in European clothes, opened the door. She was a short, buxom individual with a forceful expression on her face. I flashed her my home-made detective's ID.

'Just what is this?' she demanded. 'Pimpernel Investigations? Look, this is a bail hostel and if you want to see any of our clients you'll have to approach them with a court order in the usual way.'

'It's not your present clients I'm interested in,' I explained.

She began shutting the door in my face. 'If you're another Albert Clark groupie, you can get lost! We're sick and tired of it.'

I hadn't come this far to have doors slammed in my face. I pushed the door back and tried to get money out of my wallet.

'You pervert!' she shouted. 'You're worse than Clark.'

I beat a retreat.

When I turned back towards the Land-Cruiser, a skinny looking teenage prostitute was sitting on the wing. She was grinning cheekily at me.

'That's Fauzia Khan,' she said. 'We get a lot like you round here trying to look over the Clark house.'

'Do you mind?' I asked, trying to get the door open without manhandling her.

She didn't mind. She stayed on her perch. 'Have you read the book?' she asked conversationally.

'Just get out of my way,' I said roughly.

'Don't be like that. I can get you in there without upsetting Fauzia.'

I looked at her closely. She was wearing dark tights, a broad red belt and a dirty white singlet through which I could count every one of her ribs. I took her for a smack-head. She got the wrong idea about my inspection.

'See something you fancy, then?' she asked with all the optimism of her kind. She rubbed her hand over her crotch and spat out the gum she was chewing.

'How would you get me in?' I asked.

'Same way as we always get in; round the back. Fauzia guards the door but there's people in and out all day long by the back way. I can show you, but you'll never get in wearing those clothes. The others will soon suss out that you're not a resident.'

Five minutes later I was in her room trying on her boyfriend's clothes.

'Sure there isn't anything else I can do for you?' she said, pointedly, as I pulled on a pair of two-tone denims about two sizes too small and a floppy yellow and black T-shirt with a picture of Marcus Garvey on it. I gave her fifty pounds, which she tucked in the top of her belt. I ran my hands through my hair a few times trying to shape it into an appropriately unkempt style.

'Hey, you'll do all right,' she said. 'What's your name?'

'Cedric Liptrot,' I replied with a grin.

After all my preparations, the house was a disappointment. My idea was to check it out for secret passages and hidden cellars. There was no cellar, and if there'd ever been passages, residents occupied them now. The place was a rabbit warren of tiny cubicles.

Hardboard partitions were everywhere, dividing up the rooms Clark would have known. The only interesting spot was a brick built annexe to the kitchen with an odd slanting entrance. It stood between the angle of two outer walls making a curious, windowless room.

It was there that Fauzia Khan trapped me.

'You again! I'm phoning the police,' she rapped when she caught sight of me.

'Don't. It's that Cedric Liptrot. You know he wrote the book,' my guide explained.

This fascinating news stayed Fauzia long enough for me to establish that she'd found this unexpected space during alterations. It had previously been hidden behind some deep, solidly built, fitted shelves. There never had been a door. It was a secret chamber all right.

'You have informed the police about this?' I asked.

'Why should I? We're sick of sightseers without providing additional attractions. Besides, Albert Clark's behind bars and is likely to stay there.'

'Was there anything in the room when you opened it?'

'Just a couple of old leather straps like you use for tying up suitcases,' Fauzia said defensively. I shook my head and she looked mildly embarrassed. At least, she dried up about phoning the police to complain about my unauthorised search of the premises.

I spent the rest of the afternoon checking out all of Summergill's other properties. They were just ordinary homes in terraced streets in working-class parts of the town. I felt bleak and empty. Kath was slipping away from me. It was hard even to remember her face. I kept going. There might be some clue, however tenuous. The occupants knew nothing of Summergill. They paid rent to a property agency in the town centre.

After those humble premises, Summergill's old home, now occupied by George and Rita Hanley and their two sons, came as a complete surprise. It was in an exclusive suburb, one with many large secluded mansions. Summergill's former home was not quite in the mansion class but it was imposing enough. I guessed it would sell for at least £300,000, or so – not bad going for a repair man. The house was much more modern than Clark's, a very large 1930s era corner semi-detached with bay windows, mock-Tudor beams and an arched doorway leading to an entrance hall. There was at least half an acre of land attached, running right round the corner and down the sideroad. The front of the house was open to the street, easy to observe across a well-tended lawn and garden. School was out and the family was eating their evening meal in the front room.

The house bristled with security devices. As my eye ranged over the view there seemed to be burglar alarms and motion sensors on every surface. There was even a large floodlight mounted on a steel post in the middle of the side lawn. The chances of there being a secret room here appeared to be remote. This type of dwelling is standard from one end of the country to the other. The large garden, surrounded by a low stone wall with a wooden fence above was more promising. There was a range of outbuildings, joined to the house by a wide tarmac drive. They were well back from the road, screened from view by a hedge of Leylandii and a high-lapped timber fence and gate.

How do you knock on someone's door and say, 'Excuse me, I'd like to check your outbuildings for secret chambers.' There isn't any way. No friendly prostitutes could smuggle me in here.

I sat gazing at the respectable suburban scene from across the road. Slowly the blood began to pound in my veins. The primary school headmaster drove a top-of-the-range BMW. It was a real executive limousine in a metallic silver colour. Hanley must be an incredibly well-paid headteacher. Perhaps he had as many as four or five hundred children in his school, but there was no way he could afford a car like that. As well as the BMW, there was a new VW Polo. This man did not own the house he lived in, but presumably rented it from Summergill. He threatened to sue the police just because they asked a perfectly reasonable question about Kath at 3 a.m. He'd never heard of Chillgate Farm. What was he hiding? Why plaster the place with alarms and sensors?

It took all my self-control to stay seated in the car. Hanley must know something. Was he one of Summergill's accomplices? A police car cruised past and I decided it was time to withdraw. I drove down the sideroad. A high fence, running along the sideroad, screened the garage and other buildings from public view. I slowed down long enough to see that access would not be easy, there were plenty of alarms. There were no buildings overlooking the property at the back. Summergill's grounds adjoined a cricket club.

I cruised round the neighbourhood for a while, getting the feel of the area, before resuming my vigil parked diagonally across the road from the house, just at the limits of observation. A boy of about eleven came out of the side door and began skating up and down the path on rollerblades. He made a little game for himself, setting up milk bottles and a little jump as an obstacle course. Then he got out an orange ball and a long street-hockey stick and started flicking the ball up and down the path. Before long the ball went over the fence at the bottom. The kid retrieved the ball and returned to his game, leaving the gate open. Almost at once a man, presumably Hanley, emerged from the house, lectured the kid and swiftly closed the gate. Hanley moved nervously and rapidly back into the house as if fearful of daylight. His whole emergence was quick and lizard-like. He was an insignificant-looking guy, a mirage of a man. If I'd rubbed my eyes I'd have missed him. As it was, I not only saw him but got a glimpse of the back of one of the outbuildings. There was a heat exchanger attached to its wall, such as you would find on a coldstore or refrigerated room.

Keener than ever for a view, I drove into the cricket club. There didn't seem to be anyone about, so I climbed up into the score-box, a dilapidated brick building about twenty feet high, standing at the corner of the cricket pitch nearest to the house. There were no windows looking over the Summergill property but by shoving my head and shoulders right out of the side window and twisting round I managed to get a view over the enclosed area. It contained five sturdily built wooden buildings of different sizes. One was obviously a garage, another the cold-store and the rest of indeterminate purpose. All entrances were padlocked.

'What the hell do you think you're doing?' a gruff voice demanded as I left the score-box. I was confronted by a tall stoop-shouldered man of about seventy. He had the type of ruddy complexion that you only get from being either a hill farmer or out on a cricket pitch in all weathers.

Deciding that honesty was the best policy I showed him my homemade ID card and explained that I was trying to observe his next-door neighbour.

'What's the snide bugger been up to then? Cheating on his wife?' he asked in friendly enough way. I kept my explanation vague and brief.

'I suppose I should phone him and tell him that there's someone spying on him, but we don't like Mr Hanley much in this club.' He explained that he was the club secretary and that they'd had trouble with the neighbours for years. He was ready enough for a chat when he saw that I was harmless.

'Hanley's bad enough, never lets us have any balls back, but the previous owner, Summergill, was a real monkey. We had to get the law on him. A lad climbed over the fence to get his ball and he was savaged by two wild dogs Summergill had in there,' he said, gesturing towards the bottom of the garden. 'We used to have the practice nets right up here, near the clubhouse but we had to move them.'

'What happened to Summergill?' I asked eagerly.

'Our solicitor got him to promise that the dogs would be chained up but he had the dogs destroyed and the present, much higher, fence put up.'

I'd already checked to see if Hanley was in the phone book but he wasn't listed. I asked the cricket veteran if he had Hanley's number,

'Aye, but you'll have to come inside for it,' he replied. Once in his office, I noticed that he had a Polaroid camera, which the club used for team photos. He let me use it for a consideration.

Using the score-box again, and other positions, I was able to get some interesting shots of the property and its unusual outbuildings and fancy cars. They wouldn't be enough on their own to convince even Cullen, let alone Pinnock, but they were evidence. Exactly what wrongdoing they were evidence of, I wasn't certain.

Later I sat in a nearby pub car park trying to work out my next move. Should I just barge in on Hanley, get him by the throat and shake him until he talked? No, he had a wife and two sons I'd have to silence as well. If the Summergills were keeping Kath alive somewhere any sort of warning from Hanley could be curtains for her. Burglary was also definitely out. In the end I decided that I had more to lose than gain from a direct approach. With time, and a bit of luck, I might have been able to tap Hanley's phone. He must be in touch with Summergill. As I sat furiously thinking that time was the one thing I didn't have, an idea came to me.

I went into the pub and phoned Hanley. I had to know if he knew Summergill.

'It's Dennis here,' I said when he picked up the phone. 'Have the police been round again?' My imitation of Dennis Summergill's clipped military accent was barely passable but fortunately was enough to fool Hanley.

'What are you doing phoning here?' he asked angrily. 'I've told you to always use the answer phone.' With that he slammed the phone down. It took me five minutes to get back to his house. As I entered the road I saw the BMW pulling out of his drive.

I followed.

He took all kinds of shortcuts along back streets. It was difficult to stay with him. I thought for a while that he might be going up to Chillgate Farm but the hour-long drive led us to a village school in Pateley Bridge. He pulled into the schoolyard, shooed away some children from the playground, and let himself into the building.

I discreetly inspected the premises. The name G. Hanley was listed as headmaster. From an outside view the school appeared to have no more than two class rooms, three at the most. There was no way that Hanley was driving a BMW on the salary he drew from here. One of my father's theories is that the secret criminal mastermind is a myth. Career criminals always reveal themselves by some aspect of their lifestyle. Unless Hanley could show that he'd won the lottery, he had questions to answer. At least in my mind. I drove back down the road to the same lay-by where I had shared tuna sandwiches with the Liptrots. It was only last night but it already seemed like weeks ago.

My patient vigil was rewarded after half an hour

when Hanley's distinctive silver BMW went past in the Bradford direction. It was now quite dark. I drove back to the little school and parked round the back. I took a tyre lever out of the boot and made my way forward. I could easily see into all the school rooms with the help of a torch. It took a moment to locate Hanley's office. His answer phone sat on the desk conveniently close to the window. I smashed the window, reached in and yanked the phone out, cord and all. An alarm went off, but I was on my way back towards Manchester.

One of the advantages of the off-road vehicle was that it had an excellent field of view. I sat on the main road across from my flat scanning all points of the compass for half an hour before I decided that there were no police in attendance. Then I phoned just to check if anyone was waiting for me, not that they'd have answered if they were. Lauren Caulfield had installed herself again. She was on her own.

'What the hell are you doing here?' I demanded, when I came in carrying my loot. 'You never did tell me how you got in the first time.'

She gave me a wintry smile. 'You were right, Dave. You said the CID would be parked on my doorstep and they were. I've spent most of the day sitting in coffee bars. In the end I thought this would be the safest place as they already searched it.'

I laughed. 'That's a little disingenuous of you, Lauren, and if you think you're safe here you must be joking. You came here for the same reason you did last night and for the same reason you followed me down to Macclesfield last week. You want to unload your guilt about Billy Fox. Philip Pinnock won't put up with it so I'm elected.'

'Spare me the amateur psychology, Dave,' she said. 'You've got a low opinion of yourself if you think I'm only here on a guilt trip. I'm here because I want to be. I admit that at first I was hoping to make Phil jealous but it's been over with him for a while. I'm so stupid it just took me a long time to work that out. He only ever thinks of himself, but you, you're obsessed with other people. You won't rest until you've found Kath. I think it was when you pulled Cedric Liptrot off me that I realised what my feelings were.'

I was feeling slightly hysterical. I started laughing. She inflicted a very martyred, long-suffering look on me.

'If you're so smitten you can tell me what it is about Billy that convinced you that he didn't do the killings. You don't need to worry about your reputation now. By the time Phil Pinnock's done with you, you won't have one.'

She blushed furiously, looking far more youthful than a woman in her early-thirties had any right to. 'I found out last month,' she said. 'I told Phil right away but all he wanted me to do was to shelve the findings.'

'What findings?'

'I found that Billy was a mosaic . . . he had a population of cells in his body that had an extra chromosome. No one had thought to do a chromosome analysis of his blood.'

I must have looked at her blankly because she carried on explaining.

'With a Down's Syndrome person all the cells have one extra chromosome but with a mosaic like Billy it's only some of the cells. In Down's Syndrome the effect of the extra chromosome can be severe. Sufferers sometimes die young from leukaemia, duodenal atresia or congenital heart defects. With Billy the effect was much less. It left him rather small in size but the main results were his love of music and his immense suggestibility.'

Lauren's manner was clinical throughout this explanation.

'Would he have been capable of violent crime?' I asked.

'It's unlikely.'

'Could he have killed if someone put him up to it?'

'Again, that almost impossible. Part of the reason for his suggestibility was the strong feeling of empathy which he would have felt. If he had seen he was hurting a third party he would have been too upset to carry on. It's just within the bounds of possibility that he might have done it once but fourteen times? No way.'

'So what happened?'

'Billy felt immense loving warmth for his friends One of them, the true killer, won his sympathy and coached him to say everything that he told the police. The sad thing is that he would never show the same sense of self-preservation that a non-afflicted person might. If we'd still had capital punishment Billy would have walked to the gallows agreeing that he was guilty. The questioning must have reinforced his previous conditioning.'

Lauren had tears in her eyes as she spoke. I made no move to take her hand or offer sympathy. If she'd spoken out earlier Dennis and Dean Summergill might be in prison by now.

'Don't look at me like that. Don't you think I've tortured myself enough? Phil persuaded me to put off announcing the results and then as time went on it got more difficult. I tried to convince myself that Billy must have played a part in the murders.'

'Well, now you've finally admitted what you know, what are you going to do about it?' I asked coldly.

Lauren appeared to think about this for a moment. She was in control of herself again.

'I thought I'd try and put a spoke in Phil's wheel by a few judicious leaks of information to the Press,' she said, pointing to her computer. She'd cleared a space on the kitchen table and was set up for action. She still had access codes for the GMP computer files, for the Home Office major enquiry file on the Billy murders and the five most recent killings. She could also reach NCIS files on unexplained past murders. She'd already downloaded her revised theories about Billy Fox to the Press Association. At best, she might force Pinnock onto the defensive. He'd have some awkward questions to answer such as, 'Are you still looking for suspects in the Billy Fox case?'

I was doubtful if her scheme would have much effect on Pinnock. He was a man with all the answers. 'You're assuming that Pinnock is going to be swayed by scientific evidence. He hasn't been so far, has he?'

'He must be,' she said.

'Only a major break in the case is going to force him to move. It's almost as if he was protecting the Summergills. Did he ever mention them to you?'

'If they were informants, Phil would never have mentioned them. I helped him with profiling but he had informants that he never told me about.'

'Makes you think though, doesn't it? I wonder if the Summergills were informants not just about Billy but about other things. Now the shit's hit the fan with Billy, Pinnock must realise that he's in far too deep with those two to ever allow anything about them to be made public.'

The speculation about her former lover was too much for Lauren. I guessed that she'd played a much more substantial role in Philip Pinnock's intrigues than she cared to think about now.

'Look, get real, Dave!' she snapped. 'I can't help you with that at all. What I'm into now could be the biggest thing that's happened in criminal investigation for years and I'm going to crack it. I'm going to stay here and comb through the data. Don't forget there's still a serial killer on the loose out there – or even a whole gang of them! There must be more names . . .' Her eyes were gleaming at the prospect of fresh discoveries,

'Well, if that's what turns you on,' I said doubtfully. My eyes lingered on the whisky bottle sitting on the table next to the computer. I wondered how much of her inspiration came from that.

'There's all this new information about animals and taxidermy and God knows what else,' she explained eagerly. 'I'm going to get onto the RSPB for their list of suspects and cross-reference them against my own lists of potential serial killers.'

'There's a lot more information than that,' I said. I showed the print-outs of the various addresses owned by Summergill Senior, the photos of George Hanley's home and described Albert Clark's secret hiding place. Last of all, I plonked the answer phone on the table. It took me a while to get it wired up and running.

Hanley had not erased the tape. It held many messages. The first ones we heard were disappointing – school meals were unable to deliver vegetarian sandwiches, Jimmy had measles and would be off all week, then mingled among the school messages were more sinister ones. An Asian voice said, 'Mr Razak would be able to take delivery of his order on Tuesday. Would Mr Hanley please confirm availability?' A Scots accent enquired more bluntly, 'What's happened to my snow leopard? Let me know at once.' Then I felt as if someone was squeezing my heart, I heard Dennis Summergill say, 'George, we're shutting down for a while. Don't answer any client enquiries. The weather's getting rather warm in Manchester.'

'That's it!' I shouted. 'A link between Summergill

and Hanley. Hanley must be handling the delivery end of the taxidermy business. He's got a perfect front and he's handily placed to keep an eye on Chillgate Farm.

'I don't like to pour cold water, Dave, but that message doesn't actually prove anything. After all it's only you who claim that it's Dennis Summergill. He could deny it. Nor does it say that he's got Kath as a prisoner.'

'Hanley must have told Dennis that the old lady had visitors up at Chillgate yesterday. I bet he watches the place like a hawk,' I said.

'There was someone else who could have told Dennis. Have you forgotten that Cedric Liptrot could have told him. After all he was a neighbour of Clark and Summergill in Bradford. You mustn't overlook the chance that he played some part as well.'

'No. Hanley's a shifty beggar, living in the lap of luxury on the proceeds of crime –'

'Doesn't that match what you've said about Cedric Liptrot?' Lauren asked.

'Maybe,' I said to cover my confusion. Then I shook my head, 'He couldn't . . .'

'Psychopaths are very cunning, Dave,' Lauren said. 'Think of how he jumped at me without any warning.' I think she was perversely pleased to have shaken my conviction that the Summergills were guilty.

'Right,' I said, 'I'm going to see if I can get some official backup for another search of 13 Hamer Lane and I'm not going through your ex-boyfriend this time.'

'Good luck, then, but I must carry on with this,' she said.

'Will you be safe here?' I asked.

'Phil Pinnock won't be round again,' she said confidently. I hadn't got her attention. Her eyes were locked on the screen of her laptop. She'd plugged a transformer into the wall and was working on mains electricity. There was nothing to stop her spending days analysing information.

'I didn't just mean Pinnock!' I said angrily. 'Do you think the Summergills are just going to sit back quietly while you sieve out the data that's going to send them to prison for life?'

I don't think she really took in what I was saying. Lauren had the true computer nerd's ability to focus her total attention on a small screen for hours at a time.

'Lauren! Promise me you won't go prying round at the Summergills' home.

By reply she gave a grunt that could have been taken as affirmative. I was wasting my breath. There are other drugs besides crack and brown. The woman was hooked. God knows, I'd have preferred to be investigating a homicidal bunch of Yardies myself. At least they were straightforward, they shot at you when you got on their case, whereas here, breaking out of one blind alley just opened up another one.

For a moment the memory of Cedric launching himself at Lauren during that meeting at the Metropolitan University came back to me. Then when we were at Chillgate Farm, Cedric had gone back to the car while I'd spent almost an hour looking for scraps of bone near the incinerator. But then he couldn't have . . . could he? There wasn't time. The police said Enid Maxwell had struggled fiercely against her assailant. His mother wouldn't have been so unaffected. There were a thousand reasons why it couldn't have been him.

The idea of Cedric as a killer was just too hard to swallow but there could be some link still unexplained between the Liptrots and the Summergills. Was there some connecting thread between all three Clark, Summergill and Cedric? But what? Was there some clue in Lena Liptrot's constant fantasising about Cedric's origin? Maybe they were all related.

I needed help to find out, but where was I going to get it? I looked at Lauren Caulfield, humming and clicking away to herself. No help from her. There was only one person I could turn to.

'You! You crazy bugger,' Cullen said when I phoned him on his home number. 'Where are you? Pinnock's got half the detective strength of the GMP out looking for you.'

I took the fact that he hadn't hung up immediately as a sign that he was at least willing to listen. I swiftly told him what I'd found out in the last few hours.

'The tape's not evidence of anything except of a crime committed by you,' he said at last.

'Won't you at least let Sinclair know?' I pleaded. 'I can't believe that you can't reach him.'

He grunted indecisively.

'What's happening about your own enquiries into the animal racket?'

'Shelved. Pinnock's prioritised things a bit differently now that Mr Sinclair's in Wales.' I knew it cost him something to say what he said next – 'I'll take him the tape, but I'll need the actual cassette, not just your say-so about what's on it. You'll have to trust me enough for a meet.'

Understanding Cullen's problems didn't make me any more anxious to put my pretty head into the noose of a possible trap than I had been before. It was only when he agreed to run a check into Cedric Liptrot's family background that I arranged to meet him in the car park of the giant Sainsbury's supermarket in Regent Road, Salford. It was open until ten on Fridays and the car park was vast enough for me to select a deserted spot to meet Cullen.

Keeping a weather-eye open for a police tail and for the Summergills in their grey van as well, I left Chorlton and headed for Salford. I'd agreed on 9.30 p.m. for the meet, and so had some time to waste. I parked in front of a furniture warehouse in the far corner of the retail site. I was partly screened by bushes. I could observe the comings and goings from there.

I occupied myself while I waited by updating myself on the story of Billy Fox's death as it gradually unfolded on radio bulletins. There was going to be a major scandal. Opposition spokesmen were already questioning the Government's competence in running the prison service. A leader of the Prison Officer's Association blamed government penny-pinching on overtime and cut-backs in training as the likely causes. The Home Secretary blamed administrative error and said that the police were already at the prison making the fullest possible enquiries and that he could say nothing that would prejudice the outcome. VICPAC's solicitor blamed police time-wasting for the failure to discover where the victims were buried. SPROAC claimed that stereotyping Billy as a violent black man led to a lack of attention to his needs by the Prison Service.

The enquiry into the murder of Enid Maxwell seemed to be on the back burner now as far as the media were concerned. Nor were there any reports that the police were combing Manchester for a private detective. I supposed that Pinnock intended to give everybody a cheap thrill when he got hold of me. My gloomy foreboding ceased when I saw Cullen's blue Ford Sierra drive into the car park.

As instructed, he pulled into the largest clear area. I gave it five minutes just to check that no one else was around and then drove alongside. Cullen was standing by his car. I gave him the tape without getting out of my car.

'Cedric Liptrot and his mother, Lena. Do you think you could dig out their dates of birth, birth certificates and anything you can find about Cedric's father or any of his relatives. Maybe Mrs Liptrot had more than one husband. I'd be really grateful,' I said.

He shook his head dubiously, got in his car and drove off. He didn't say a word to me throughout.

'The place of intuition in detection is in danger of being neglected and treated with contempt because of the commitment of many to "scientific" methods and logic. In geometry the shortest distance between points is a straight line, but in the map of the human mind there are very few straight lines. Intultion is often the surest guide through the thicket of facts presented to us by the forensic scientists.'

From *The Lateral Thinking Detective* by Dr James Christopher B.Sc.(Crim) Ph.D, page 15.

19

Friday evening – Saturday morning

To lose one female was a misfortune – to lose two would be sheer carelessness. I decided that the best place for me to be was back at the flat with Lauren, come what may. It could only be a matter of time before Pinnock sent his rumble-squad round again. Meanwhile, she needed looking after. When I got into the flat after another elaborate, and probably quite useless, checking process to see that the police weren't in residence, she had gone. I told myself that if there was one thing that was predictable about Lauren Caulfield, it was that she was unpredictable. I phoned the number listed in the book for her, but put the receiver down at once when a male voice answered.

I went in the kitchen. All her apparatus remained, piled up on the kitchen table just as she'd left it. The IBM laptop was open and switched on. It displayed a phone number on an otherwise blank screen. Feeling grateful that Lauren had left some means of keeping in touch, I dialled the number.

The voice of Dennis Summergill answered. 'Ah, Mr Cunane, you've finally arrived. How gratifying to hear from you. I believe we've met once before. That was you, the other day, pretending to be delivering something from a mail-order company, wasn't it?'

I felt hot and cold at the same time. My knees began to give way. I sat on the chair next to the phone.

'Come on now, Mr Cunane, or can I call you Dave?' Summergill's tone was that of an old friend renewing an acquaintance. His voice fitted everything I'd ever been told about psychopaths being charming as long as they get their own way. I cleared my throat. 'Ah, you are still there, then,' he said. 'It wouldn't do for you to lose control. There are two people here who are counting on you for a very great deal. Why don't you take a shot of scotch to steady your nerves, I believe you like the occasional stiffener.'

'Where did you hear that?' I managed to ask.

'Sauce for the goose is sauce for the gander, Dave. I believe you've been spending a lot of time checking up on me. Surely you don't mind me extending the same courtesy to you?' Again he gave a friendly chuckle, as if he was my favourite uncle discussing how I'd gone on at some football match. I realised that I had to encourage him to keep up the friendly banter.

'Technically speaking, Dave, you could say I've had my eye on you since you took employment with that repellent nuisance, Cedric Liptrot. I knew Cedric would never manage to find out anything for himself, so I watched carefully to see who he would find to be his eyes and ears this time. You know that old dragon of a mother wrote his last book for him, don't you? I knew he'd need help to do the job on Billy and it seems as if you've been acting as eyes, ears and *brain* for him this time.

'Anyway, enough of that. You and I have more pressing matters to deal with. Listen carefully, Dave. You are going to drive down to Bootle Street Police Station. You are going to alert the waiting press and television people there, and then you are going to confess to the murders of Yvonne Clutterbuck, Stacey Shawcross, Lisa Dolan, Carter Gumbs and Enid Maxwell. Did you get that, Dave? They've seen you coming in and out of Bootle Street often enough for them to believe you. Shall I say the names again so you can write them all down?'

'I know the names,' I said faintly.

'Fine! Aren't you curious as to why you're going to do all this, Dave?'

I cleared my throat, but didn't speak.

'I'll take that as a "Yes",' he said with a sickening little giggle. 'The reason is, Dave, if you don't oblige me by doing this little favour, two friends of yours, Ms Headlam and Dr Caulfield, will both suffer fatal skull-fractures some time between midnight and four a.m. Don't let their confidence in your ability to protect them be totally mistaken.'

I must have given an involuntary moan at this. Whether it was of relief that Kath was still alive, or of horror at Summergill's other news, I couldn't say.

'Eh! That got your attention didn't it, Dave?' Summergill showed his pleasure at my discomfort with a full, prolonged laugh. 'Now, Dave, or perhaps I'd better show my gratitude for the service you're going to do me and call you "Sir!" eh? At any rate, I expect there are all kinds of schemes churning through that fertile brain of yours at this moment. You are thinking of how you can get the police involved, isn't that right?'

He was wrong, and maybe that was his first mistake.

That wasn't my first thought. My mind had leapt towards the pump-action shotgun I'd confiscated from Zara Pilatski and I'd already visualised using it to blow Summergill's head clean off his shoulders. I began to recover from the initial shock and get some control over my responses. I needed time to think of some way out and I also needed some clue as to what he'd done with the missing pair.

'You're really well round the loop, aren't you Summergill?' I said. 'On your previous form Kath and Lauren are already dead. Why don't you give yourself up?'

'Oooh! That's risky talk, sir. There's going to be a price for that. Dean! Mr Cunane wants to hear from Kath. See to it, will you.' I realised that he was addressing his odious son. A moment later I heard Kath screaming very loudly in the background. My hair stood on end. The scream was impossible to fake. Kath's voice expressed overwhelming fear of a painful and imminent death in a way that no words could convey. I felt defeated. There was more. 'Now kindly get Dr Caulfield to oblige in the same way,' Summergill ordered his son. His voice had now lost the amused, self-congratulatory tone. He sounded as cold as death.

'No!' I shouted. Whatever they were doing to their victims was probably worse than I was imagining, but I couldn't stand for more of that noise. It may be that my plea had an effect, or that Lauren was less injured than Kath, but she didn't scream. I could hear her cursing and shouting and then the noise was abruptly reduced in volume as if an intervening door had been shut.

'Wearying noise to listen to, isn't it? Believe me, I know every register that the human voice can reach,' Dennis Summergill said, all charm again. 'Dean and I find these sessions can be very wearing, so to save you having to listen any further, full instructions will arrive by e-mail on your friend Caulfield's computer. So this is goodbye and I'd like to say it's been a real pleasure making your acquaintance.'

He then hung up. I feverishly dialled 1471 to get the number only to hear 'number withheld' as I expected. My hand was shaking. How did you set the laptop up to receive e-mail? I'd only seen it done once. Heedless of possible police, or any other surveillance, I ran out of the flat and down to the lock-up garage on the ground floor. I was praying that Pinnock's search hadn't extended this far and that the Remington shotgun was where I'd left it. It was. I hurried back up and re-assembled it on the kitchen work surface. I checked the action a couple of times. It was working. Those few simple mechanical processes calmed my nerves. Holding the gun in my hand gave me the feeling that I could hit back. Maybe I'm just as psychopathic as Dennis Summergill.

The bottle of whisky was still in place beside the computer. There was about a quarter left. I had a solid belt and then turned to the machine. Fortunately, it was designed to be idiot proof and I soon got Summergill's e-mail message.

> *Mr Cunane you will immediately go to confess as arranged.* **<grin>** *When word of this is released, and* we ***will be*** *monitoring the news channels,* **:-o** *Dr Caulfield will be released from our custody. She will phone you on your mobile number. We know that the next part is asking rather a lot of you but we have confidence in you.* **;-(** *We would like you to arrange a fatal accident for yourself* **:-a ;-(** *Our suggestion is that you run into one of the concrete abutments on the M56 but you may well have your own ideas on what is most convenient. Following this we will release Ms Headlam. Her injuries are not severe* **<sigh>** *and could be taken to be self-inflicted, so we are*

confident that despite the story she and Dr Caulfield may tell they will not be believed. **;->** *Their rantings will be put down to the efforts of two love-crazed women seeking to clear the name of the mass murderer they were so deeply involved with. When I found how closely you were monitoring my movements I realised just how convenient you were going to be, Mr Cunane.* **;-)** *Even if at some future date your friends manage to clear your name, Dean and I will be long gone.* **<grin>** *We only need a few days start to establish ourselves in another location. Any hint .of premature police involvement renders this agreement invalid.* **:->** *Thanks once again for your co-operation.*

P.S. Dr Caulfield and Ms Headlam will be dead by one a.m. if you fail to comply. **88**

As I scrolled through the message again, stuffed with coy little e-mail 'Smileys', I realised that I was dealing with a suffocatingly stupid, vain, but at the same time, completely deadly man. How could an adult, a man in his fifties, bother to interlard his messages with those odd little humorous punctuation marks? Even odder was his idea that I was going to commit suicide to please him. Before going towards the door I checked that I had a full load of shells in the magazine of the Remington. I had and there were enough spares for a reload. I blessed Zara Pilatski again.

Summergill was a true psychopath and he was obviously now coming to the boil. Boiling over. In his cunning, he imagined that I was simple-minded enough to believe what he said. He must have thought he was still dealing with Billy Fox. His scenario was obvious to a child of five. I would confess and receive the message from Lauren on my mobile. That would be the last thing Lauren would ever do. He would kill her, probably leaving her body somewhere near my flat; likewise with Kath. Meanwhile, I would have removed myself from the scene permanently, and while the police were sorting out exactly what had happened, the Summergills would decamp.

Nice one Dennis!

I was certain that Philip Pinnock wouldn't take much persuading that I was the perpetrator when the corpses of his ex-mistress and Kath turned up outside my flat, or office, or wherever. A bloodstained club hammer would be found with one of them. Naturally, the spate of local murders would cease after my demise, lending further verisimilitude to Summergill's plot.

'So what was new there?' I asked myself. Pinnock already had most of the GMP out looking for me. What I had to do was to get myself down to 13 Hamer Lane, find where Dennis was hiding Kath and Lauren and get them out. Nothing much. There was no use me even thinking of contacting the police or those few friendly coppers of my acquaintance. Kath and Lauren would be dead before I could finish explaining. It was down to me. As I reached my front door it crossed my mind that Kath and Lauren were already dead. Probably Summergill had already recorded a phone message from Lauren. He'd shown sufficient cunning for any treachery.

My intuition was that Kath and Lauren were at 13 Hamer Lane. I hadn't had time to check whether Summergill had other properties in Manchester but Cullen had and there were none listed. Summergill must be at Hamer Lane and that was where Kath and Lauren would be, alive or dead. I carefully repositioned the shattered front door with as much care as I could, and replaced the police tapes that were holding it together. Carrying the gun under a coat, I headed for the Land-Cruiser which was parked on the road a hundred yards away from Thornleigh Court. As I got in the vehicle, a car slid past me and parked outside the flats. The occupants of the back seat, two young men, twisted round to see who I was. Then their car shot into reverse, covering the distance between us in seconds. It swerved to prevent me driving away but I was already in gear. I raced past it. Pinnock's lads had finally arrived for a check-up on the flat. They were right on my rear bumper. If they'd come half an hour earlier they might have been able to prevent Summergill taking Lauren away.

I crashed the lights, and roared away up Edge Lane in the direction of Stretford. They followed. Edge Lane gets its name because it was the edge of the arable land in the Mersey Valley. On my left, behind a ribbon of semi-detached houses, lay the open spaces of the former Mersey water meadows, devoted nowadays to sports pitches and nature reserves. I knew that if I could get the off-road vehicle onto the Meadows I would have a chance to lose my pursuers. My prospects in a prolonged chase on roads were dismal. I'd no idea what the top speed of the Land-Cruiser was but it couldn't be high. At the first turn, I violently spun the wheel to the right, hoping everything I'd heard about stability of high centre-of-gravity vehicles was untrue. I survived and found myself rushing down a narrow road towards Turn Moss, a large open area with several football pitches laid out end to end. In seconds I was out into the green space, bumping across the far from level ground at sixty.

They were still with me but not overtaking. I wondered how long it would take them to get the helicopter after me. I could only hope that it was in action on some remote part of the GMP's patch. I crashed through a hedge at the end of the pitches and onto an area of marshy ground. With four-wheel-drive engaged, my vehicle shot ahead. The danger now was that I would be trapped in the maze formed by the

Bridgewater canal, the steep Mersey river dikes and the motorway embankments. All those morning runs now paid off. I raced down the bumpy land alongside a cemetery and crossed under the canal at Cut Hole Bridge. I paused for a second. In the distance I could hear the wail of sirens.

There were a few streets of old terraced houses on my right, almost engulfed by the concrete pillars carrying Chester Road high above. I raced under the road and then out onto open ground again. It was rougher land than before, the wheel jerked and jumped in my hands. Driving across open fields in the pitch dark with the lights off is not to be recommended. I was coming up to the next obstacle, the M63 motorway which carried ten lanes of traffic high above the valley at this point. There was just one narrow road under it, through a concrete tunnel, and finding it was like trying to thread a needle in the dark. I made it, through and out the other side. Looking back I could see headlights all across the open ground behind me, at least four cars now in pursuit. The helicopter couldn't be far away.

In front of me there was a maze of swampy fields, steep-sided drainage channels and, dead ahead, a sewage farm with all kinds of settling tanks and other impassable barriers. Again, luck was with me. Briefly switching the lights on I located the gate leading through the sewage farm and smashed through it and into the fields beyond. There was no chance to congratulate myself. I knew that I was heading in the wrong direction, away from Manchester. Beyond the sewage farm there was a small dairy farm with a track leading towards Urmston. It ran alongside the motorway embankment. Pursuit was very close now. It could only be moments before I encountered vehicles vectored onto me. I put the car into low gear and crawled up the steep bank.

It laboured and chugged but reached the top. Snatching a glimpse behind, I saw the original CID pursuit vehicle slam to a halt at the bottom of the slope. All that was between me and the motorway now was a thin fence. The helicopter still hadn't put in an appearance. The Land-Cruiser smashed through the puny fence and I found myself on the road. There was other traffic but it wasn't heavy. I joined the stream just as the helicopter switched its searchlight on somewhere ahead of me, over the meadows to my left. If I'd still been down there the helicopter would have located me in seconds with its thermal imaging device. I hoped I was now indistinguishable from other traffic. There were plenty of four-wheel-drive vehicles on the road.

I turned off the motorway at the first interchange, which was at Davyhulme, and headed back to Manchester by minor roads. I was feeling as churned up as if somebody had included me amongst the ingredients for a giant omelette. The shotgun had fallen on the floor and I wasn't sure what to do next. All the aggression I'd been full of a short while ago had evaporated.

It was all down to me. There was no one else to do what was needed. Detective Chief Superintendent Pinnock had refused to believe that Kath was missing, despite all the evidence. Even if I could get Cullen or Sinclair to believe me about the possibility of a secret room at the Hamer Lane address, the chance of another search was low. I had to give it my best shot and hope that I could do what was needed myself. I drove slowly towards Withington, constantly checking my mirror for police interest. My hope was that the last thing Summergill would be expecting would be a sudden attack on his home.

I drove slowly up the narrow road behind Hamer Street, intending to check out the mews garage first. It was in complete darkness, as was the house behind. There wasn't even a chink of light anywhere. I sat for a long while wondering if I was doing the right thing and then climbed over the back fence by the same route I had used before. There was no sound, no trace of occupants but my senses told me that the Summergills and Kath and Lauren were here somewhere. I crept up to the back window. The ground-floor windows were solidly shuttered and I knew that there would be pressure pads and movement sensors even if I could get past the windows.

An upper-window was not quite flush with its frame, as if not firmly shut. I decided to give that a try. I checked my watch. It was midnight, normally regarded as a bit early for burgling but I had no choice if I was going to take Dennis's deadline seriously.

Although my elbows and knees were very tender from my early-morning adventure of shinning down the side of Thornleigh Court, I reckoned that I should be able to make it up to the roof of the kitchen by climbing onto the handily placed wheelie bin and taking a jump for the guttering. Using my belt, I improvised a sling for the Remington.

Hostility must improve agility because I found myself on the sloping roof of the kitchen and checking out the window in seconds. As I jumped off the bin it fell over with a crash but nothing else stirred. In the distance a cat gave a shriek, but there was profound silence from 13 Hamer Lane. My progress was apparently undetected. It's amazing how high the walls of a house can seem when you're pressed right up against them trying to climb. The window was just beyond my reach. Heaving myself onto the window ledge with one arm, I struggled with the window with the other. In the end the window catch, which hadn't been tightly shut, gave way to brute force and the window swung open. After another prolonged struggle to get purchase on the walls, I managed to lever myself up onto the window frame and then push my body half inside the building. If anybody had caught me then, I'd have been completely helpless so I wriggled desperately to get through the narrow space. The gun started digging painfully into my back and I had to twist round to free it.

Realising that I was in danger of panicking, I counted up to twenty and then made another, less frenzied attempt to free myself. Patience was rewarded and I found myself facing into the room with my two hands resting in the basin of a massive Victorian sink unit, large enough to bath a whole regiment of servants in. I heaved myself in. The unit gave a groan and pulled away from its wall fastenings as it took my weight, but it didn't give way. Partly to get my breath and partly to orient myself, I sat down on the floor beside an equally enormous Victorian bathtub and waited in silence for a full five minutes. Apart from distant traffic noises there was no sound at all.

Eventually, fearful that I might have staked everything on one last throw and lost, I opened the bathroom door and stepped out. Holding a pencil torch between my teeth, and the shotgun in both hands, I scanned round the landing. I was on the middle floor. When they built these places the architects were trying to impress on their clents that they were buying their own mini-stately home in the suburbs. In this case they succeeded very well. The wide staircase from the ground floor opened onto a gallery that extended along three sides of the building. Besides the door I'd just come through, there were six others. The gallery was crammed with glass display cases. Creepy looking glass eyes winked back at me wherever I shone the light. The space to walk along was confined to a narrow strip along the wall, thickly covered in old newspapers. It was hardly elegant but there was no noise from the floorboards as I listened outside each door in turn.

I decided to search the rooms on the top floor first. The stairs leading up were narrower. There was a nasty musty odour blended with a reek of formalin. There were no locked doors. One room was Dean's bedroom. At least, I decided that it must be Dean's. There was a filthy looking unmade bed in one corner. Unfortunately, he wasn't in it. Clothes lay round the room in jumbled heaps. Hard-core porn magazines lay here and there, but above all there was a horrible smell. The lower layers of debris must have started to rot. In another room I found old suitcases containing female clothing. The name on the cases was Edna Summergill, presumably the long-departed wife of Dennis and mother of Dean. I shuddered as I wondered just how she'd departed from this house. One room, with a wide skylight letting in enough starlight for me to see without the torch, was set up as a taxidermist's work room. The remaining rooms were storerooms crammed with more of the glass cases.

I checked all rooms for possible secret cavities. There were none. If there was an attic, the plan of the house meant that it must be very small.

When I reached the head of the stairs, intending to search the middle-floor rooms, I heard a noise from below. I stood perfectly still, my eyes trying to penetrate the gloom. Then I saw Dennis Summergill creeping up the stairs in the dark. His head was turning from side as he went.

I let him get onto the middle landing before I came up behind him and jammed the gun into his back.

'Mr Cunane,' he said pleasantly. 'We were expecting you earlier. What kept you?'

Before I had the chance to speak, I received a sharp, violent blow on my right shoulder. I knew that someone had shot me. Still holding the gun, I put my left hand over my shoulder. My fingers touched feathers. A broad-shafted dart was sticking out of my shoulder blade. Summergill was looking at his watch.

'Five seconds, I think,' he said. A numb feeling spread down my right arm. The Remington tumbled from my nerveless fingers and seconds later I felt myself slumping forwards to join it on the floor. The last thing I remembered was the front page of the newspaper that my face crashed into before I lost consciousness. It was the *Daily Telegraph* and the headline was 'Fourteen Murders Discovered in Manchester'.

The Legend of Procrustes: in Greek mythology Procrustes, whose name means hammerer or stretcher, was a son of the god Poseidon. He was a serial killer who preyed on travellers on the road to Athens. He ran an inn and gave his unfortunate guests the choice of two beds. Short people were forced into a long bed and stretched to fit. Tall people were put in a short bed and cut down to size. The hero Theseus dealt with Procrustes as he had dealt with others: Theseus cut his head off to make him fit in a bed.

The meaning of the myth may be that it is wrong to try to fit facts to preconceived ideas.

20

Saturday, 22nd September

I came round in a darkened room. I was lying on my back. When I tried to move my arms and legs there was no sensation. Panic roused me to full wakefulness. My first thought was of the *Daily Telegraph* headline I'd impacted with. How cheeky of Summergill to use that particular issue as part of his carpet. Then I remembered crashing to the floor with the anaesthetic dart in my shoulder. Had I lost the use of my limbs? More panic flooded through me. I tensed the muscles in my arms and legs and tried to move again. Gradually it dawned on me that I wasn't paralysed from the neck down. I was lashed very securely to a frame. Even sideways movement of the head was difficult. As my eyes became accustomed to the dim light, I was able to make out details of the ceiling above me. It was a curving brick vault painted with white distemper that was peeling off, leaving bare brick.

I must have lain there dreamily for an hour or so, wondering where the Summergills had taken me. The place looked more like a mortuary than anything, but at least it was quiet. The room was pervaded by a sharp reek of chemicals. My confused mind couldn't distinguish what they were, though one was very familiar. I struggled to recall it. Thoughts were passing through my brain very slowly. I went over every move I'd made in the house. Had they known I was there from the moment when I climbed the back fence?

Eventually, there was the sound of someone coming downstairs. The noise was very muffled, as if I was located in the dungeons of a medieval castle. A door opened behind me, again with a heavy creaking sound. The first sensations of alarm were already arriving in my mind before Dean Summergill pushed his ugly face up against mine and shone a torch into my eyes. Spittle from his open mouth dripped onto my face.

'The bastard's awake, Dad!' he bellowed before swinging his fist into my face for a sickening blow. The next few moments weren't really worth remembering. Dean thumped my head and body with all his strength for what felt like an eternity. The lingering effects of the anaesthetic meant that there wasn't much pain. I lurched in and out of consciousness. The only thought in my mind was that this couldn't actually be happening.

'Weigh on, lad!' the more cultivated voice of Dennis Summergill intervened, just as Dean was really warming to his task of bashing my ribs in. There was a certain unmistakable lip-smacking relish in the way he spoke. Hope that the reprieve would be more than temporary was shattered by his next words. 'There'll be plenty of time for that later. Flailed ribs aren't one of the injuries we want him to have, but a bit of general bruising won't do any harm considering the width of Dr Caulfield's shoulders. We want to have a little chat with Mr Cunane first.' Dean reluctantly ceased pounding me. Icy cold water was poured over my face. It ran down onto my clothes.

The shock of the beating and then the cold made my thoughts run even more slowly and disconnectedly than before. I struggled to recall the words. Caulfield's shoulders? What was he on about?

I wondered how I could ever have been so stupid as to imagine that my spur of the moment raid would surprise a cunning psychopath. Summergill had set his trap. He bent over me and unfastened something outside my peripheral vision. The band round my temples came free. Then he grasped my hair and pulled my head up. Still gasping from the beating and the cold water, I managed to form a more complete impression of my surroundings. I was in a kind of narrow little alcove, the curved walls of the ceiling matched the curved walls of the tiny room.

Dennis let my head go but I struggled vainly to keep it up. He turned away from me and went to an oil lamp fixed on the wall and fiddled with it for a moment. It came to me that that was one of the odours which I had tried to recognise before – paraffin. There was another familiar sweetish smell mingled with it that I couldn't identify. A greenish-yellow light flooded the narrow cubicle. For the first time I noticed the ominous reddish-brown splash marks on the walls of my little prison cell.

They left me for a while but I could hear them rattling around in another room. There was shouting, terminated by an abrupt yell that stopped suddenly in the middle of a rising note. Suddenly, every inch of my body was flooded with fear. I recognised the voice.

They had Lauren Caulfield in the next room. I'm not boasting, but I didn't feel much fear about myself. What was going to happen to me, would happen. I suppose that's mainly stupidity. I can't feel that what happens to me is of great concern, but that sudden, sharply cut off, yell of Lauren Caulfield's turned my body into jelly. It was so out of character for her. What about Kath? Was she still alive as well? Every trace of dreamy lethargy left me. My brain was racing.

That was the state my captors found me in when they returned. I was feebly struggling against the restraints and trembling with fear and rage.

'Well, smartarse, I'm sure you're feeling pleased with yourself now,' Dennis said genially. Again there was that note of relish and deep pleasure in his voice. He was almost purring. His son gave an approving little giggle at his father's wit.

'You certainly gave me more trouble than Dr Caulfield or Ms Headlam did, Cunane. The good doctor folded up sweetly as a nut when young Dean here stunned her,' he chuckled at the recollection. 'Handy little thing, isn't it?' he asked, holding up a black plastic object. I could just make out the words 'Z-Three' on it – an electric stun gun that worked by passing a huge voltage between two electrodes projecting from the end.

'Whatever did you imagine you were going to do with that enormous shotgun? It takes me back to my days in Malaya – an armed man coming after me. Still we coped. Dean thought the stun gun might not be sufficient in your case so we dug out the dart gun. It's unfortunate really, there might be traces of anaesthetic in your blood when they find you. We'll have to cross that bridge when we come to it. You don't use cocaine, do you?'

My mouth was too dry to speak. I struggled to get words out.

'Don't trouble yourself. Shut up or I'll send you to bye-byes again,' he said, waving the stun gun in front of me. 'This is the part I like, when I tell my guests what's going to become of them. I must say you're rather disappointing so far, Cunane. I thought you'd hold up a little better than this. Someone as hard to discourage as you . . . I've been to a lot of trouble watching you but when I heard from George Hanley what you'd been up to in Bradford, I knew that a permanent solution was required.'

At last I managed to croak some words out. 'I bet you're brave with helpless girls aren't you? Undo the straps if you want to see how well I'm holding up.' It was hard to form the words with numbed tongue and lips. Whatever they'd used in the dart, Novocain or something, it must have been a massive dose. If they had undone the straps, I doubt if I could have stood up.

Dean responded to my goading by starting forward to strike me again, but his father restrained him. 'Leave it. He's only trying to wind us up,' he said. 'I've had plenty of practice in killing well-armed enemies. I was in Malaya during the terrorist emergency and I was trained to kill using stealth and evasion . . .'

'Yeah, a bit different from creeping up on dopey young girls. That's all you can manage now, or do you leave that for Dean?' I sneered.

He got really angry. 'Who are you to stand in judgement over me, Cunane? A jumped-up, money-grubbing little detective? We know all about you. I must say I expected a better standard of abuse. But we're going to give you a special treat, believe me. Did you like the scenario I worked out for you earlier? You could have spared yourself all this unnecessary pain if you'd played your part as asked.'

'You're crazy,' I muttered.

'Far from it,' he said. 'I didn't really think you'd co-operate in your own demise. That was just Plan A. It was the unlucky Mr Carter Gumbs who gave me the idea for Plan B. We thought we might arrange for Ms Headlam to have a hammer blow, Dr Caulfield to have defence injuries and another fatal blow. Then your career in crime will be terminated by this,' he said, holding up a kitchen knife. 'Shocking this domestic violence, isn't it? Don't you think the Manchester police will be happy to have caught the Manchester Basher?'

I started laughing hysterically. The knife he was holding was the one which Lauren had snatched up from my kitchen to gralloch her ex-boyfriend Pinnock with. 'What a crazy you are! Can't leave it alone, can you? But did you have to involve your son? God! The poor bugger has enough of a handicap with that face of his, without you involving him in your sadistic games.'

'I see what you're trying to do, Cunane, but whatever you say won't make a scrap of difference,' he said. He spoke a little too calmly to be convincing.

'What have you done with them?' I demanded.

That amused both of them. They tittered like a pair of silly schoolboys. Dean started to say something but Dennis hit him in the mouth. 'It's not your turn. They're mine,' he told him. 'They're still alive, Cunane, but not for too long,' he said, hefting a mason's club hammer into my line of sight. Both striking surfaces were heavily crusted with blood and hair. He noticed me scrutinising it.

'Yes, I know it'll take a bit of convincing for the police to believe that you're the Manchester Basher. However, when they get the forensic report on this hammer, which they'll find clutched in your hand, they'll be well on their way. There's hair and blood on this hammer from Yvonne Clutterbuck, Stacey Shawcross, Lisa Dolan and the interfering Carter Gumbs. The haematologists will have a field day identifying all the blood groups, but they'll do it, don't worry.

He sounded so pleased with his own cleverness that it was almost a shame to correct him.

'Very clever, but you've made one vital mistake,' I said.

'Playing for time?' he asked nonchalantly. 'You wouldn't believe some of the bargains Dean and I have been offered down here. Some of our poor darlings were ready to sell us their own grandmothers when they knew we wanted their pretty heads for our collection.'

Dean giggled at his father's witticism.

'But you've made a fatal error this time,' I insisted.

'I don't think so. Dean and I are the most skilled operators anywhere at this game. I call it my Gestalt Theory. I make a little picture, then I leave it for the police to fill in the details. You see, when they find a piece of material evidence, and there'll be plenty of other bits in your flat besides old Skull-cracker here,' he said, 'they make up the story themselves. You'd be surprised at the corroborating evidence they'll come up with . . . the friends who always knew that you were a murderous bastard. Of course, unlike poor Billy Fox, you won't be around to hear what they say. He revelled in the adverse publicity.'

'That's fine, but the person in there isn't my girlfriend. She's Lauren Caulfield, the GMP forensic psychologist. She's the mistress of Detective Chief Superintendent Philip Pinnock and in no way involved with me. No one's going to believe that she'd let me or anyone else get within a hundred yards of her with lethal intent or help me to kill Kath,' I continued, improvising desperately.

'Dean, a word!' Dennis said sharply to his son, for all the world like a teacher inviting a recalcitrant pupil to step outside the classroom.

By revealing Lauren's identity I might have bought us a short reprieve . . . or maybe they'd kill us all now, out of panic. I'd know very shortly. I could hear them arguing outside the door. Dennis's method of questioning his son involved a fair amount of slapping and punching from the sound of it..

They stepped back into my dungeon again. Dennis raised the hammer above my head and brought it down but stopped it with the palm of his hand before it made contact.

'I'm big enough to admit a mistake,' he said, bringing the hammer down again, this time onto the framework to which my restraining bonds were fastened. 'Your frankness has earned you a slight stay of execution. Normally, I like to despatch my customers within an hour or two of their arrival, as it were,' he said with a grin. 'Dean tends to get a little excited with some of our female guests, don't you? He likes them to linger longer. Some of his young ladies have grown quite fond of him.'

Dean gave a helpless grin, as if being accused of overeating or something equally trivial. I could imagine what Dean's excitement was due to, he was already salivating in anticipation of the thrills to come.

'Wheel the good doctor in, Dean. We're going to give her a real treat. I think Ms Headlam had better stay where she is though.' While speaking, he rubbed his hands together like a craftsman making his hands supple before a delicate procedure. 'As the doctor is so interested in my work, I think it's only fair to give her some hands-on experience.' He sniggered at his own cleverness.

'As for you, we're going to arrange for you to be found on a patch of waste ground. You'll be company for the corpse of one of our young homeless. Does that suit you, Mr Cunane?'

Dean returned pushing a hospital gurney to which Lauren was securely strapped. Her eyes were open, but there was no response in them. I looked again at the cart she was fastened to. It had nothing to do with hospitals. It was a pathologist's gurney similar to the one I'd seen poor Stacey Shawcross being loaded onto at her postmortem. 'Small world,' I thought. That was where I first crossed the path of Lauren Caulfield. The gurney had lots of slots and a drain for the blood to run off for easy cleaning. It was made of some sort of plastic.

'Don't be alarmed, Mr Cunane,' Dennis said reassuringly. 'We had to give her a little shock earlier to ensure ease of handling, but she'll come round soon enough. We had intended that she should die in your flat. But now I'm afraid I shall have to let Dean have his fun with her, then she and Ms Headlam will disappear completely with not even her head left for anyone to grieve over. Those people in VICPAC are very ungrateful to want whole bodies back, aren't they?'

Then turning to his son, he said, 'Dean, show Mr Cunane the instruments we'll be using for his little operation.'

Dean dashed off eagerly. 'This is a cellar under the mews isn't it?' I asked Dennis with genuine curiosity.

'Well done, Cunane,' he said patronisingly. 'You've got further than your plodding friends in uniform. Yes, when the house was built, the first owner was a wealthy eccentric. He had a cellar built under the stable block for his own little experiments in surgery. It's linked to the house by a passage running to the cellar. There was nothing secret about it when we bought the house. It was strengthened and enlarged for use as an air-raid shelter in the war. The estate agent actually showed us round. It didn't take me long to disguise the doorways, I can tell you.'

'Is this where you brought all your victims before

their heads ended up in Billy Fox's cupboard?' I asked. I was curious about just where Billy fitted into the story.

'Interesting you should say that, Cunane. Billy Fox was a bit like you . . . an intriguing challenge that had to be fitted into my plans. He played a very useful role, as you shall eventually.'

'Summergill, the criminal mastermind?' I sneered.

'Not far short of one,' he said proudly. 'I discovered Billy Fox's secret, which is more than you or anyone else ever did, or is likely to do now. But I suppose it's fair to say that I did have the advantage of knowing him. Billy Fox had a mild form of a rare condition called Klinefelter Syndrome. He had two populations of cells in his body. Some of his cells had the normal sex chromosome XY, others had an extra one making XXY.'

It was startling to hear him confirming Lauren Caulfield's belated discovery. I didn't let on that I already knew. There was always the chance that Summergill was wrong. Another investigator might discover the truth about Billy.

By this time Dean had returned with a bundle in his hand. He paused at the door to listen to his father's lecture.

'So you persuaded him to help you kill those girls?' I said, prompting Dennis to continue.

'Tell him, Dad,' Dean insisted. 'Tell him the truth. No one else will ever hear it.'

'Billy was my son's friend. His soul mate in many ways. It was through Dean that I got to know him.'

'Tell him, you old sod!' Dean shouted. 'I want someone else to know.'

'All right, calm down,' Dennis said soothingly. The flare-up raised a flicker of hope in me. Dennis took the bundle from Dean and began unwrapping it. 'You must realise, Cunane, that I have a tremendous interest in human anatomy and physiology,' he said. He untied the end of the bundle revealing a long package of scalpels and other surgical instruments. He held up a scalpel with a wickedly curved blade to the light for my inspection. 'Yes, I doubt if there are many anatomists in this country with my massive experience in dissection. When I first saw Billy, I recognised that he was an interesting specimen.'

'You bastard!' his son interrupted.

'No, on the contrary, Dean. You fill that description better than I do. Your mother and I never did tie the knot.'

Dean cleared his throat menacingly. I waited for him to attack his father but he didn't. I guessed that he never would. Dennis was in complete control.

'OK! Dean, that's enough!' Summergill senior rapped and Dean subsided like a wolf hound on a choke chain.

'You must excuse my son's manners, Mr Cunane,' Dennis continued smoothly. 'Dean himself suffers from an affliction that makes him sympathetic to creatures like Billy. It makes him short-tempered. The ingrown hair in his face gives him hell sometimes but he won't grow a beard as he's been told. It's had a terrible effect on the poor lad's sex life, hasn't it, Dean?'

Dean reached across the frame I was lashed to and grabbed his father's arm in a powerful grip. Dennis twisted free with contemptuous ease.

'Weigh on, Dean. You'll get plenty of chance to release your aggressive feelings later. You can show Mr Cunane just how strong you are.' Dennis's voice was dripping with contempt for his son. They were both equally mad, but then why should I have expected the relationship between these two psychopaths to be like that between a normal father and son?

'Now you must excuse us both, Mr Cunane,' Dennis said with great charm in his voice. 'Dean and I only get the chance for one of these heart-to-hearts when we have a guest down here in the cellar with us. Then I can usually divert him with the prospect of a little sexual relaxation at the expense of our visitor. It's you being a man that's made him so edgy. As for Billy, suffice to say that I took him to a private hospital under a false name and they did a chromosome analysis that confirmed my diagnosis. They wanted to put him on hormone replacement therapy, but Dean and I were quite happy with him as he was, weren't we, Dean?'

'Billy was my friend. You didn't need to grass him up,' Dean said.

'Dean doesn't understand how the police work, Cunane. He won't accept that they need an offering from time to time to keep the public happy. Our luck was bound to run out, just as it did for poor Albert Clark in Bradford. I told Albert, time after time, to be more careful but he wouldn't listen. He was too infatuated with himself. I had to leave him to it in the end. Without me to guide him he soon fell into error. I ask you . . . leaving the tools of his trade on the back seat of his car while cruising through a red-light district. Was that sensible?'

'Stop bragging, Dad, and tell the bastard what you've got in store for him,' Dean said. He didn't sound angry with his father any longer.

'Yes. Well, Cunane, we thought we'd give you the benefit of our surgical skills to remove some extraneous parts of your anatomy. You won't be needing them much, anyway. I believe Pinnock, the plod in charge of the investigation into the so-called Manchester Basher, is looking for a loner suffering from some sort of psychosexual mutilation. So, we intend to make sure that you fill the bill, Cunane. After you've had your little operation the police are going to find your body hanging at the scene of the next Basher murder. They'll think your wounds were self-inflicted. There are plenty of forensic psychologists who will be only too pleased to explain why you maimed yourself, if not your friend Caulfield here. There are lots of cases in the forensic pathology textbooks. It won't be too hard to arrange. We'll hang you up in here first. There's a very convenient stanchion up there.' He gestured to the ceiling where a rusty metal hook protruded through the brickwork. His eyes followed my gaze.

I kept my mouth shut. The merciless expression of self-satisfied cleverness on his face told me that there was nothing he would enjoy more than to hear me beg for mercy.

'Hard man, eh?' he said with a little sigh at my lack of reaction. 'Well, you have a reprieve for the moment. We have to go and find a suitable victim and that might take us some time.' He swept out of the room rather like a prima donna who's just failed to receive an ovation of the length she expected.

Dean leaned over me, favouring me with his curry-scented breath. 'I'm going to leave these where you can see them,' he said, carefully arranging the open instrument wallet in my line of sight. He put them on a little ceramic tray on a stand. 'You'll be screaming for mercy when we get back – they always are. Billy Fox knew nothing about those murders. Dad set him up and coached him in what to say from that book your friend, Liptrot, wrote. He sat up for hours with him, laughing his head off at the mistakes.'

'Come on, Dean. Plenty of time for fun later,' came the muffled voice of Dennis, echoing round the solid vault of the chamber. Dean left, slamming the heavy metal door shut behind him. There was the sound of bolts sliding home and faint receding footsteps and then the place was as quiet as a grave.

I called out to Lauren, but she was still stunned. By straining my ears in that silent place I could just hear her breathing. I became aware that my body was a mass of aches and pains from the beating Dean had handed out. For the moment checking out my body gave me some relief from thinking about what lay ahead. I was sore but in one piece for the time being. The gurney was hard, it was digging into me at several places but then it was designed for corpses.

I could move my head from side to side and my hosts had kindly left the lamp burning so that I could inspect their torture kit. I looked round the room. There was nothing that could be of the slightest help to me. Then I began checking my bonds. I was pressed flat against the plastic gurney by leather straps which came up through slots and were fastened underneath me. There were two loops round my upper arms, and another round my shoulders. Simliar loops held my thighs and legs.

I strained with all my strength against the leather. Nothing budged. I tried again and was rewarded with a very faint creaking sound. By twisting my head I could see there was a crack in the plastic where Dennis had smashed the hammer down. It was a start. I was determined that they would not find me lying helpless on that table. I told myself that none of their previous victims had been strapping types like myself. Surely I could free myself. I tried again. Nothing moved. There wasn't even a creak from the leather. I tried to concentrate my strength into my right arm and the right side of my body. Still nothing moved.

I began to try to strain rhythmically, timing each heave by the number of breaths I took. Something must give, I told myself. I was still fully clothed with the straps passing over my clothing. If I could just get free at one point I would be able to squirm out of the other fastenings. After what must have been at least a hundred heaves I felt a slight feeling of movement in the bonds against my right shoulder. I could lift my shoulder about an inch above the table, possibly the buckle on the strap had been deformed when Dennis lashed out with the hammer. I kept on trying but nothing else was ready to give. I could have wept in frustration.

'Dave, is that you?' asked Lauren. The sound of her voice startled me.

'Thank God you've come round,' I said. 'I thought they'd killed you. Have you seen Kath Headlam?'

Lauren didn't speak for a long time. I thought she was about to tell me that Kath was dead. 'I'm sorry Dave, but she's in a bad way. She's almost completely traumatised. That bastard Dean was doing something to her . . . Dennis stunned her. She's deeply unconscious.'

A wave of frustration passed over me. Despite everything I'd been proved right. I'd found Kath but there wasn't a thing I could do to help her, Lauren either. She'd been working in my kitchen when a pair of workmen arrived. Lauren assumed I'd sent them. They went round the flat checking for damage, then they got to work mending the door. The next thing she knew was when she woke up in the room next door with Dean looming over her. I told her about Dennis's plans for our future.

Lauren didn't start shouting. She kept her scientific cool. 'This kind of planning is so typical. Summergill will probably change his plans several times yet. He gets a tremendous thrill from being in control of things.'

When I asked her what they'd done to her she wouldn't say. We both lapsed into silence for a few minutes. Then I started struggling again. It was futile. I lay back and rested for a while. Perhaps if I tried flexing the powerful muscles in my thighs one of the lower straps might give way. I tried for a long while. There was a slight loosening but not enough to give me freedom. The only parts of me still capable of movement were the head and neck. I tried twisting my head first to the left, then to the right.

At last something was happening. My body was moving horizontally along towards the head of the table. It was only a very slight movement but it was enough. I was able to twist my neck more fully and get my teeth into the leather strap that ran across my shoulders. There was a tremendous feeling of relief when my teeth bit into that leather strap. For the first time I had leverage. Bracing my head against the strap I tried to force myself upwards and pulled forwards another couple of inches. The strain on my neck from holding the position was terrific, but there was no more chance of movement, so I chewed on that hard dry leather for all I was worth. In my mouth it felt as if it was at least half an inch thick, but reason told me it couldn't be. It would never be flexible enough to restrain me if it were.

I chewed until I felt my teeth coming loose. After about an hour the leather was soft and pliable enough for me to try biting through it. There was no way on earth I was going to succeed. Human teeth are just too blunt to chop through thick pieces of tanned and hardened leather, at least in the time available. I gave up. Lauren wept in frustration. Her bonds were even tighter than my own, and the only thing she could move was her fingers but not enough to get them onto the fastenings.

We tried rocking our gurneys and this time she was able to help. The small amount of movement she had in her fingers, combined with levering my head back against the edge, was just enough to push my tray off the trolley. They were designed to hold a motionless corpse not a struggling victim. I went down head first onto the floor, knocking Dean's torture kit off the stand on my way down. I blacked out when my head hit the deck. I've no idea how long I was unconscious but, when I came to, fear of the would-be killers returning was the main thought in my mind. I was upside down with my head jammed against the floor. My legs and body were still in the air, fastened to the gurney that was firmly wedged against the trolley. I was able to see the reason why I hadn't bashed my head in. The floor was made of worn and uneven wooden setts that looked as if they'd originally been laid in the streets.

By heaving and straining desperately, I was able to get one of Dennis's scalpels into my mouth and I used it to saw through the previously softened leather with a jerking motion of my head.

It took a further hour before I severed it. I lay back gasping in triumph. Then fear took over again. Suppose the Summergills chose this moment to return? I sobbed with frustration. I was still fixed to the gurney tray like a Sunday joint waiting to be carved.

'There's a crack in the plastic at the top,' Lauren said. 'If you could work on that . . .'

I began straining my head against the floor, trying to lift up my whole body with the muscles in my neck. At last, the part of the tray beneath my feet slipped free from the table and crashed to the ground with a heavy impact. For the first time I had some luck. I felt the plastic crack as it hit the ground. It snapped completely through into two parts. My back and shoulders were free and I was able to get onto my feet and crash against the iron door until the remaining part of the tray splintered, releasing my arms and legs. I was free.

At that moment we both heard faint sounds from above. The killers were coming back. I rushed to

Lauren's gurney. My fingers were numbed, there were more fastenings than I could possibly release in the time. I tried the door. It was locked.

'Save yourself, Dave,' Lauren gasped.

I picked up the bits of broken gurney and hid them in a corner. I replaced the instrument stand and turned down the flame on the old-fashioned paraffin lamp as low as it would go. Then I lay on top of the trolley hoping that they wouldn't notice that I was no longer pinioned.

'Our only hope is that they don't notice that I'm free. We'll howl and shout to distract their attention and I'll try to surprise them. It's our only chance,' I told her.

From what sounded like a long way away, I heard the faint noise of a door opening. I began screaming and shouting. The fear in my voice wasn't entirely simulated either. Lauren joined in. We must have been realistic enough. When Dennis Summergill flung open the door there was an expression of sadistic pleasure on his face at the sound of other human beings suffering that I'll never forget. I saw him looking down at me in that dim, greenish light. There was a look of pure pleasure on his face. He resembled a gourmet about to consume a favourite feast. He stepped forward eagerly for a close look into my face. I swung over and kicked his head with all the strength in my right leg. He went down as if poleaxed with barely a grunt and I lunged off the table, down on top of him, and pressed the scalpel into his evil heart.

I must still have been roaring my head off. Summergill's eyes popped open in surprise when the thin blade went into his chest. With fear spurring me on, I twisted the handle from side to side for all I was worth. I only wished I had the carving knife in my hand. I'd have taken his heart right out. I suppose I should have cut his throat but I couldn't bring myself to do that. To my horror, before dying, he managed to raise himself on his elbows and look at me, still with that wicked gleeful look on his face. Then he groaned and slumped back.

Dean came in. 'Get off him, Dad,' he said fretfully. 'You promised me a chance – 'Then he leapt back in fear as he realised his mistake. It was lucky for me that he didn't try to attack. He was powerfully built and I was weary. Even so, the threat of being locked up in the cellar again galvanised me into action. I got up and chased after him waving the bloody scalpel in my hand.

Through the open door there was a much larger vaulted room and leading off that a narrow passage lined with what looked like large new bookcases. I ran headlong after Dean. The cases had people in them! I pressed myself back against the wall for a look. The first case held a display of an orang-utan; the next, a mountain gorilla, artfully posed. I'd stumbled onto the Summergills' other little sideline, the trade in illegal stuffed animals.

The delay nearly gave Dean the chance to get away. I reached the door at the far end of the corridor just in time. Dean was feverishiy trying to barricade it shut, when I cannoned into it. It quickly resolved into a pushing contest in which my greater weight won.

Dean was halfway across the floor of the cellar under the main house when I caught up with him. I dived at him and he crashed to the ground. He was squealing in terror as if I'd already stabbed the scalpel into him. He was attempting to defend himself with the stun gun. He tried to shove the electrodes into me but I twisted it out of his hands, pressed it to his neck and pulled the trigger. I got a mild jolt myself but he went rigid, his eyes rolled back into his head until only the whites were showing. Unfortunately, he was still breathing.

Satisfied that he was incapacitated for a while, I went

back into the dungeons to release Lauren and find Kath. The passage leading to them was wide and braced with new-looking concrete pillars and roof joists. The display cases filled the gaps between the pillars. There were other primates, bonobo chimpanzees, common chimpanzees, lowland gorillas; a whole inventory of endangered species. Sickeningly, each case was carefully labelled with an estimate of the existing population of the animal it contained. There were only six hundred and fifty mountain gorillas left, I noted.

I felt fierce joy that I had managed to reduce the population of Summergills by fifty per cent.

The rooms where we'd been held were only one part of what appeared to be an elaborate secret dungeon. One wall was covered by an immense drape made of some heavy material, which partly accounted for the muffled sound as the Summergills entered and left the garage/mews side of their premises.

Kath was in the next cell to mine. She was trussed up as I had been. There didn't seem to have been any obvious physical injury and she was fully clothed, but she was deeply unconscious. She was breathing rapidly with a very deep snoring sound that I'd never heard from her before. Something was very wrong. There was no response when I shook her.

When I reached Lauren I could see she was exhausted by the strain we'd been under. It didn't take me above two minutes to unfasten all the buckles that held her. I helped her off the trolley and she clung to me for a moment. Then a croaking noise came from the body of Dennis Summergill.

'God! He's still alive,' I said, looking round for the scalpel.

'No, it's the death rattle,' Lauren said confidently. 'The last bit of breath was passing through his throat.' I looked down. There was plenty of blood and

Summergill looked dead enough. I didn't feel like checking too closely.

'Come on. Help me get Kath out,' I urged.

'She's only drugged. I'll never get another chance like this,' she said stubbornly. 'I want Philip Pinnock here. I want him to see this before anyone else does.'

I was staggered. It passed human understanding. We'd just escaped by the skin of our teeth and she wanted to hang around. Deciding that her experience must have unhinged her, I grabbed her firmly by the arm and tried to lead her to Kath's cell. She pulled against me. I let her go.

'There's a stairway up here,' I said, pointing. 'We don't need to go out past Dean. This must be where they brought us down.' I ran up the stairs and pushed at the heavy reinforced doorway at the top. It wouldn't budge. Then studying the hinges, I realised that it opened inwards. It was a false door opening into the back of a cupboard just like Albert Clark's. I could see into the mews from between cans of paint and tools on the shelves. I started shifting them but then realised that the cupboard itself was on castors. It slid aside. Our way out was clear.

'And when I found the door was locked,
I pulled and pushed and kicked and knocked.
And when I found the door was shut
I tried to turn the handle, but –'
From 'Humpty Dumpty's Song' by Lewis Carroll

21

Saturday morning

Rage now mingled with the feeling of relief at our deliverance. Lauren stood her ground. Was there no end to her contrariness?

I went down to her again, intent on extracting her from the scene.

'I'm not going and neither are you. Kath will be all right for a few more minutes,' she said firmly. 'All I'll be able to tell the police is that somebody rendered me unconscious in your flat, using a stun gun.' At this she pointed to the stun gun that I'd brought back from the house with me. I'd dropped it outside the door of our cell. 'That stun gun. I'll bet it's got your fingerprints on it.'

I strode forward angrily. Perhaps I should retrieve the gun and use it on her again, anything to get out of here. She moved to block my path.

'Lauren,' I begged, 'be reasonable. Sinclair will believe us. He's already got his sights on Dennis Summergill.'

'Will he believe me when I tell him that when I returned to consciousness the first thing I saw was you stabbing a scalpel into Summergill's chest? Think about it, Dave.'

'Don't be stupid!' I said. 'That was the most sensible thing I ever did!'

'Oh, do what you want!' she said, angrily turning away when she saw that her threat wasn't working. 'But I'm going to save my career, and Phil Pinnock's as well, by getting him here to wrap this up.'

'What makes you think Phil wants anything to do with you? As for your own career, Sinclair is your best bet. He'll reinstate you if you withdraw that database you sent to the Press Association. You can say it was a hoax by a computer hacker,' I said glibly. 'The Press Association are waiting for you to verify it before they release it.' Some of that sounded close enough to the truth to be convincing to me.

'You don't understand,' she said sadly. 'I've invested too much in Phil's career to throw it all away now. I know he'll come back to me if I can show him the way out of his troubles. It's the way we've always operated. We need each other! You don't need me, Dave. You don't need anyone!' she concluded angrily and then turned on her heel and started up the tunnel towards the house.

I sighed. Pimpernel Investigations gave up doing matrimonial cases years ago. Like all private detectives I'd met scores of estranged couples where one partner thought the other would return to them if they just pressed the right buttons. It hardly ever works like that.

Even so, I wasn't totally convinced that Lauren's motives were simply to blackmail Pinnock into being her lover again, or to retrieve her own career as the oracle of the GMP. Lauren had had an awful long time to think while I was struggling to break free from that wretched mass of plastic and leather. Had she hatched some complicated plan for revenge, I wondered?

Kath was still snoring, but not as loudly as before. I undid the straps and covered her up with my jacket, thinking that she'd be all right for a couple of minutes longer while I tried to get Lauren to see reason. Why are scienfists so irrational about their private lives, I wondered? I had more time to look around when I went along the passage than I had last time. The entrance hatch between the cellar of 13 Hamer Lane and the passage was extremely cunningly disguised. The whole cellar was walled with pine panelling including the back of the heavy door to the dungeons. There was a light metal-frame shelving stack just pushed to one side of the door. When the door was in place and the shelving pushed up to the wall no one would suspect the existence of a secret door unless they had an idea of what to look for. A search of the mews and the house would have come up with what Pinnock found in the first place – zilch.

This time, though, there was some incriminating evidence in the cellar besides the hecatomb of illegal animals awaiting discovery. Dean Summergill lay where I'd left him. He was stirring back into consciousness. Whatever voltage I'd given him wasn't enough to stun his ox-like carcass for long.

Rolling him onto his back, I pinioned his shoulders with my knees and put the scalpel to his throat. 'We want a chat with you, Dean. Now Dr Caulfield's very kind. She thinks I shouldn't kill you, at least not until you've answered her questions, but as far as I'm concerned I'd rather top you now and leave you in the dungeons with your Daddy. No one will ever find you there, will they?' Lauren looked at me disdainfully as I spoke, but I'm not a copper and I didn't feel like being polite to an individual who only minutes ago had been intent on torturing us.

Dean was in no doubt at all that he was in mortal danger. All the strength went out of him. His eyes were almost bursting out of his head with fright. 'I'll tell you anything you want to know. Just ask me,' he blubbered. 'It was all his fault. I'm glad he's dead.'

I couldn't believe what I was hearing. I let out a shout of rage so savage that it frightened me to listen to it. Lauren jumped back three paces.

'You filthy pig! You raped those girls and tortured them. Your father as good as told us,' I screamed. I was on the edge of losing control. I shoved the bloody scalpel at him. All thoughts about poor Kath were forgotten.

Dean certainly felt that his last moment had come. His head went back. He fainted. Putting the scalpel to one side I roughly slapped his face. There was no response. I rolled him over again, pulled his jacket down over his arms and then tied his hands behind his back with his belt.

'Get upstairs and check out the house,' I snarled at Lauren. 'I'll really flip if I stay down in these damned cellars much longer or are you going to insist that I keep him here until you get dear old Phil onto the scene?'

She must have believed me because she shot up the cellar steps like a rabbit bolting from a stoat. I could hear her moving about above me. With any luck, I hoped, she might head straight out of the house and into the street.

Dean groaned and then started letting out a series of self-pitying little moans. I got hold of his collar and hauled him to his feet. Without giving him any respite, I pushed him up the cellar steps. The door opened into the old Victorian back kitchen that was now the Summergills' main living room. I recognised it at once from the description Kath had given. I moved the curtain for a look outside. It was still pitch dark.

Lauren came back into the room. It was too much to hope that she'd have normal human reactions.

The place was littered with half-eaten meals congealed on plates. Pride of place was taken up by a narrow glass case, the lower part of which was filled with soil. As I looked, I saw things moving about inside it . . . ants. It was the live-ant display mentioned by Kath. I felt my skin crawl with revulsion.

I brutally kicked Dean's legs from under him and he crumpled into a heap in front of me. He had some explaining to do, but before I could ask a question he started pleading with me in a low tone of voice.

'It wasn't my fault. It was all him,' he whined.

'What was?' I said impatiently.

'Look at that,' he said, gesturing towards the ants with a shake of his head. 'He put that there to remind me. He says human beings are no more important than ants. He did it all. I'm sure he killed my mum when I was just a kid. He said a monster would come and get me if I told anyone. He's always been crazy. Go and look in his bedroom, he has all these photos of stars and planets and things from America. He says human beings are insignificant.'

I looked at Lauren. She was studying Dean with the same expression of fascinated abstraction that she'd shown with her laptop computer yesterday. I relented to the extent of deciding to allow her to 'investigate' for two minutes more. If she was able to repair her relationship with the horrible Pinnock at least it would get her off my back and simplify things to that extent. Two minutes wouldn't hurt Kath. I couldn't go down for her and leave Lauren with this drivelling maniac. She'd probably have him lying on the sofa for a counselling session when I got back.

'Get moving!' I yelled. 'Find the phone! Get lover boy over here if that's what you want.'

'Sorry,' she murmured, 'but this is absolutely fascinating. I don't think anyone's ever had such immediate material from a serial killer. She managed to tear herself away for a moment and search for a phone. My own mobile had gone the same way as my watch. I felt a shiver up my spine when I recalled the way this pair of killers had collected trophies from each of their victims.

Dean was still feebly protesting his innocence. He was rambling on about being just as much a victim of his father as any of the others.

'Oh, shut up!' I said, giving him a push. 'It was you who killed at least half of those women, wasn't it? You're trying to cover it up because you know I'll kill you.' My tone must have been convincing because he began blubbering again.

'I didn't, I didn't, I didn't,' he said over and over again as if repetition alone would convince me. The whining was getting on my nerves. It was all I could do not to start lashing into him. The low, sincere tone he was using was particularly jarring. Then it struck me that Dean had been preparing for this event for years. He must have known that eventually their crimes would be found out and have been pondering on every word that he would say. The only thing that had gone wrong with his preparations was that I wasn't a policeman bound by man-made laws and judges' rules. I decided to let him know this and see if I could rattle the truth out of him before Pinnock arrived.

'Listen, Dean,' I said, 'I've killed your father and whatever way the police look at it I'm sure to be going down for a few years for manslaughter at the very least. So ridding the world of your presence is going to be like a little extra bonus for me. They won't give me much more for killing you both than for just doing your dear Dad.'

I wasn't sure how much truth there was in that. Surely, with Lauren to back me up, I could get away with self-defence? But there was no way of being certain how the Crown Prosecution Service might jump, or that Lauren might not carry out her earlier threat to drop me in it. She was unpredictable enough for anything.

I took the bloody scalpel out of the pocket of my jacket and laid it down on the table beside the ant nest. Dean looked sideways at the knife and shuddered.

'Please, just give me a chance,' he begged with that appalling sincerity of the guilty.

'A chance to do what?' I asked. 'I'll listen but you'll have to convince me that you're telling me the truth.'

'You don't understand,' Dean said eagerly. 'Dad's always killed people. I think he killed my mother. He told me she'd gone away to live in Wales when I was nine. I think he only let me live so he could abuse me.'

'You did your share of that, scumbag!' I told him. Lauren came back in.

'He's on his way,' she said. I never thought it would happen, but a surge of relief swept over me at the thought of Pinnock arriving.

I turned back to Dean. He mistook my relieved expression for one of pleasurable anticipation at the thought of killing, a sensation with which I was sure he was well acquainted.

Once he'd got started, the words came tumbling out of Dean. The main message of his story was that everything was Dad's fault. Dad had killed his mother, he'd abused Dean, and then he'd joined up with Albert Clark for a murder spree in Bradford. Dad had been the driver and the look-out man for Albert. Once, they used Dean to lure one of the women into their car but that was as close as Dean had ever come to murder. Dad had decided to leave Bradford after quarrelling with Albert.

In Manchester they were making a good living from

the house-repair business and the taxidermy racket. Dean had begun to hope that what had happened in Bradford was all a bad dream until one day when Dennis came home early. He was excited. He told Dean that he'd been fixing a curtain rail in the flat of this girl. She'd opened up to Dennis. She was paying too much rent. Did he know anywhere cheaper? Dennis did. He convinced the girl that she'd have to do a secret flit so that they could still go on drawing the old high rent from social services. She must tell no one where she was going. That same night Dennis went to collect her, trailing Dean along unwillingly as look-out man. She had all her bags packed. They loaded her stuff into their van and drove her round to the mews at the back of the house. Once they got the car in the garage that was it. She never came out. Dean took no part but he heard her screaming for days. Then she stopped. The funny thing was that no one missed her. They studied all the papers closely for weeks but there was no mention. Dennis went round to the flat where she'd lived and no one had even been round to ask questions.

After that, they 'moved' lots of girls. Dennis even went out recruiting them at the animal shelter in Moss Side. He always checked them out first to make sure that they had no one interested in them. The idea for the heads had come later, after Dennis had met Billy. He fitted Billy up as the murderer and then handed him over to the police.

As Dean went on and on with his story, my anger with him didn't lessen. The way he told it he was the innocent party, victim of his own father's machinations. I think Dean had forgotten to whom he was talking. It was only a few minutes ago that he'd been eagerly vying with his father for the privilege of cutting me up. Still, the story held up in parts. If he ever told it to a court there would be some who would say that he'd never had a proper chance.

'Did you kill tonight?' Lauren asked quietly.

This jerked him out of his self-serving ramblings. 'Oh, no. We couldn't find a single one of the little tarts. All the usual places are empty. There were tramps and dossers, but no girls. Dad said it would break the pattern if we did a man. He was going to risk it and keep you here for a while until the fuss died down and then pin the blame on you.

I picked up the scalpel and rapped the table with it. Dean's story was a pack of lies, but without months of questioning it was hard to see how anyone would get the full story out of him. He hadn't mentioned a word about the part played by George Hanley in Bradford or about Kath. It was like father, like son. Dennis had prepared Billy Fox as his alibi and Dean had been working out how he would blame everything on his father. I didn't know what to do next. Wait for Pinnock, I supposed, then get Kath. I rapped the scalpel down on the table again. Then an answering sound came from behind me.

I swung round in fright. The instrument I was holding slipped through my fingers. Emerging from the top of the cellar steps was Dennis Summergill's head. He was crawling up the steps. I'll believe until my dying day that the colour of his face was blue, but blood from the wound I'd inflicted had run into his eye sockets. The face was glaring at me with the harsh intensity of one of those paintings Van Gogh did when his sanity was going.

As I quickly stood to defend Lauren and myself, there was an angry rattling at the front door. Lauren dashed off to let Pinnock in. I was only alone in that cluttered little room with the two self-confessed killers for about a minute but it felt like a week.

'Dean, Dean, help me!' Dennis was moaning as Pinnock ran into the room.

'Christ, Cunane! What have you done?' were the first words out of Pinnock's mouth. I swear I'll have them carved onto my tombstone, if I ever reach the stage where somebody wants to provide me with one. At any rate, those words will always be etched on my memory and will always qualify any friendship with a copper, even DS Cullen.

'You gob-shite!' I shouted, anger and rage sweeping away all the fatigue that had been mounting in my tired body.

'Philip, it's not the way it looks,' shrieked Lauren. It did no good. Pinnock jumped at me and tried to grapple me to the ground. I rolled over and crashed into the ant hill, pulling him down with me. The case smashed and ants poured out over us. The whinging Dean leapt to his feet, transformed in an instant and swinging a heavy kick at me as he passed. Dean headed towards the cellar door. I saw him struggling to help his father to his feet as Pinnock engaged me in a head lock. The belt had come off Dean's wrists so he must have been working free all the time he was feeding me his sob story.

Meanwhile, I was giving Pinnock as good as I got. All the rage and fear of the last few days went into the solid blows I landed on his body but he had no intention of letting me go. I was sure I'd have downed him, he had weight and motivation on his side but I was desperate for freedom and stronger than him. Lauren leapt onto his back and began pulling him off.

'Let go! You bloody bitch!' he screamed at her.

'So much for hopes of romance,' I thought as I wrenched his arm off my neck. I caught a glimpse of Dennis, he was now propped up against the cellar door. Dean was hampered from joining in the fray because his beltless jeans had slipped down over his fat thighs. He was rapidly hitching them up.

Suddenly Pinnock was on the floor with Lauren astride him. My first impulse was to get the hell out fast and so, fortunately for all of us, was Dean's. He slung Dennis over his shoulder and went down into the cellar. There was no way I was going to let them get near Kath again.

'You're both under arrest,' Pinnock shouted at Lauren and myselm. He hadn't a clue what was going on but Lauren had. She knew where Dean and Dennis were headed. Once through the dungeon and into the mews they'd be away to some other secret hide-out. If they had George Hanley quiefly beavering away for them in Bradford, how many other secret confederates might they have? Dean hadn't even begun telling us about the murders.

'You've got the wrong man!' Lauren screamed. 'It's the Summergills, not Cunane!' At that she let Pinnock go and headed down the bolt hole.

Pinnock struggled to his feet and looked at me. 'She's right,' I said.

The sight of the secret passage must have convinced him that he'd made a terrible mistake, perhaps it made him desperate to make up for his error. I did what I should have done in the first place – went to phone Sinclair. I went out into the dusty hallway, lined on both sides with cases of mouldering stuffed animals, looking for the phone. It wasn't near the door and it took me a moment to trace the old-fashioned phone cables along the ceiling to the landing on the stairs. The hallway was pervaded with that same sweet chemical odour I'd noticed in the dungeons. I realised now that it was formalin – one of the tools of their trade. Were they preparing to bottle Lauren and Kath's heads when their plans went astray?

It only took a moment to alert Sinclair, back in his own home from Wales. This time I was careful to do what Lauren had neglected. I told him that the Summergills had kidnapped us and were the murderers and that Pinnock was with us, going mad. I flung the front door open to speed his entry.

I raced back into the kitchen and only hesitated a second before plunging back into the cellar and down the passage. It was in total darkness. A reek of paraffin hit me like a wave. I could hear the others moving about but the thickness of the vault walls and the echoing hollowness of the place made it difficult to locate where the sounds were coming from. I flattened myself against the cold, damp wall and crept forward, racking my brain to remember the layout of the place. All I could think was that Dean would be trying to get up the steps into the mews.

I kicked something and it clattered along the ground. Instantly something heavy shattered against the wall above my head. It had been thrown from above. I was drenched in formalin. I bent down in horror, my hand touched something soft and slimy. It was a human head. I let out an involuntary cry.

'Dave!' Lauren yelled. She was only a pace away from me. 'I think they've got Phil. They smashed the lamps as they came down and I think Dean clubbed him.' As she spoke another grisly missile crashed into the wall close by. I could tell what its contents were from the soft splat after the jar shattered.

I felt my way forward to her and grabbed her. She was standing in a doorway, the entrance to Kath's cell. 'He's further forward. Dave, you've got to do something.'

'Get Kath out of here!' I screamed. 'I'll help Pinnock.'

'But how?' I thought to myself. I remembered the endless TV sci-fi programmes of my childhood, glimpsed through clenched fingers while crouching behind the sofa. The aliens always lured the protagonist into a trap. Most of those were filmed in darkened caves.

Then there was the sound of a heavy door swinging open and instantly there was movement in the air, bringing relief from the vile odours accumulating in that crypt. There was even a faint trace of light. Actually real light at the end of the tunnel, and outlined against it I could see the bulky shape of Dean lugging Dennis forward to freedom.

I charged forward and tripped over the body of Pinnock, sprawled at the base of the short stairway. I recovered, and gaining the top of the steps, grabbed Dean's leg as he prepared to swing the door back into place to cut off pursuit.

I heaved; he screamed, kicked and cursed. We all came rolling down the stairs. My fall was broken by the body of DCS Pinnock. I landed on his chest and the blow revived him somehow. At least, his hand shot out and gripped my hair. I had little time to admire my first-aid technique, because almost simultaneously a heavy kick landed on my right temple. I felt myself going down with a lovely pattern of blue and white stars shimmering before my eyes.

Through a peaceful glow of near unconsciousness I could hear Lauren screaming. She'd joined the fray to assist Pinnock, abandoning Kath on the floor. For a moment, the separated lovers were gaining the upper hand but then there was a flash of white actinic light in the darkness. Dennis, still slung over his son's shoulder, and despite being apparently on the point of death a few minutes earlier, had the stun gun in his hand, feebly trying to jab it into Pinnock. I don't know whether Dennis actually stunned Pinnock. If he did Pinnock was his last victim and should be added to the roll of those he killed. What I do know is what happened next.

The whole tangle of bodies fell off the stairway a second time. Dennis was still sparking away with his stunner, presumably trying to get Lauren. He was on the bottom of the heap. After the second flash there was a faint popping sound and the whole staircase was bathed in a gentle blue flame as the formalin ignited. It went phut, phut, phut as it jumped up each step towards the garage door.

Fear of fire revived my heavy limbs. I rolled out of the immediate path of the flames and as I did so caught a glimpse of Lauren going down in a heap. Dennis must have touched her with the stunner. Dodging back to the tiny cell where I'd smashed the plastic tray I grabbed the largest piece of it and ran out to try and beat the flames away from her. Dean was standing at the top of the steps, still with his father on his shoulder, stamping out the modest clinging blue flames with his feet. I grabbed the heavy form of Lauren Caulfield and dragged her away. Kath was further down the corridor leading to 13 Hamer Lane, not in immediate danger. The fire was reviving her as well, she was sitting up, trying to take in the scene.

'Get Phil, get Phil!' Lauren screamed. I lurched back to recover him. I was too late. The creeping flames had licked their way towards the paraffin spills. A wall of orange fire exploded out of the cell door, forming an impassable barrier. There was worse to come. There was a secondary explosion from the top of the crypt steps. The Summergills must have kept a store of petrol in there. It went up. There was a jolt that made my ears pop as the air was sucked forward to feed the combustion above. Then, as the air went forward, a blowback of fierce heat swept towards me. I could hear the sound of agonised screaming above the roar as the

Summergills fried. At least, I hope it was them, and that Pinnock was unconscious or dead by the time the flames reached him. Whatever kind of ambitious fool he was, he didn't deserve to die in agony.

I tried to get to him, beating at the flames with the plastic board, trying to make a way through the searing heat. It was hopeless. As I struggled flames swept over the long drape by the steps. When it shrivelled something behind was briefly revealed and then enveloped in a wall of blue fire. There was now no hope of recovering Pinnock, dead or alive.

I'll never know how I managed to race the fire out of that passage. I tried to hustle Lauren and Kath down between the encased animals that came to life for an instant as the flames reached them. Looking over my shoulder, I saw fire searing the orange fur of the orangutan. It looked as if he were dancing.

What I do remember, was that as I reached the end of the underground corridor, the door that led to safety was swinging shut. There was a terrific current blowing towards us as air rushed in from the front door to feed the inferno behind us. I think it was the sight of that heavy door gently swinging shut that gave me the strength to drag Lauren and Kath on. The formalin on all our clothes had burst into flame and we were screaming in terror, but I was able to jam the door open against the fierce draught and haul them through. We scrambled up the stairs from the cellar and out of the front door.

Police cars were arriving as we reached Hamer Lane. I tore the burning clothes off Lauren, who to my eyes was in a worse state than either Kath or I was. Cullen ran forward and sprayed us all with a dry-ice extinguisher from his car. I lay on the ground gasping. My hands were in agony. Incredibly, there were still live ants all over me, last survivors of the Summergill household.

Sinclair came out of the shadows in the street.

'What's going on? Where's Pinnock?' he asked frantically, while trying to make sense of the sight of two people writhing on the ground in a heap of smouldering clothes. More uniformed police began arriving. In my recollection this took place in seconds, but it may have been longer. Time had been telescoped. Weirdly, the house gave no immediate sign of the underground fires that were being stoked up below.

Sinclair hesitantly went forward with two uniformed men clutching firearms behind him.

He was blown through the air, right off the top of the front doorstep, when the house went up. To describe it as a blast furnace is a total error. A blast furnace is controlled, confined by thick metal. This was much more elemental than that. It was like a volcanic eruption. Flame poured out of the downstairs windows, then out of the upstairs. The house was a mass of dry wood and flammable liquids.

Kath, Lauren and I were already in an ambulance heading towards Withington Hospital by the time the fire brigade arrived. I heard the sirens roaring past us as we went down Palatine Road. I knew they were wasting their time. Those flames were unquenchable.

'Any link with the Billy Fox case is purely coincidental. A senior officer of this police force has lost his life while completing a longstanding investigation into the abuse of animals and any attempt to link his death with previous cases he worked on is not only wrong, but grossly offensive to his memory. Having said this, we are not denying that there may be a link between those who perished in their own booby trapped premises and the Bradford killings of the 1980s. Precisely what that link was may never be determined as they are dead and Albert Clark refuses to speak. Press release by the GMP after the death of DCS Philip Pinnock

'Case Closed

When pressed on the issue, the police representative confirmed that no one was now being sought In connection with the recent murders of three young women and a man in Manchester. Furthermore, the search for the killer of Yorkshire animal lover, Enid Maxwell, has also ended, although arrests are anticipated of those who took part in the rare animal smuggling ring.' Report in the *Daily Telegraph*

22

Saturday – mid-morning

The ward sister kept coming back to assure me that my burns weren't so bad. I couldn't pull myself away from the window. Her professional concern was that the fire had traumatised me. It wasn't that. My mind has so many compartments that I was able to shunt the previous night's experiences into a recess. It was the clear light of a mild autumn day and the brown leaves scampering about in a mild breeze on the lawn below that attracted me. I vowed that I'd never go into a cellar again. I kept looking up at the sky.

Eventually a visit from DS Cullen brought me back to reality. 'Sister says you're feeling a bit ropy, cocker,' he said cheerily. I looked him over, he was smartly dressed in a dark suit, this time complete with a blue shirt. Something sinister was going down. My eyes must have glazed over because he leaned across and prodded my sore shoulder. I winced.

'Sorry, mate, but Mr Sinclair wondered if you could clear up a few points for him. He'd come himself but he burnt his hands quite badly and he also has to give a news conference at twelve.'

I grinned through the pain. I could easily imagine that Sinclair wanted us all to get our stories straight. 'How's Dr Caulfield?' I managed to croak through cracked lips. 'She was more badly burnt than either Kath or me.'

'She's sedated at the moment. Her upper back is burnt but you managed to get her clothes off before it got really bad,' he said. 'I suppose that's where practice makes perfect, eh Dave?' he said, then laughed at his own joke.

'Looks as if DCS Pinnock died a hero's death then?' he said, looking at me closely.

I grunted affirmatively and a look of relief spread across his face.

'Yes, it looks like he finally made the link between the attacks on animals and the Basher Killings. Must have come up with it on his own – that the same disturbed mind was responsible for both sets of atrocities, like?'

I tried to keep a poker face while Cullen spun me this

yarn. The story must have sprung from the fertile brain of Sinclair. That man was the spin doctor to end all spin doctors.

'We're going to put it out that he was making some kind of individual scouting mission to the suspects' house when they sprung that fire trap on him. It's better that way, don't you think, Dave?'

I gave a slow nod by way of reply.

'But, Lauren . . .' I said after a moment's thought.

'Oh, she'll back the story up, Dave. Pinnock's got a wife and children and he did die in the line of duty if you look at it one way.'

'I suppose so,' I said, and then turned away to stare out of the window again.

Cullen breathed a heavy sigh of relief. 'Mr Sinclair said you'd be sensible. We can count on you to keep shtoom, then? There might be awkward questions for you otherwise . . .'

'When have I ever done anything to damage the reputation of the GMP?' I asked sombrely.

'Yeah, well . . . er . . . I'd give you a lift home mate, but I've got to see Sinclair. He's anxious to get on with the press conference. Lucky this all blew up on a Friday night, in one way. The Sunday papers will make a meal out of it, but then interest will wane. Whereas if it had happened on a Monday, the press would've spent all week poking and probing.'

I raised my eyebrows at this cynical appraisal of the power of the press but he was anxious to go. Everything had worked out well for the GMP, at least as far as Sinclair was concerned. The cremation of the two Summergills and himself that Pinnock had caused by his stupidity was going to be presented as a heroic bit of policing. It was obvious also that no one was anxious to make enquiries into my part in the proceedings.

'That wraps it all up then, does it?' I asked.

'Well now that you ask, there are still a few loose ends. There's Kath Headlam and Cedric Liptrot.'

'There's nothing I can do for you there. Cedric's been promoted into one of the world's leading experts on serial killing thanks to Mr Sinclair and the late Philip Pinnock. No power on earth could stop him singing to the media like the proverbial canary.'

'Yes that's true, but what does he know, Dave? From what you said I believe that he was even more sceptical than the late Pinnock. Mr Sinclair has arranged to have a meeting with him. He's to be given the tapes and the video-recordings of all the meetings with Billy Fox. Mr Sinclair believes that it's a matter of public interest that he writes a truly informative account of the Fox murders and when he's done that he's to be given access to the files on the Summergills.'

I must have slumped back into the bed after this. Cullen shook my painful right shoulder, still throbbing from the wound inflicted by Dean's dart. I shrieked.

'Sorry! Are you all right, mate? Do you want the nurse?' he asked.

'What about Kath?'

'There's good news for you there, Dave. Her old TV company have had a little reshuffle at the top. There's every chance she'll be offered her old job back.'

I didn't bother to ask what favour had been traded in for this. Permission for the TV company to make a series about car crime or the vice squad was my guess.

'Well,' I said, spitefully, 'you seem to have covered everybody apart from one very important person.'

'Who's that then, Dave?' Cullen asked cheekily.

'Lena Liptrot. She must have a very shrewd idea about what really went on and she has a very commercial attitude.'

'Interesting that you should mention her. You asked for info about the Liptrot family background. I got a researcher in our office onto it right away and guess what she found?' he said tantalisingly.

'Oh, come on, Sergeant,' I said, deliberately croaking to make my condition seem worse, 'Can't you see I'm an injured man? Give!'

'I don't know about that, but I suppose I should be grateful for the tip. Anyway, Cedric Liptrot is actually the son of one of the last people to be executed at Armley Jail in Leeds. His father, an Irish labourer called Alexander McGarrigle, killed his first wife in 1948 so that he could marry Lena Liptrot. Liptrot's her maiden name. She gave birth to Cedric shortly after McGarrigle's arrest. She put her maiden name on the birth certificate but a check of the hospital records shows that Lena gave birth in a private ward and was originally entered in hospital records as Lena McGarrigle. I phoned Lena at the Ramada Hotel. It was unfortunate, really. I didn't mean to let anything slip, but I asked for Lena McGarrigle by mistake. I think Lena's going to be very quiet indeed for a while.'

I tried to laugh at this news but it came out as a protracted bout of coughing. Frying up the Summergills really had generated a hell of a lot of smoke. I coughed until the covers slipped off my bed and an angry nurse appeared to rebuke Cullen.

'There's more,' Cullen said when the nurse had rearranged me in bed. 'It doesn't look as if Lena was aware of what Alexander had done until he was arrested. She was independently wealthy and quite a catch for Alexander, who from his photographs looked something like the young Sean Connery. The only problem was that he was already married. Divorce wasn't the easy option then that it is now,' he said. 'Lena probably wouldn't have married a divorced man anyway. He solved his difficulty by strangling his wife and burying her in the back garden. The corpse was discovered three years after he married Lena.

I was purple in the face from trying to suppress a laugh and another bout of coughing by this time.

'Do you want me to go on?' he asked. Genuine anxiety at the state of my health appeared on his face for the first time since he arrived. 'Shall I bring the nurse back or something?'

'Water,' I croaked. He poured out a glass for me. I drained it and he looked on expectantly.

'How did the lovely Lena come to be an heiress then?'

'The family were in coal,' Cullen explained. 'Owners, not miners. When the mines were nationalised there was some compensation. Not much, but enough to keep her in clover.'

I lay back on the bed trying to sort out my emotions. I really was exhausted and poisoned.

'Well, I must be going,' he said after a decent interval. 'I'll see you again, cocker.'

'Yeah, and bring some grapes next time,' I drawled.

I was in hospital longer than I expected. 'Smoke inhalation and delayed shock,' the consultant said. I was on a ventilator for three days and could hardly move for several weeks after that. My complications had something to do with the massive dose of anaesthetic that I'd received from the veterinary dart as well as the smoke I'd inhaled. It was just as well that I was immobile. I was fretting about why they wouldn't allow me to see Kath. Demands for a visit were met with bland answers about her not being too well at the moment.

Kath's father came round to the hospital to collect the key of the flat. He didn't come in to see me directly. A carefully written note arrived first, borne to my bed by a highly amused ward sister.

'My goodness, Mr Cunane,' she said. 'You've got some very cautious friends. The gentleman who wrote this insisted on inspecting the sluices and the sanitary arrangements before he would enter the ward.'

I read the note.

Dear Cunane,
I shall understand if you don't wish to see me but there is a personal matter I wish to discuss.
H.Headlam
Commander RN (retd)

When he arrived Headlam examined my charts for some moments before speaking. He asked for the key of my flat so he could move out his daughter's belongings and then after many insincere enquiries about my health came round to the real purpose of his visit.

'I'm not very clear about what happened to Kath. She seems to be incoherent. According to her she was having a cup of tea with this fellow in Yorkshire, George Hankey or Hanley, or something, at this little school house. Then the next thing she remembers is waking up in this cellar belonging to these two chaps the police have down for the animal smuggling racket and all these murders.'

'Doesn't she want to see me?' I asked.

'That's just it. They've moved her out into the psychiatric wing. She's suffering from extreme shock. The only male she will allow to approach is me. She just screams and shouts if any of the doctors come near her. There was no physical damage. She wasn't . . . er . . . interfered with.'

'Is this going to be permanent?' I asked.

'The best the doctors will say is that with time and rest her mind may regain its natural balance.'

'What about her job?' I asked, thinking about what Cullen had said.

'Liptrot was very generous. She's to be paid in full and receive credit for the TV series.'

'I didn't mean that. I thought she was to be offered her old job at the TV studios back?'

He shook his head sadly. 'There's no question of that. Perhaps in time when her mind recovers. She's to be moved to a residential unit in Ambleside where I can be near her. I hoped . . .'

'I'll come and see her at any time,' I said hastily.

He seemed pathetically grateful. The Commander seemed to have shrunk and grown old. He was no longer the peppery naval officer but a man with problems that he wanted to share. When he'd gone I thought long and hard about everything. I'm not into heavy-duty guilt trips. I'd done everything I could for Kath. The only reason she was still alive was because I'd gone round to that house. The Commander on the other hand . . . If he hadn't been so unpleasant on that Sunday morning when Cullen and Gobbo called, I might have gone with Kath to Chillgate on that fatal Tuesday . . .

Then again, if I'd been strong enough to turn the Liptrot commission down in the first place . . . I spent a lot of time going over all the might-have-beens.

When I did get back to my flat after three months in hospital there was a pile of mail to wade through. It included a healthy cheque from Headstone Press, paid on behalf of the Liptrots, and a letter from Lauren Caulfield, written on pink notepaper.

My dear David,

By the time you read this I shall have left Manchester. I'm sorry that you suffered such bad effects from the smoke on that terrible night. You may be wondering why I didn't come to see you. I know it's totally unfair, but I can't stop blaming you for the death of Philip Pinnock. The speed with which he came round to 13 Hamer Lane told me that in his heart of hearts he still loved me and I blame myself as well as you. If I hadn't helped you to overcome him he might have lived.

Enough of regrets.

Thanks to help from Mr Sinclair, who won't hear a word said against you, by the way, I've obtained a post as Assistant Governor at Greenash Secure Psychiatric Prison. I start my duties next month and am looking forward to the job.

David, there is something else I must tell you because it affects us both. I believe I am with child and that the child is yours. I tell myself that it's Philip's child but, as he had had a vasectomy, it can only be yours. I intend to have the child and bring it up under the name of Philip Pinnock. In due course my solicitor will be in touch with you regarding maintenance payments.

I hope you don't feel bitter about any of this but I'm sure you're a big enough man to take all this in your stride.

Best wishes,
Lauren Caulfield

I lay down on the carpet and howled. The woman was barking mad and she was going to the right place to get help for it. I sat up and laughed until tears were streaming down my cheeks. There was something comic in the style of the letter. I'd never suspected that Lauren, the hard-nosed scientist, had this romantic, Barbara-Cartlandish side to her character. It was pure unalloyed joy to read between the lines of Lauren's letter. I thought of the microscopic sperm battling for success in that muscular, alcohol-laden body and then actually succeeding. It made everything I'd gone through look trivial. Still, she was going to have a hard time extracting support from me. The CSA would have to get their DNA sample first, and there was no way I was going to give it voluntarily.

Then I had second thoughts. The child would have enough trouble labouring through life as Philip or Philiippa Pinnock with Lauren Caulfield for a mother. I would do whatever I could for it.

I was thinking these noble thoughts when there was a rap on the door. It was Sergeant Cullen.

'Still off your oats, Dave? You look a bit flushed,' he said genially.

'No, Sarge. I've just had some very interesting news,' I said mildly.

'It's not Detective Sergeant any more Dave,' he corrected me. 'I've been made up to Inspector,' he said proudly. His interest in my health was not profound. 'The Chief Constable asked me to bring this to you. He'd have presented it himself but Mr Sinclair told him that it was best to avoid unnecessary publicity.'

He then drew himself up and very formally handed me a framed certificate.

My eyes were almost bugging out of their sockets as I studied it closely. It was a letter of commendation from the Chief Constable thanking me for my efforts to help Detective Chief Superintendent Pinnock in his struggle to apprehend the Summergills. I could see that this was a serious moment for Cullen and I received his offering in the spirit in which he'd given it. Then we toasted his promotion and my award with a glass of malt whisky each, a very small glass; and, when he'd left, I hung the commendation up in my toilet. If the GMP wanted a degree of secrecy in the affair, that was fine with me.

Was it my imagination or was there already something a little officious in Cullen's manner?

*

I took some time off work to ponder all these things. The payment I'd received from Headstone was generous enough to enable me to afford it. Apparently my health had been insured by the publisher and in addition to the fee from Cedric there was a nice sum from the insurer. Cedric's book was rushed into print to catch the fresh wave of interest Billy's death had aroused. There were trailers on the television for the series based on the book that was going out to fifteen countries across Europe as well as Australia, New Zealand and North America.

I see Jay Anderson from time to time. He sorted out his problems with the odious Mallick. There was a community meeting arranged by the local vicar at which Mallick had to admit that he was in the wrong and back down.

I used some of the money I got from the Liptrots to buy some very heavy duty, copper-bottomed pans, saucepans and a sauté pan for my kitchen. It was the one place that I felt the visit of the Summergills to my home had left violated. The expense was like a sacrificial offering and brought a feeling of sanity and calm back to my daily life.

That's a lot more than I can say for my sleeping hours. Often, just before I fall asleep I'm troubled by a memory of what I saw when the flames sweeping the Summergill dungeon enveloped that immense curtain that hung by the cellar steps. Behind the curtain, there were racks with row upon row of jars containing severed heads. No trace has ever been found. I've asked. The heat in that inferno destroyed all remains, human and animal. Only in my memory do those victims, the anonymous dead, still survive and I don't intend to forget them, however convenient it may be for others.

I visit Kath every weekend and there's been some

improvement in her condition. The doctors say it will be a long job. The Commander and I often go for walks over the Langdales. The remains of Billy Fox were cremated so no one will ever be able to prove anything about his chromosomes now.

Selected entries from

Database on 14 victims

Prepared by

Dr L.C. Caulfield B.Sc. Ph.D.

(Circulation Restricted)

MURDER: Mulligan, Sharon Jacqui Number: 1

Approx date of murder:	*Jan 1990*
Time if known:	*Unknown*
Location:	*Unknown*
Victim's last known location:	*Shared flat in Stone Bank Rd, Fallovlleld, MIC*
Police enquiries initiated?	*No*
Desc. of victim:	*Lightly built, undernourished, 4' 10" tall, very pale complexion, hollow cheeks*
Description of location:	*Semi-derelict squat. Now demolished*
Date of last sighting of victim:	*25 Dec 1989*
Condition of body:	*Torso not found, head preserved, signs of decay*
Body parts found:	*Head, preserved in Fonnalin (11% solution)*
Position on shelf:	*No.4, lower shelf*
Cause of death:	*Not known, decapitation not ruled out*
Presumed age at death	*18*
Occupation of victim:	*Student*
Hair colour:	*Brown*
Eye colour:	*Hazel*
Ethnic origin:	*European*
Sexual orientation if known:	*Hetero*
Frequency of sexual contacts:	*Active, 2 boyfriends*
Education:	*Alcock & Brown HS. 6 GCSEs. City College*
Special interests:	*Animal rights*
Number of close friends	*2*
Number of relatives visited in previous year:	*I*
Religion:	*C of E*
Name of next of kin:	*Shaun Mulligan, half-brother*
Maritial status of parents:	*Unmarried, father not known*
Dysfunctional family?	*Yes*
Medical history:	*Serious kidney infection, abortion at age 16, treatment for STD at St Luke's Clinic.*
Previously known to social services?	*Yes*
Previously on 'at risk' register?	*Yes*

Previously in care of local authority?	*Yes*
Previously known to police?	*Yes*
Nature of criminal offence:	*Shoplifting – 2 cautions*
State of dental hygiene:	*Poor, 3 caries, 3 loose fillings*
Result of postmortem Dental examination:	*Teeth broken by grinding. Tongue partly severed by biting*
Spectacles?	*No*
Cranial index:	*1.02*
Pathologist's description of facial expression:	*Rigor despite softening effect of formalin*
Identifiable possession:	*Pottery mug, labelled Sharon – present from Blackpool*
Financial status:	*No bank or savings account traced*
Possible defence injuries:	*None detected*
Bruises:	*At base of r.jaw*
Semen stains:	*None detected*
Fibre traces:	*Cotton – long fibre egyptian*
Random victim?	*May have been targetted as drug abuser*
Stalked victim:	*May have met Fox, social contact*

NOTES:

Facial expression and dental evidence suggests that Sharon Mulligan died in great fear. This suggests that decapitation was not the immediate cause of death. The mouth was open contributing to the expression of horror. The jar containing this victim's head was on the bottom shelf and was the only one facing away from the room. The state of preservation of the head was good but it had been exposed to air for some time before being placed in Formalin and there was some decay. This, together with the unpleasant gaping aspect of the jaw, suggests that this head was the first to receive the preservation treatment.

The victim's brother did not report the disappearance to the police because he thought Sharon might have her own reasons for disappearing – possible criminal offence which she had been involved in. Brother would not explain further. This victim was a heavy user of crack cocaine – high concentrations found in serum traces.

LINK WITH FOX:

Shaun Mulligan, the victim's half-brother, was at primary school with Billy Fox. The mug labelled "Sharon – a present from Blackpool" was identified by Sharon's brother. Fox was using it as a shaving mug.

MURDER: Lee, Diana Number: 1

Approx date of murder:	*Apr 1993*
.Time if known:	*Unknown*
Location:	*Unknown*
Victim's last known location:	*72 Kelmscott Road, Chorlton, M/C*
Police enquiries initiated?	*No*
Desc. of victim:	*Small. 5′ 2″ tall, well built with long black ponytail. Cheerful and pleasant expression noted*
Description of location:	*Furnished flat in Vic. House*
Date of last sighting of victim:	*Mar 1993*
Condition of body:	*Torso not found, head preserved*
Body pails found:	*Head, preserved in Formalin (10% solution)*
Position on shelf:	*No. 5, upper shelf*
Cause of death:	*Not known, decapitation not ruled out*
Presumed age at death	*18*
Occupation of victim:	*Unemployed, waiting to start college*
Hair colour:	*Black*
Eye colour:	*Dark hazel*
Ethnic origin:	*Anglo/Chinese*
Sexual orientation if known:	*Hetero*
Frequency of sexual contacts:	*Not known*
Education:	*A. Lincoln HS M/S 8 GCSEs. Albigensian VI form*
Special interests:	*Volunteer in animal shelter*
Number of close friends	*3*
Number of relatives visited in previous year:	*2*
Religion:	*RC*
Name of next of kin:	*Evelyn Park – Aunt*
Maritial status of parents:	*Deceased*
Dysfunctional family?	*Yes*
Medical history:	*Appendix removed (age 12)*
Previously known to social services?	*Yes*
Previously on 'at risk' register?	*Yes*

Previously in care of local authority?	*Yes*
Previously known to police?	*Yes*
Nature of criminal offence:	
State of dental hygiene:	*Poor, teeth stained, many caries*
Result of postmortem Dental examination:	*Evidence that teeth had been ground– pieces of broken teeth residue in mouth*
Spectacles?	*Yes*
Cranial index:	*1.13*
Pathologist's description of facial expression:	*Calm, tranquil – relaxed as in sleep*
Identifiable possession:	*Ball point pen engraved with name*
Financial status:	*£72 in building society account*
Possible defence injuries:	*Signs of slapping on both cheeks*
Bruises:	*Faint on face*
Semen stains:	*None detected*
Fibre traces:	*Strand of blue nylon cord (washing line in the hair*
Random victim?	*Likely*
Stalked victim:	*Possible*

NOTES:
Diana's head was among the best preserved which may account for its prominent place on the top shelf of the trophy cupboard. Diana was similar to other victims as a single girl without any particularly close relationship with a friend or relative. Her landlady assumed that Diana had simply done a flit owing a months rent. Benefit had not been claimed since March and Diana had funds in the building society which would suggest that there was no immediate financial problem. Diana's clothing and property had been entirely removed from her flat in Chorlton. Diana's disappearance was not reported and there was considerable difficulty in finding someone willing to identity the head. Faint finger marks on face suggested a large hand.
Diana was eventually identified by her former social worker, Angela Mallory. There is no evidence that Diana Lee ever was in the same care home as Fox – she was much younger. Mallory strenuously denies that there was ever any contact with Fox through her agency. Her spectacles had been taped onto the head as with No. 6.
Diana's long pony tail had been removed - roughly cut off with blunt scissors.

LINK WITH FOX:
It is not known how Fox met Diana Lee. The possible link through social worker Mallory has been thoroughly investigated, so far no evidence has come to light proving that Mallory introduced victim to Fox. Billy Fox worked at the Abraham Lincoln HS as a technician in 1989.
The pen belonging to Diana was found behind Fox's bookcase.

MURDER: Greene, Janet Wilhelmina Number: 12

Approx date of murder:	*Mar 1994*
Time if known:	*Unknown*
Location:	*Unknown*
Victim's last known location:	*41 Egerton Close, Fallowfield*
Police enquiries initiated?	*Yes*
Desc. of victim:	*Average height. 5′ 4″, full figure, dowdily dressed, overweight*
Description of location:	*Rented top floor flat*
Date of last sighting of victim:	*Mar 1994*
Condition of body:	*Torso not found, head preserved*
Body pails found:	*Head, preserved in Formalin (11.5% solution)*
Position on shelf:	*No. 3, upper shelf*
Cause of death:	*Not known, decapitation not ruled out*
Presumed age at death	*21*
Occupation of victim:	*Full time university student*
Hair colour:	*Dark*
Eye colour:	*Hazel*
Ethnic origin:	*European*
Sexual orientation if known:	*Hetero*
Frequency of sexual contacts:	*Not known*
Education:	*Scargill HS Leeds*
Special interests:	*Environment, animal rights*
Number of close friends	*8*
Number of relatives visited in previous year:	*2*
Religion:	*Lutheran*
Name of next of kin:	*Ulrika Greene – Mother*
Maritial status of parents:	*Divorced 1985*
Dysfunctional family?	*Yes*
Medical history:	*Admitted to psychiatric hospital twice – acute nervous hebephrenia. Required regular medication*
Previously known to social services?	*Yes*
Previously on 'at risk' register?	*No*

Previously in care of local authority?	*No*
Previously known to police?	*No*
Nature of criminal offence:	*None*
State of dental hygiene:	*Good*
Result of postmortem Dental examination:	*No damage to teeth, remains of capsule found in mouth – Temazepam*
Spectacles?	
Cranial index:	*1.25*
Pathologist's description of facial expression:	*Relaxed, peaceful*
Identifiable possession:	*None found in Fox's possession*
Financial status:	*On student grant: loan facility unused*
Possible defence injuries:	*None*
Bruises:	*None*
Semen stains:	*Strong fluorescence*
Fibre traces:	*Short black woollen fibres in hair as No. 11*
Random victim?	*Unlikely*
Stalked victim:	*Likely*

NOTES:

The head had been manipulated post mortem to produce an almost grinning expression on the deceased face. There were no signs of struggle and this together with the remains of the Temazepam capsule suggests that she was heavily drugged after her abduction. The victim shared a flat with two other female students. She had remained in the flat during vacation – for study purposes. When the flatmates returned for term they found that Janet had moved out, to live with her boyfriend as they assumed. It was only a week later when the boyfriend called looking for Janet that they realised she was missing. No alert was raised until the university History Department had contacted her mother, now resident in Osnabrück, Hanover, Germany, that an effort was made to establish Janet's whereabouts. Even then the police were not informed for three more weeks. It was assumed that Janet had left the university following warnings by her Academic Tutor in February. Eventually at her mother's insistence an extensive check was made of psychiatric hospitals and institutions and homes for the destitute. Sightings of a female answering Janet's description, subsequently proved to be another person named Greene, persuaded the Police that she was living rough in London. Among several, valuable items missing with the victim were Meissen figurines inherited from her German grandfather (see list below). DNA tracing proved to be impossible – sample too small.

LINK WITH FOX:

None immediately apparent.

Egerton Close is near Fox's flat & the only viable suggestion seems to be that Fox had spotted her in the streets & followed her to her home.

MURDER: Aldritt, Maeve Patricia Number: 14

Approx date of murder:	*Jul 1994*
Time if known:	*Unknown*
Location:	*Unknown*
Victim's last known location:	*61 Birtch Gardens, Rusholme*
Police enquiries initiated?	*Yes*
Desc. of victim:	*Small. 5′ 1″, slightly obese, dark haired. had a slight speech defect and very short sight*
Description of location:	*Semi-det house shared by nurses*
Date of last sighting of victim:	*Jul1994*
Condition of body:	*Torso not found, head preserved*
Body pails found:	*Head, preserved in Formalin (11.5% solution)*
Position on shelf:	*No. 2, middle shelf*
Cause of death:	*Drug overdose possible*
Presumed age at death	*22*
Occupation of victim:	*Nurse at St Mary's Hospital*
Hair colour:	*Black*
Eye colour:	*Brown*
Ethnic origin:	*European*
Sexual orientation if known:	*Hetero*
Frequency of sexual contacts:	*Was engaged*
Education:	*Convent, Ballinrobe, Mayo, Ireland*
Special interests:	*Football fan – Manchester United*
Number of close friends	*21*
Number of relatives visited in previous year:	*12*
Religion:	*RC*
Name of next of kin:	*Eilis Aldritt (Mother)*
Maritial status of parents:	*Father deceased*
Dysfunctional family?	*No*
Medical history:	*Had a tendency to stoutness and had tried various 'slimming cures' including amphetamines*
Previously known to social services?	*No*
Previously on 'at risk' register?	*No*

Previously in care of local authority? *No*
Previously known to police? *No*

Nature of criminal offence: *None*

State of dental hygiene: *Good*
Result of postmortem
Dental examination: *No damage to teeth*
Spectacles? *Yes*
Cranial index: *1.1*
Pathologist's description of facial expression: *Tranquil*
Identifiable possession: *Set of pearl rosary beads found in Fox's possession*
Financial status: *£2700 in Deposit Account at Bank of Ireland*
Possible defence injuries: *None*
Bruises: *None*
Semen stains: *None detected*
Fibre traces: *None*
Random victim? *Unlikely, often in company*
Stalked victim: *Had complained about a Peeping Tom*

NOTES:
Head was very well preserved and had a calm expression. There were traces of tape having been applied to the mouth. Maeve Aldrift was the last victim (as far as is known) and possibly the unluckiest. She was nervous about the neighbourhood and rarely left either the hospital or the house except in company of her boyfriend or another nurse. On the day she disappeared she was alone in the house and it is thought that her killer gained access on some excuse. An external water pipe had been damaged some days previously. Miss Aldrift had also complained to her fellow residents that there was a black man acting as a Peeping Tom from some waste ground behind the house. Unfortunately they did not report this and discounted her fears because of her known nervous temperament. On her disappearance the police mounted an extensive search of the area, they questioned a number of known sex offenders because of the Peeping Tom connection. A considerable amount of Miss Aldrift's personal effects including clothing and personal souvenirs were missing from her room. Her fiancé, Joseph Talbot, was questioned extensively regarding the disappearance. When he committed suicide in October 1994 Police enquiries were concluded. Talbot must also be regarded as a victim in the case.

LINK WITH FOX:
None known prior to the murder. Report of a black Peeping Tom and external damage to Miss Aldrift's house may be linked to Fox.
Her rosary beads were found in Fox's possession.

FOR INTERNAL USE OF G.M.P PERSONNEL ONLY

Author's Note

MOSAIC SYNDROME

This syndrome is a variant of Klinefelter Syndrome, a chromosomal abnormality that is characterised by an extra X chromosome in the cells of the body (XXY). Unaffected males have 46 chromosomes including one X and one Y chromosome that make up the pair of sex chromosomes (XY) In the case of mosaicism not all the cells in the body are affected. There are two populations of cells in the body, one set with XXY chromosomes and one with XY. The symptoms of an individual with mosaicism are generally less severe than those of one with full Klinefelter.

The signs and symptoms of Klinefelter Syndrome may not be detected until puberty or even adulthood. Symptoms vary with individuals and can be treated by hormone replacement therapy. About one in eight hundred males are affected.

For the purposes of this story it is suggested that Billy Fox, with undetected mosaicism, was very suggestible both as a child and adult. He was shy, apprehensive and passive. His sex drive was low, as was his sense of self-esteem. He readily accepted responsibility for the misdeeds of others as a way of enhancing his own feeling of importance and was an easy victim of a certain kind of 'persuasive interviewing'.

Billy Fox is a fictional character and there is no intention to suggest that those afflicted with chromosomal abnormality are more prone to wrongdoing than anybody else. Billy is a victim not a culprit.

Also by Frank Lean

Red for Rachel

David Cunane is Manchester's most off-beat private eye. Fond of the booze, fatally attracted to the wrong women, champion of the lost cause, he walks a thin line . . .

Rachel Elsworth is missing. Nineteen years old, she has vanished into the city's seamy underworld. Her father employs Cunane to find her. Rachel's trail leads Cunane into the maze of Manchester's criminal fraternity; and right to the heart of police corruption.

As Cunane finds himself drawn further and further into a web of deceit and danger, he realises that someone will stop at nothing to find Rachel before he does. Even murder.

'This is the kind of stuff the English thriller has been begging for' *GQ*

'Wicked as they say . . . the author should give up his day job' *Time Out*